P9-DGZ-012

MEDICAL LIBRARY
NORTH MEMORIAL HOSPITAL

POTIONS, REMEDIES AND OLD WIVES' TALES

BOOKS BY W. W. BAUER, M.D.

AMERICANS, LIVE LONGER!

HEALTH, HYGIENE AND HOOEY

HEALTH QUESTIONS ANSWERED

EAT WHAT YOU WANT
    (With Florence Marvyne Bauer)

STOP ANNOYING YOUR CHILDREN

SANTA CLAUS, M.D.

YOUR HEALTH TODAY

HEALTH AND SAFETY
    DEVELOPMENT PROGRAM, ELEMENTARY
    AND SECONDARY TEXTBOOKS
    (With Gladys Gardner Jenkins,
    Helen Shacter and Eleanor Pounds)

MOVING INTO MANHOOD
    (With Florence Marvyne Bauer)

TO ENJOY MARRIAGE
    (With Florence Marvyne Bauer)

POTIONS, REMEDIES AND OLD WIVES' TALES

POTIONS, REMEDIES AND OLD WIVES' TALES

W. W. BAUER, B.S., M.D., LL.D.

Formerly Director of Health Education and
Editor of *Today's Health* for the
American Medical Association

Doubleday & Company, Inc.
Garden City, New York

WZ 309
B344

Library of Congress Catalog Card Number 69–10977
Copyright © 1969 by Florence Marvyne Bauer
All Rights Reserved
Printed in the United States of America

2285

for
  "Polly"
    and
      "Nan"
        who
          helped
            me
              so
                much

CONTENTS

How superstitious are you? . . . some common expressions
and how they began . . . do witches fear horses? . . . "upper
crust" . . . "pig in a poke" . . . "letting the cat out of the
bag" . . . "the cold shoulder" . . . "white elephants" . . .
"red-letter days" . . . "baker's dozen" . . . "in the swim" . . .
"eating your hat" . . . "Here's looking at you" . . . "p's and
q's" . . . "fly-by-night" . . . walking under a ladder . . . black
cats . . . four-leaf clovers . . . thirteen at table . . . three
lights from a match . . . walking around your chair to change
your luck . . . starting something on Friday . . . clock striking while your eyes are crossed . . . blowing out birthday
candles . . . stepping on a crack . . . a rabbit's foot . . . first
star at evening . . . breaking a mirror . . . to spill the salt
. . . a spider, morning and night . . . star over your shoulder
. . . observation, experience and interpretation . . . belief in
the supernatural . . . basic similarity of beliefs from various
origins . . . religious backgrounds . . . relationships between
belief in myth, magic, folklore, medicine and religion . . . the
worship of trees . . . *The Golden Bough* . . . mistletoe . . .
plants, herbs and flowers . . . what folklore means today . . .
fire . . . the wheel . . . lenses . . . stars . . . astrology and
astronomy . . . natural phenomena . . . early experimentation
. . . historical clinical experiences . . . early man, not stupid.

Chapter Two: FOLKLORE, RELIGION, MEDICINE 27

Folklore influenced by fear and the impulse to be helpful . . .
Greek and Roman deities related to medical folklore . . .
nothing grows without a purpose . . . the doctrine of signatures . . . the significance of numbers . . . color symbolism
. . . taboos . . . how medical folklore spreads . . . Mexican
botanical remedies . . . astrology . . . the Zodiac . . . doctor-
priests . . . herb doctors . . . knowledgeable "Grannies" . . .
psychology, credulity and faith . . . who are we to scoff?

Chapter Three: WITCHES, WITCHCRAFT AND
WITCH DOCTORING 45

Wit, wisdom and witches . . . wizards . . . malignant spirits
and demons . . . good witchcraft . . . testing for witchcraft
. . . witch-prickers . . . trials in seventeenth and eighteenth
centuries . . . animal disguises . . . mental and emotional
factors in illness . . . witch doctors—suggestion and hypnotism
. . . divination . . . prophecy . . . ESP.

Chapter Four: MAN'S EMERGING IMAGE OF
HIMSELF 61

"The proper study of mankind is man" . . . ancient relics,
paintings, sculpture . . . real progress made of man's internal
organs in Alexandria . . . Hippocrates and his idea of the
"four humors" . . . mistaken concepts of organ functions
(heart, arteries, liver, brain) . . . Aristotle and herb medicine
. . . Aretaeus of Cappadocia . . . the paradoxical Galen . . .
Galen's fallacious doctrine of spirits . . . Galen's "laudable
pus" . . . quick survey of progress through the centuries . . .
Vesalius the anatomist . . . dissection of human corpses
. . . histology (microscopic anatomy) . . . anesthesia . . .
bacteriology . . . surgery and asepsis . . . twentieth century
shows fastest progress . . . X ray and radium . . . electronics
and medicine . . . man's debt to chemistry . . . health education and healthful living . . . the kind of people who fall for
fakes . . . separating truth from fallacy.

its products . . . goats . . . the horse . . . geese . . . mice and
rats . . . hamsters and guinea pigs . . . apes and monkeys . . .
chickens . . . animals in scientific research . . . the uses of
blood . . . the heart . . . the liver . . . the brain . . . the
skeleton . . . glands of internal secretion.

Emotional health a problem now as formerly . . . good appearance boosts self-esteem . . . some thoughts on vanity . . . baths
and bathing . . . soap is just soap . . . medical uses of soap
. . . hair, beards and wigs . . . hair restorers, ancient and modern . . . fallacies about hair . . . the art of make-up . . . early
American cosmetics . . . colorings, powders . . . softening of
the skin . . . perfumes . . . modern beauty miracles.

Sickness in pioneer days . . . doctors and dentists scarce and
poorly educated . . . superstitions about teething . . . birthmarks . . . warts . . . the "rheumatiz" . . . fever and chills
. . . bowel inflammation . . . common remedies for bowel
problems . . . accidental injuries . . . snake, bee and spider
bites . . . stones and other kidney diseases . . . skin ulcers
. . . boils and carbuncles . . . mouth infections . . . headaches
. . . lung conditions . . . croup, coughs and colds . . . goiters
. . . folk medicine is still with us . . . Sam Levenson on
Mothercare . . . chicken broth . . . childbirth . . . psychology
of the witch doctor . . . old-time country doctors . . . folklore
and the modern quack . . . homeopathic magic . . . contagious magic . . . the healing touch and the king's evil . . .
Grandma was often right!

Active ingredients in folk medicines . . . identified by modern
chemistry . . . alcohol . . . anesthetics . . . ancient drug mixtures . . . opium and its alkaloids . . . laughing gas . . .

INTRODUCTION

Do you like cabbage?
Do you *eat* cabbage?
W*hy* do you eat cabbage?
Probably you do not eat it for the reason given by the Roman philosopher Marcus Portius Cato. He advised those who expected to drink liberally at a banquet, to eat five leaves of cabbage dipped in vinegar. "This," he said, "will make you as fit as if you had had nothing, and you can drink as much as you will."

This might be easy to brush off with an indulgent smile as just another ancient superstition, and evidence that they had their way-out ideas back there just as we have them today. We eat crackers or swallow olive oil or butter to help us hold our liquor.

But wait. Here's the whole story. An amino acid derived from cabbage juice is being used today, with promising results, in the treatment of alcoholism.* Add also the facts that cabbage seeds were used in Egypt to prevent drunkenness and the modern use of sauerkraut juice for that morning-after letdown, and you have to pay attention.†

This is not an isolated example. It is part of a pattern which emerges when one studies ancient and modern herbals and centuries-old ways of treating the sick and injured, in comparison with modern ways. Cabbage juice may not prove to be a cure for alcoholism, just as digitalis leaves did not cure heart diseases.

---

* Prof. William Shive, Department of Chemistry, University of Texas, Austin.
† Kreig, Margaret, *Green Medicine*, Rand McNally, Chicago, 1964.

Real cures are rare, and doctors use the word with caution. Even quinine, the oft-quoted "pattern" for a curative drug, is not always successful against malaria. Parasites and germs can develop defenses against drugs. As my late associate Dr. William Bolton phrased it, "Germs Fight Back."

Even so, the numerous and increasingly impressive examples of how folk medicines underlie modern medical advances, compel us to regard these traditional remedies with more respect than has often been the custom. In my half-century of medical experience, and especially when I was very young and knew so much more than I know now, I used to have lots of fun ridiculing strange, popular ideas about medicine. These came to my attention through rural medical practice, public health experience, radio and television contacts, medical writing and editing for nonmedical readers, and the extensive correspondence arising from these sources.

I am less ready now to point with derision, but by the same token, I am not prepared to accept every claim at face value.

There must be, and indeed there seems to be, a reasonable middle ground where one can weigh the evidence impartially and, at least to a certain extent, credit much of folklore with a basis in fact, while continuing to reject that which at this time appears to be without scientific support. This sympathetic and objective overview was suggested to me by my friend and associate Dr. Cyril Solomon of New York, to whom I make grateful acknowledgment for giving me the impetus which developed into this book.

In the following pages I have tried to explore the vast store of information and to select a limited number of examples which will indicate as fairly as possible, the growing scientific interest in medical folklore today.

W. W. Bauer, B.S., M.D.

Chicago
Illinois
1968

POTIONS, REMEDIES AND OLD WIVES' TALES

Chapter One

HOW DID FOLKLORE BEGIN?

How superstitious are you?

Do you know why people nail horseshoes over their doors, or paint them on their automobiles? For good luck, of course! Yes, but it all began with the idea of warding off witches. And how do horseshoes ward off witches? Why, witches are afraid of horses. Who says? Well, now, if they were not afraid of horses, why would they ride on broomsticks? But if you rely on horseshoes, be sure to nail them open side up—otherwise the magic runs out.

Don't laugh. Here are some more tall tales from the past.

You probably use a lot of pet phrases in everyday conversation, just like the rest of us. But what did they really mean in the beginning?

You may speak of some VIP as belonging to the upper crust. The upper crust of what? Of a pie. When wheat was scarce, thrifty housewives baked the lower crust of their pies from rye flour, reserving the more expensive wheat for the upper crust, which showed.

Do you ever turn down a bargain offer and say you never buy a pig in a poke? What's a poke? A poke, in farm and mine talk, is a sack. Farmers used to tie their underweight pigs in sacks and try to sell them without letting the buyer see them. The buyer knew that if he opened the sack and let the pig out, he would have to chase it through the market-day crowd and catch it. So he bought it sight unseen. That's buying a pig in a poke.

And what about letting the cat out of the bag? That came from the practice of some really tricky farmers who put a cat in the bag instead of a pig, and when the purchaser got home he "let the cat out of the bag."

Probably the farmer that pulled those tricks too often got a cold shoulder from future buyers. This was a cold cut of second-rate meat, usually from the shoulder, served to guests who stayed around too long or otherwise displeased the hostess. When they had been given a cold shoulder a few times while others got hot roasted prime cuts of meat, they were likely to take the hint.

Have you gone to a white-elephant sale recently? Where did the idea of a white elephant originate? Oh, that seems obvious—just something expensive and useless. Right, and it originated in Thailand, where all white elephants automatically belonged to the king. Since they were expensive to feed and keep, the kings made a habit of presenting a white elephant to a subject whom they disliked. And, of course, one does not refuse gifts from a king, even if they are ruinous. Or ugly, as I found out in Germany when I commented on some atrociously ugly royal gifts in a castle.

We speak of memorable events as "red-letter days," perhaps because calendars commonly have important days printed in red. Originally, in Rome, the good days were called white-letter days, the bad days, black-letter. Even today we speak of a black day when misfortune overtakes us.

Where does the term "baker's dozen" come from? And why is a baker's dozen thirteen, the unluckiest number of all? That's because Henry VIII of England decreed that a baker's dozen of rolls must weigh at least a certain weight, or the baker would lose his head. The extra roll was added as a sort of life-and-health insurance.

Are you in the swim, socially?

That idea originated from the fact that schools of fish were called, and sometimes still are, a "swim." For a fisherman to drop his bait in such a swim usually meant good fishing, and that's how that began.

Have you ever said that if so and so happened, you'd eat your hat? Perhaps you might explain this by thinking that hats of straw, felt, feathers or fur would make pretty poor eating, but that isn't exactly the right answer. *Hattes* were a highly in-digestible "food" containing eggs, veal, dates, saffron and a lot of other stuff and things, and eating them was a real chore. So when a TV set shows you a hat with a chunk out of the brim, you'll know better!

When you propose a toast, do you say, "Here's looking at you?" Why? Because, in the days of personal combat among knights or peasants, tankards with glass bottoms were used to permit the drinkers to keep an eye on each other while drinking, thus forestalling treachery. This is closely akin to the origin of the handshake, which originated from the practice of extending the open hand to show that no weapon was being carried.

When you were young, you were told to mind your p's and q's, often by prim parents who wouldn't have used the expression if they had known its origin. It came out of the tavern, where the bartender tallied the pints and quarts of liquor as they were consumed. The guest was expected to mind his p's and q's if he did not wish to be overcharged.

The phrase "fly-by-night" has come to mean some rather disreputable character or action. It came from the fact that people in trouble often escaped by night in a horse-drawn vehicle or sedan chair. These were known as "flies."

Other common expressions, actions or beliefs which have come down from the distant past, include*:

- never walk under a ladder; not merely to keep from getting a bucket of paint down your neck, but to avoid violating the Holy Trinity by walking through the triangle formed by the wall, the ground and the leaning ladder;

- a black cat crossing your path means bad luck, but not in ancient Egypt, where black cats were deified; this tradition is of European origin, where witches were supposed to be able to change themselves into black cats, and back again;

- four-leaf clovers are good luck, because Eve was supposed to have taken one along when she and Adam were expelled from Eden; five-leaf clovers are unlucky, but no good explanation for this seems available;

* Much of the factual material contained in this passage comes from the book How Did It Begin?, by R. Brasch, David McKay Company, Inc., New York, 1966.

- sitting down thirteen at table is regarded as an indication that one of the group will die before the year is out; insurance statistics indicate that among *any* thirteen persons one death is likely to happen; the story goes back to an old Norse legend of a banquet with twelve gods invited, plus one angry uninvited guest; it is also related to the fact that Jesus and his disciples at the Last Supper numbered thirteen, of whom two were soon dead;

- if you refuse to take a third light from a match, your action stems from the experience of soldiers in trenches, who found that by the time the third man lighted his smoke, the enemy had time to spot and kill him;

- if the cards run against you in a poker game, walk three times around your chair; I was unable to find any explanation of origin for this, beyond the traditional significance of the number three;

- never start a new project on Friday; Friday the thirteenth means double-trouble; it was on Friday that Adam and Eve were supposed to have eaten of the forbidden fruit; Friday was also the day of the crucifixion of Jesus;

- if the clock strikes when your eyes are crossed, they will stay that way; if its owner dies, the clock will stop; if a clock stops, it foretells a death: clocks and time have always been associated with human life; clocks may stop and death occur coincidentally; when death occurs, the winding of the clock may be forgotten, as "time stands still"; modern research on sleep and other body functions is based on the concept of a biological clock;

- blowing out birthday candles makes wishes come true, but only if they are not spoken out loud; this is based on the lighted candle being a symbol of life to be kept burning until extinguished at one puff; this seems somewhat strange reasoning; the modern view is that blowing on a cake to be eaten by others is unhygienic;

- "step on a crack and you'll break your mother's back," we used to chant as we avoided all cracks and junctions in sidewalks; I have been unable to find any explanation for the origin of this idea;

- carrying or touching a rabbit's foot means good luck; the foot, a phallic symbol, coupled with the rabbit, well-known for its fertility, was accepted as a sign of creativity, a positive influence;

- breaking a mirror means seven years of bad luck, and not only because it is expensive and broken glass may cut you; the tradition is based on the still-water reflection so easily disturbed by ruffling the surface, plus the concept of allowing one's image to be smashed as a bad omen; mirrors were also believed to foretell the future, and their breaking was regarded as a deliberate act by an inimical god to deprive man of his ability to foretell coming events;

- don't spill the salt, or if you do, throw some over your left shoulder; supposedly this may be based on Leonardo da Vinci's "Last Supper," where the salt on the table was spilled, and Judas was shown with his left hand raised as if throwing something over his shoulder;

- there's an old German proverb:

Spinne am morgen,	Spider in the morning,
Bringt Kummer und Sorgen.	Trouble and mourning.
Spinne am Abend,	Spider at night,
Ist Glücklich und labend.	Luck and delight.

I never got to the bottom of that one, but I have memories of my grandmother, who killed spiders in the morning, but was careful to do them no harm toward evening. I don't like 'em at any hour.

Spiders have been feared because of their occasionally venomous bites, some of which may be fatal—black widow, the tarantula, and the brown house spiders in particular. Spiders do not bite human beings unless they are interfered with.

Spiders have also been associated with good omens. Robert the Bruce, King of Scotland, watched a spider try six times to start its web, and succeed on the seventh. This encouraged him to try again after losing six battles. Another spider story is told about Bruce, and also about the Prophet Mohammed and a king of ancient Babylon—how a spider rapidly spun a web across the mouth of a cave in which the person was hiding, and so deceived the searchers into thinking that he could not possibly be in there. This is another indication of the universality of folklore.

- see a star over your left shoulder, with money in your right-hand pocket, and recite:

> "Star light, star bright,
> First star I see tonight
> I wish I may, I wish I might,
> Get the wish I wish tonight!"

I wish I may, I wish I might, know the facts and know them right, to tell where this wish so bright, was first conceived and brought to light.

These and many other beliefs had been repeated over and over, mainly by word of mouth, sometimes seriously, sometimes with amusement. How did they originate? In many instances, who knows? It is plain that they have been influenced by religion, experience, and interpretation of cause, effect or coincidence. Sometimes they seem baseless, but often they contain more than a shred of truth. In any event, they are examples of the kind of thinking out of which came myth and magic, and finally medicine. Their bearing on medical folklore is that most of such influences, benign or malignant, attributed to these circumstances revolve around life, health, disease and death.

It is worth considering how much of what we "know" today will become myth in the unforeseeable future.

Probably the exact beginnings of folklore will never be established beyond doubt, but some pretty shrewd conclusions can be drawn from existing evidence, in addition to the traditions cited above. In the tombs of antiquity, in statuary and ancient scrolls, in the writings of poets, historians and philosophers; in the religious rites which have come down through the centuries, and in the Scriptures of the various religions, there is dedication enough that man, in his efforts to understand his world, created myths and legends. Some of these are fanciful to the extent of incredibility in the light of modern science, but others are so close to the truth that they have become the basis for modern medical procedure. Some are admittedly allegorical, but even some of these show indications of well-directed observation and intelligent interpretation. The commonly assumed attitude of scornful skepticism needs to be replaced by a more objective evaluation to separate the true from the false, and to give due credit to the accumulated wisdom of the race.

Man, looking about him at a fascinating, complex and sometimes frightening world, endeavored to explain what he saw, heard, felt, wanted or feared. This was in part an effort to satisfy a natural curiosity, but also it was an attempt to fulfill a need for security against perils, for success in procuring food and shelter, and for finding relief from illness and injury. With his inborn mysticism, which has persisted down to the present day, man sought to find a reason behind the phenomena which he observed. Dimly he perceived that somehow these things did not just come about; they had to have a creative power behind them.

In practically every culture we find a belief in some form of supernatural influence upon man and his world. Thor, the thunder god of the Norsemen; the Manito, the Great Spirit of the American Indian; Isis and Osiris, the chief gods of the Egyptians; the moon deity Nannar of Sumerian Ur; the bearded "fair god" Quetzalcoatl of the Mexican Toltecs and the sun-god pyramids of the Aztecs; all are examples which show not only the diversity but the similarity of religious belief as an explanation for the world and its mysteries. In India there was born the Brahman belief, centered about a trinity—Brahma, the Creator of the Universe, Vishna, its preserver, and Siva who represents both destruction and reproduction. The Greeks created a whole galaxy of gods and goddesses, many of them endowed with attributes anything but admirable, and the Romans adopted them, with variations. Roman theology finally descended to the low level of emperor deification, including some characters like Caligula, whom a schoolboy unwittingly characterized with great accuracy when asked to write an essay about him. He had not studied his lesson, but he was not stupid. He wrote: "The less said, the better!"

The diversity of these beliefs, and others, is striking, but there is also a strong thread of similarity. In all theologies, the gods were represented as creators, benefactors, controllers, avengers and destroyers. They were concerned with life, death, illness, misfortune, good fortune, love, reproduction, virtue and wickedness. In the Egyptian world of the dead and the American Indian's happy hunting ground there is indication of a single basic origin. Indeed, the Brahman trinity, the father-mother gods of the Egyptians and the Christian Trinity are among the many indications which have led both theologians and scientists to conclude that man's original religion was monotheistic, a belief in one God, Creator and Ruler of the universe. The Judaic Scriptures, which tell of the dispersion of man as a punishment for aspiring to the status of deity when he built the tower in the plain of Babel, are cited as the beginning of diversities in religious belief.

Any scrutiny of early beliefs in the closely related areas of religion, myth, magic and medicine show the strong trend toward personalizing natural phenomena such as sun, moon, stars, earth, sea, clouds, rain, thunder, lightning, plants, animals, springs, rivers, and mountains.

Trees were prominent among objects of veneration or worship. They appear very early in the Old Testament, where in the "garden eastward in Eden," there grew two special trees. One was the tree of life, the other the tree of the knowledge of good and evil, and Adam and Eve were prohibited from eating of the latter. And in the Apocalypse we read of the "tree of life, which bare twelve manner of fruits, and yielded her fruit every month; *and the leaves of the tree were for the healing of the nations.*" (The italicized phrase is the motto of the American Public Health Association.)

We find the tree of life also in the Aztec "cosmic trees" pictured as surrounding the fire-god Xiuhtecutli, and related symbolism appears in ancient Assyria, Babylon, Arabia, Asia Minor, Central and South America and the Far East. Among the trees so venerated are the Egyptian sycamore, the palms and cedars of the Hebrews and the Christians, the oak and the ash of Norsemen, Celts, Druids and Teutons, and the cassia and bo (pipal or fig) trees of the Far East. An interesting example of the gradual progression of ideas is a woodcut of the fourteenth century showing the serpent which tempted Eve, with the face and bust of a woman, twined around the trunk of the tree of knowledge. Except for the face and bust, and the leaves on the tree, it bears a startling resemblance to the caduceus, the ancient symbol of modern medicine, a serpent twined about a staff.

The Norse have a legendary world tree, Yggdrasil, an evergreen ash whose branches overshadow the whole universe and, together with the trunk and the roots, are said to bind together heaven, earth and "Hel," hell the primal abyss where the tree is believed to be rooted. Related to this tree was additional symbolism, such as its leaves representing the clouds, its fruits the stars.

On the branches were said to live the four cardinal winds. An eagle on the top branches symbolizes the air, the falcon the lookout for the gods. The squirrel running up and down the tree signifies rain, snow, hail and running water, and was supposed to be stirring up strife between the eagle above and the serpent-monster below. The monster represents the volcanic power which gnaws constantly at the earth's foundations.

The three stems which constitute the trunk of the tree represent three separate concepts. The center stem supports the earth; the second typifies the warm south where dwell the past, present and future and where the gods sit in judgment; the third represents the cold north where all the wisdom of man flows from the supposed origin of Ask, the first Norseman, reputed to have sprung from such a tree. This is about as complete a picturization of legendary belief as one can imagine in a nutshell.

In like manner, not to belabor the point, there are the legendary beliefs that:

The rod of Aaron, which turned into a serpent when Pharaoh demanded a sign of power, and swallowed the Egyptian asp, and then turned back into a rod again, is the forerunner of all the "magic wands" of fable and the modern prestidigitator.

The pipal or bo tree of the Orient is revered because of the tradition that Buddha sat under such a tree for seven weeks while attaining the perfect knowledge of nirvana.

The fig tree was sacred to the ancient Hebrews as assurance of peace and abundance; to Christians because of Jesus' frequent mention of it in his parables; Moslems called it the tree of heaven.

The cassia, an evergreen of southern China, is credited with conferring immortality upon whomever eats of its fruit; the Chinese regard it as a sacred tree of life, a celestial world tree.

The Egyptians regarded the date palm as the tree of the year; palm wine was esteemed as a potent medicine, and the date palm remains to this day an important factor in sustaining life in the desert.

In similar fashion, special virtues have been attributed by various peoples to the peach, the pomegranate and the sacred hand-of-Buddha (a citrus tree). Most particular significance is attached to the oak, well known as one of the three trees of British legend—oak, ash, and thorn.

In Sir James George Frazer's study of magic and religion, *The Golden Bough*, we read of ancient sanctuaries, often found in natural woods or groves, or even consisting of the groves themselves. Trees were invested with personalities, even regarded as having souls. The American Indians regarded the shade of the cottonwood, one of the most common trees in the Upper Missouri River region, as possessed of an intelligence which would be helpful to them if the tree were properly approached. Many other such legends could be cited, but none more common nor more significant than those pertaining to the oak.

The oak is a tree of great stature. It lives a long time. It stretches out strong, protective branches and creates a wide area of shade, signifying shelter and protection. Its fruit feeds birds and small animals and, before the development of farming, was an important food for man. In Arcadia, the priest of Zeus dipped an oak branch into a spring on Mount Lycaeus in token of a prayer for rain. The Roman Jupiter's temple on Capitoline Hill was said to have been built by Romulus beside a sacred oak; Roman military victors were crowned with oak leaves. The marriage of the ancient king of Rome to Egeria, the oak-nymph, in the sacred grove was an evidence that the kings themselves were regarded as oak-gods. The name of the Celtic *Druids* is defined as meaning "oak-men," and much additional evidence demonstrates that the oak was worshiped as the patron of the thunder and the rain. Abraham received the Angel of Jehovah in an oak grove.

Oak is listed as a source of tannin, useful in processing leather, and "has been used as an astringent." Tannic acid, once touted for healing burns, is now out of favor, and so are tea leaves. Even the herbalists admit that internal use of tannin is likely to "derange the bowels." It is also listed as a corroborant, which is to say a stimulant. Actually, the oak plays no significant part in modern medicine. Its history does, however, typify the origin and growth of folklore, and is paralleled by many other beliefs relating to plant life.

Medical myths pertaining to the oak tree include:

To get rid of gout, pare the sufferer's nails and clip some hairs from his legs; stuff these in a hole bored into an oak, close up the hole and rub it with cow dung. If the patient is free for three months, the oak has the gout;

To get rid of the "ague" (fever), one pegged a lock of his hair into an oak; the patient then wrenched himself free, leaving his hair and his ague with the tree.

THE GOLDEN BOUGH

The alleged virtues of the oak were shared and in some ways surpassed by its principal parasite, the mistletoe, the "golden bough" from which Frazer's collection of ancient myths takes its name. The mistletoe, like other parasitic plants, was greatly revered, perhaps because of its mysterious ability to grow without roots or other apparent source of sustenance. It was regarded virtually as a cure-all, especially for the "falling sickness" (epilepsy), because it was itself unable to fall to the ground. This line of reasoning by analogy is a common source of legend, fable and superstition, and plays a leading role in both medical and other folklore.

The golden bough was so named because a cut branch of mistletoe, kept for a while, assumes a golden-yellow shade which affects stem and leaves as well as berries. It was considered a cure-all in many parts of the world.

The Roman Pliny describes remarkably similar Italian and English legends. The mistletoe had to be cut without using iron, so golden implements were used, or the plant was pelted with stones, and it had to be caught before touching the ground. Then, by wearing it, women were supposed to be assured of fertility; the same effect was supposed to occur in cattle. Chewing it, and laying a piece upon an ulcer was practiced to promote healing. In modern times, as late as 1925, the Ainus of Japan used mistletoe as food or took it as a health-giving tea; they also strewed chopped-up leaves over the gardens to assure fertility. And in African Senegambia the natives have virtually the same beliefs about mistletoe as prevailed in England, Italy and Japan. This again argues a common source for much if not all of folklore.

A Norse god, Balder, is mythically related to the huge bonfires lighted on St. John's Eve in Scandinavian and Teutonic countries. He is said to have been killed by a bough of mistletoe and burned in a great fire. This connection has given the name "oil of St. John" to a mistletoe decoction supposed to be possessed of great curative powers.

In modern medicine, the mistletoe has little place. The European herbalists consider it useful for raising blood pressure; those in America value it for reducing blood pressure! It is useful also, according to American sources, for relief of toothache by chewing the leaves. The berries, however, have produced death. The American medical texts seem to regard mistletoe as obsolete. It does not even appear in all medical dictionaries.

Not only trees, but plants and herbs of all kinds have been highly esteemed for their medicinal values, often closely associated with religious or ritual concepts. Many of these ideas have proved to be the forerunners of modern scientific remedies, and will be the subject of special consideration later. Here are a few of those which have not, for the most part, found a permanent place in the medical world of today, though in many instances their use was logical enough in less scientific days:

Clover, Greek and Roman symbol of good and evil, according to an old folk-rhyme:

> "One leaf for fame,
> And one for wealth,
> One for a faithful lover,
> And one to bring you glorious health,
> Are in a four-leaf clover."

But a five-leaf clover is unlucky. In herbal lore, the various kinds of "clover," belonging to a number of plant families, are recommended for loosening coughs and sore throats (especially if used with honey), good for bowels and kidneys, useful as poultices; "clearing obstructions of the sight," skin eruptions and ulcers; poultices; alterative and tonic actions; charm against witches and evil; keeping moths out of clothing; treating dropsy, diarrhea, menstrual disturbances, and keeping up the strength of the patient. The physician of today writes them all off.

Cornflowers were supposedly created by transforming the body of a Greek youth into flowers. Their medical reputation was based on a mythical claim that the centaur, Chiron, wounded with a poisoned arrow, covered his wound with cornflowers, and got well. It's a lovely story, but that's all.

Crocus was held in great esteem by the Romans for adorning their marriage beds because, supposedly, the couch of Zeus and his bride Hera was so adorned; also it was regarded as a heart tonic, a cordial and love potion. Later it became a hair dye—saffron yellow. It may still be good for the latter use.

Hawthorne trees were ancient symbols of hope. Their branches furnished decorations for the altars of Hymen, Greek goddess of marriage, and supplied torches for Grecian nuptial chambers. A tea of the leaves was used in Rome as a charm against sorcery and witchcraft and for the protection of the newborn. It plays no part in modern medicine.

Such examples could be multiplied many times. They make the point that folklore has its fallacies as well as its shrewd and correct conclusions. But so does science. By no means every experiment succeeds. Many a promising theory fades under the impact of experience, further experimentation or clinical trials. We do not abandon medical—or other—science, because of its failures. Instead, we hold fast to its established facts, keep an open mind, acknowledge our errors and shortcomings, and work harder to establish the truth more firmly.

We owe a similar attitude to the ancient beliefs of our forebears. We should neither accept them blindly nor reject them without full and fair investigation. We owe much to the experience of previous generations. As expressed by Dr. Bruno Gebhard, founder of America's first exclusive health museum in Cleveland and pioneer expert in health education, "Grandma is not always wrong." Grandma, he explains, is the personification of the cumulative experience of the human race. But she isn't always right either (Chapter Nine).

TREES

Man's appreciation of trees did not stop with veneration. He soon learned to put them to good use. We read in the Old Testament how Solomon was instructed in the building of the temple to use the finest woods. Among these, the cedars of Lebanon are still cherished today. Planks of fir were also specified. Noah built the ark of wood. Fires were lighted by the friction of wood against wood, as Boy Scouts are taught to do to this day. The ships of the Phoenicians, famed mariners of ancient times, were built of wood, as were the galleys of the Romans, the ships of the wide-ranging Norsemen, and the clipper ships of New England, to say nothing of the warships in such fleets as Nelson's at Trafalgar and Commodore Perry's on Lake Erie. Ironclad ships, built of wood, are hardly more than a century old, and now the only remaining wooden ships are treasured historical relics, except for pleasure craft.

Trees also supplied man with food. The fig tree, Biblical symbol of fertility and fruitfulness, still serves the Oriental, and visitors to California are regarded as barbarians if they dislike fresh figs. The date palm too is a world-wide source of food; not only the fruit, but the leaves of the heart, which are used for salads. The peach, the pear, the apple, the plum, the pomegranate, the cherry, the orange and lemon and grapefruit, the olive and its oil, the plantain and the breadfruit, all contribute to human nutrition.

Man, the most destructive of animals, has not appreciated the trees and forests. He has ignored the Old Testament injunction, "Thou shalt not destroy the trees thereof by forcing an axe against them; for thou mayest eat of them, and thou shalt not cut them down (for the tree of the field is man's life). . . ." The destruction of forests by indiscriminate cutting, threatened to waste the wealth of the nation until government and business adopted less destructive practices. Denuding vast areas of trees turned fertile lands into deserts, creating alternate droughts and disastrous floods. In our cities, parklands with trees are being ruthlessly sacrificed in favor of motor roads, unless embattled citizens call a halt to the sabotage. When the forests are gone, so are the birds and the animals, and the plants which depend upon the trees for their shelter and protection. And man is poorer by the loss.

Since trees have meant so much to mankind, it is not surprising that medicinal virtues should be attributed to them. The oak does not figure prominently in folk medicine, except as indicated previously, but many other trees do. Following are some of the more important medical items which have figured in folklore; other useful ones will be discussed in detail later:

- Calabar beans, a West African "ordeal poison" by which guilt or innocence of an accused was supposedly determined, contain an alkaloid, physostigmine, useful in eye conditions;

- licorice root, a popular flavoring in confections, useful in disguising bad-tasting drugs, and sometimes still used for treating inflammatory conditions in animals and man;

- Malabar kino, harvested from Oriental trees as maple sugar is from maples; used for diarrhea and dysentery;

- araroba or Goa powder is made from the sap of a Brazilian tree, and was extensively used in treating skin diseases in the form of chrysarobin; it is related to rhubarb, senna and other popular laxative drugs;

- balsams of Tolú and Peru supplied similar mixtures derived from tropical trees, and were extensively used for antiseptic dressing of wounds in the preantibiotic era;

- gums, such as tragacanth from trees in the Middle East, and acacia (gum arabic originating in the Sudan) are useful in making pharmaceutical preparations such as tablets;

- senna leaves, derived from an African and East Indian shrub, have been widely used as laxatives, and were common ingredients in so-called "patent" medicines, especially those recommended—by their promoters—for "curing" constipation; the stems and the fruit pods have had similar uses;

- oil of cloves, the traditional family remedy for toothache, comes from a tree indigenous to the Moluccas or Clove islands and is now cultivated in Zanzibar; it is more useful as a spice than as a medicine;

- the oils of fennel, caraway, dill, coriander, and other spices were commonly used as so-called carminatives, which were intended to redden the stomach lining with more blood and so promote digestion;

- asafetida is mainly noted for its offensive (fetid) odor, but was long esteemed as the ingredient of amulets to be worn for the prevention of communicable diseases; this is an interesting indication that medical folklore is not all nonsense, since we now recognize that these diseases are spread by close contact, which the stinky amulets effectively discouraged;

- manna, a sweet sap from trees growing in Sicily, was used as a laxative for children.

This list could be extended indefinitely, but enough has been cited to establish at least the following basic points about medical folklore:

- it cannot be dismissed as undiluted nonsense;

- it had a basis in observation and experience;

- it had a limited usefulness;

- much of it has now been scientifically validated;

- it has been the basis for many modern medical methods;

- it deserves respectful attention;

- it should be discarded when disproved or superseded as knowledge progresses.

THE MEANING OF FOLKLORE TODAY

These legends and traditions lead us to consider why man, in his arrogance, tends to look with a supercilious eye at his historical predecessors, as if he were more intelligent than they.

Our language is filled with evidences of our contempt for what has gone before. Manners, fashions and morals change almost overnight; so do the meanings of words. "Passé," once the fashionable term for the outmoded, is now "out," and even that is no longer "in." By the time these words can be published, they too may be outdated. Physicians and other scientists have tended to look with amused tolerance at medical ideas prevalent in the past, when these did not inconvenience them. When they did, tolerance was replaced by exasperation. In my younger days, I now confess with a somewhat red face, I turned up my nose too many times at the "strange and misguided" ideas which prevailed in the past and which are, to a great extent, still current.

Time and experience should bring tolerance and better understanding, as well as the wisdom to look more closely at cause and effect, and to reserve judgment until all the evidence is in. Just a quick look into the past should cause us to have a new respect for the ingenuity and the cleverness of our distant ancestors. They did, after all, originate many of the advantages we take for granted today.

FIRE!

Where did fire come from, and through whose discernment?

In nature, fire may arise from a stroke of lightning or the slow combustion of dry flammable materials. Somewhere, sometime in the distant past, someone captured fire, tamed it, learned to produce it, controlled it to a degree, and was occasionally destroyed by it. No one knows exactly when this happened, nor to whom. But what a world of progress it opened up!

First in primitive fashion, then with greater refinement, man learned to warm himself with fire, to cook his food with it, to work metals, to make glass, to communicate by means of smoke signals, to turn water into steam and steam into power, to mine and burn coal and later gas and oil, and to build the internal-combustion engines on which our civilization now depends so completely, and which may even ruin us if we do not find means to keep them from poisoning our air. To cap the climax, man now uses fire to create refrigeration. Atomic power will soon supersede traditional fire for many purposes, and who knows where that will lead?

Modern science now recognizes the slow combustion which takes place in the living cell. This is called metabolism, the true fire of life, as yet not fully understood. We know the calorie (heat) values in foods, and how the body transforms them into heat and energy and—unless we burn them up with physical activity—into fat. We know that all this takes place because of oxygen, the invisible and odorless gas which makes life on earth possible. Oxygen was discovered in 1774 by Joseph Priestley who never really knew the full significance of his discovery.

Fire is at the heart of the space explorations, which depend directly upon propulsion fuels, and indirectly upon the use of heat in the processing of practically everything that is required for space flights.

Electricity is among the most important expressions of energy derived from and closely related to simple and primitive fire.

Somebody way back there had his eyes open and his mind on the ball, when he learned how to make and to use fire.

WHEELS

It is a truism and a cliché to say that the world goes around on wheels, and yet it is the simple truth. Some of the work the wheel did in the ancient world, and still does, to make life more livable, may be suggested by the following uses for wheels: primitive oxcarts with wooden wheels still used in many parts of the world, as are water wheels and mill wheels. The wheel principle is the basis for rollers on which buildings are moved; balance wheels in watches, clocks and heavy machinery; automobile gearshifts and transmissions; shopping carts; gocarts; motor-driven tools and motors themselves; pulleys; steering mechanisms for automobiles, ships and other vehicles; propellers for ships, planes, helicopters; electric fans and air conditioners; telephone dials; movie camera spools; potters' wheels; spinning wheels; carrousels; Yo-yos; roulette layouts; one-armed bandits; cams; casters; and tires.

What would we do without wheels?

The earliest picture of a wheel was made in what is now Iraq in Lower Mesopotamia, then known as Sumer, about 3500 B.C. It is of a sledge mounted on four well-made wheels. Early wheels were often made of boards fastened together, then cut to a circular shape. Spoked wheels appeared about 200 B.C., and were used on war chariots because of their lightness. The first tires were made of leather. Later, metal tires were shrunk onto the wheels after being heated. Wheels appeared separately and apparently independently in the Orient and among the Aztecs, Incas and Mayas. The other American Indians continued to use the drag.

Yes, but what has the wheel to do with medical lore?

Consider the ambulance, the plane and the helicopter, all vital factors in rapid transportation of the sick and wounded to hospitals on battle fronts or in our traffic-choked cities. In the hospital or elsewhere, the clock is essential for many medical purposes such as timing dosages of drugs or the length of exposure to radiation. The laboratory centrifuge has numerous uses. Revolving drums driven by clockwork play a large part in the recording of research findings. Anesthetics are administered with the aid of motor-driven equipment. Open-heart surgery depends on mechanical heart-lung machines. The wheel chair and the stretcher cart are familiar in every hospital corridor. So are the food carts and the library wagon, as well as portable instruments like the X ray. The electrocardiograph, and encephalograph are motor driven. Air conditioning aids recovery for almost all patients and is essential in treatment of allergies of the hay-fever type. The wheel principle makes the modern artificial limb possible, with its jointed movable parts, a great improvement over the traditional peg leg. In rehabilitation, wheels for exercising shoulder joints aid recovery from disability due to disease or injury. The pulleys used in neck, limb and spine traction for arthritis or following injuries or spinal disc disease are modified wheels.

Medicine as well as industry owes a debt to the inventors of the wheel.

Does it occur to you that somebody, way back there, must have had a brain, and known how to use it?

LENSES

Man has pretty good eyes; better than those of many animals, less keen than those of some birds. Yet his distant vision is limited and he cannot see the microscopic things that influence his well-being or his very existence. And his eyes are not always normal. But somewhere along the path of history some man—

or woman—took steps to provide man with aids to his vision. We know them now as spectacles, microscopes, telescopes and other instruments, all depending on the lens.

There seems to be no indication that lenses were widely used in ancient times. Sculptors did learn very early how to carve certain substances under water for better optical conditions. An ancient rock crystal found in Iraq in 1845, was ground like a small convex or enlarging lens. In the eleventh century, an Arabian astronomer investigated the principle governing the action of lenses upon light, and by the thirteenth century, lenses were common both in China and in Europe. America's contribution was the bifocal invented by Benjamin Franklin to overcome the nuisance of having two pairs of spectacles.

Until the invention of plastics, glass was the material of which most lenses were made. Glass is among the oldest artificial substances still in use; a charm of blue glass believed to have been made in Egypt about 7000 b.c. is still in existence. Glassmaking flourished in the Mediterranean region and spread all over Europe. The fame of Venetian glass blowers has come down undiminished from ancient times to the present.

The lens is useful because it bends or refracts the rays of light. The convex lens makes things look larger, and helps to correct eye defects such as far-sightedness. It is employed in microscopes, telescopes, opera glasses and binoculars, slide and film projectors and cameras. It also has the effect of bringing distant objects closer. The concave lens acts in an opposite manner. In the spectroscope, where the purpose is to break down or analyze white light into its color components, a different type of lens—a prism—is used. Prisms are useful, too, in some forms of eye-muscle weakness.

Lenses, and the materials of which they have been made, are the outcome of a succession of keen observations, beginning far back in time. At some period back there, someone observed that melting sand, soda ash, and crushed limestone together (perhaps accidentally) resulted in the remarkable substance we now know as glass. Not only in lenses, but in many other ways, glass has contributed greatly to man's comfort, his health and safety, his enjoyment of beauty, and his industrial progress.

Stupid people—our ancestors who pioneered these discoveries?

STARS

The human necessity for explaining everything took form early in recorded history. The ancient Greeks peopled the skies, the earth and the underworld with fictitious deities like the moon goddess-huntress, Diana, and the god-king, Jupiter. They established what may be among the oldest bits of folklore, astrology, which is still used as a guide for living by considerable numbers of persons —enough to make it worthwhile for the daily press to publish astrological horoscopes. Closely akin to this superstition, but based on sound scientific grounds, is astronomy.

Astronomy is the oldest of the sciences and, like many another, it grew out of folklore, and many mistakes were committed in the course of its growth. And yet, more than 4000 years B.C., Egyptian priests watched for the rising of the Dog Star, Sirius, because they knew that when Sirius first rose before the sun came up, the time was at hand for the annual flooding by the Nile, upon which Egypt depended for its agriculture, as it still does today. This phenomenon, occurring in the hot Northern Hemisphere summer, gave this event its name of "dog days," to which rabies was mistakenly attributed, and often still is.

At Abu Simbel, the great temple was so constructed that at sunrise, the rays penetrated through two great halls to fall upon the gigantic figures of the sun gods Amon Ra of Thebes and Ra Horakhti of Heliopolis, enthroned with Ramases and Ptah of Memphis. The engineering of the pyramids also indicates an accurate orientation with the sun and the stars.

At about the same period in history, eclipses of the sun were predicted by the Chinese, who built an observatory in 2608 B.C. in order to check and correct their calendar. Two thousand years earlier, the Sumerians of lower Mesopotamia had mapped the skies and identified the constellations as we know them today, had established the ten signs of the Zodiac and invented the sun-dial.

The motion of the earth around the sun was recognized by a sharp observer in the third century B.C. He was scoffed at for seventeen centuries by the *smarter* people who came later. Even the philosopher Aristotle believed that the sun revolved around the earth. It was not until 1543 when Copernicus published his book proving Aristotle wrong, that the true concept became known. Even so, he met bitter opposition before his proofs were accepted.

Even before telescopes were available, man had learned much about the heavenly bodies. Without this knowledge, navigation would have been impossible, since the magnetic compass came much later; radio communication, radar and sonar later still. Yet man had learned to sail around the globe, and while he did not always know where he was going, most of the time he knew where he was. Perhaps the first ship to sail out of sight of land was a Greek vessel in 350 B.C. This voyage began at a Greek port and ended in the British Isles. Some of the instruments that made such navigation possible included:

- the *astrolabe*, invented by a Greek astronomer, Hipparchus, in 130 B.C.; it consisted of a sighting device without lenses, pivoted in the center of a circular disc marked in the 360° of a circle; it enabled the mariner to observe the position of the stars;

- the *quadrant* appeared about 1430; it was a quarter-circle marked off in degrees, with a plumb line by which the elevation of the stars could be noted;

- the *cross-staff* and the *backstaff* were somewhat similar devices by which the angles of the horizon and the elevation of the celestial bodies could be calculated; the backstaff enabled the mariner to shoot the sun while facing away from it to avoid staring directly at it;

- the *octant*, an early form of the *sextant*, appearing about 1730, was based on principles similar to those of the cross-staff and backstaff;

- the early—twelfth century—*mariners' compasses* were pieces of magnetized iron floating on straw or wooden platforms in vessels of water;

- an accurate chronometer first became available in 1759 to replace the pendulum clocks which were impossible to use on a tossing ship; this instrument had a balance-wheel device which compensated for the rolling of the ship;

- the *log and log line* method of measuring the ship's speed, sometimes in use to this day, originated in the sixteenth century; it was a chip of wedge-shaped wood weighted along its curving arc, attached to a line in which a knot was tied every forty-five feet; this trailed behind the ship in the water; the speed of the ship was calculated from the number of knots unreeled in the line each thirty seconds. This was known as dead reckoning.

Today, of course, ships sail with confidence, guided by magnetic compasses, communicating by radio, protected against collision by radar and against underwater dangers by sonar. Somebody had to invent all these aids. Whoever thought of the first steps in this progression, must have been almost as smart as we think we are.

OBSERVATION

It all began with Adam.

". . . whatsoever Adam called every living creature, that was the name thereof." (Genesis 2:19)

We've been at it ever since—observing, naming, classifying. Some of our forebears have been pretty keen at it, too. The aphorisms of Hippocrates, father of medicine, 400 years B.C., are descriptions of diseases which have scarcely been altered, to say nothing of being surpassed, to this day. He had no modern instruments to help him delve into the mysteries of human structure, function and behavior. He did have sharp eyes, keen ears, sensitive touch and perceptive understanding, just as the best physicians have to this day.

Characteristic of the true scientist of any era is the ability expressed by the late Dr. Albert Chesley, Health Commissioner of the state of Minnesota, who insisted that his staff learn "to *see* what they look at"—not what they thought they saw or wanted to see, but what there really was to see. Our ancestors must have had that capacity to a remarkable degree, since they lacked the modern paraphernalia which now gives aid to the five senses, and because they were unable to experiment in the modern manner.

They did have that sixth sense—imagination.

EXPERIMENTATION

The ancient and medieval scholar could augment his observation with experimentation only so long as he limited his materials to inanimate objects and to some animals. There was much opposition to the use of animals, as there is today, and scientists have always had to fight the prejudices of those who valued animal life above human life. Even the dissection of the dead was banned for religious reasons until relatively modern times. Early physicians like Galen "reasoned" by analogy from known anatomy of pigs to describe internal human anatomy, and in consequence were led into errors. These were perpetuated for many years, until such scientists as Leonardo da Vinci, Michelangelo and Vesalius finally unveiled the real facts by dissecting human corpses. Except in Alexandria, Egypt, this could be done only by robbing graveyards for many centuries, running serious risks of death or imprisonment.

Today, there remains constant need for scientists to defend their experimentation against the efforts continually on foot to curtail the use of animals in laboratory work. Some of this opposition is based on sincere if misguided conviction, and so commands respect even while it must be opposed. There is, however, an important element of self-seeking in the leadership of the so-called antivivisection movement.

CLINICAL EXPERIENCE

The physician has always relied heavily on bedside observation as a check on research and laboratory findings. Today, the doctor has many instrumental aids which were not available to medical men of the past:

- the stethoscope was not devised by Laënnec until around 1819;

- Vierordt introduced the pulse tracing in 1855, although a thoughtful Egyptian doctor-priest-philosopher, some time before 2500 B.C., advised counting the pulse and observing its behavior in order to judge the heart action of his patient;

- Pasteur's researches in bacteriology opened the door to that branch of medicine about 1860;

- Auenbrugger developed the technique of chest percussion about 1761 and it was ignored until 1808;

- blood pressure measurements were first made by Stephen Hales in 1733, and practical instruments for clinical use date between 1860 and 1880;

- instruments for exploring the esophagus (gullet), the bladder, stomach and lower bowel, the breathing tubes and larynx and the depths of the eyeball came much later;

- the X ray dates from 1895.

Since the turn of the century, scientific progress has moved at an accelerated pace, bringing such new weapons as electric cautery, laser beams, radium and its emanation radon, radioactive isotopes and cobalt, physical therapy, and cameras that take pictures in "living color" of hollow organs such as the stomach. Advances in surgery, obstetrics, anesthesia, preventive inoculations, knowledge of nutrition and many other branches of medicine fill volumes of books and journals.

All these helps were unknown to the physicians of earlier days. Yet they have given us, in addition to the amazingly accurate clinical observations of Hippocrates and the ancients, many excellent descriptions of disease predating the modern diagnostic aids. Some of these have been so classically correct that they will always bear the names of their discoverers:

- Parkinson's disease, described by James Parkinson in 1819, is still recognized by the same symptoms;

- Richard Bright in 1827 wrote the first accurate description of the principal form of chronic kidney diseases;

- Moses, leading the Israelites out of Egypt, laid down sanitary and hygienic principles now largely supported by scientific evidence;

- Aretaeus of Cappadocia, in the second or third century B.C., handed down graphic accounts of pneumonia, pleurisy and other diseases;

- Thomas Sydenham (1624–89) described malaria, scarlet fever, measles, dysentery, gout and chorea (St. Vitus's dance), and distinguished measles from scarlet fever for the first time;

- William Hunter and his younger brother John made numerous additions to medical knowledge in the middle eighteenth century;

- Oliver Wendell Holmes of Boston in 1843 declared the contagiousness of childbed fever, a view supported by the clinical experience of Ignaz Semmelweiss in Vienna, thus revolutionizing the practice of obstetrics.

Medical history teems with chronicles of the great men of ages past, who added to medical knowledge bit by bit. But these were physicians; what have they to do with folklore? Just this. The "physicians" of ancient times and even up to the modern era, bear only the slightest resemblance to the highly trained doctor of today. They do have much in common—keen minds, devotion to professional objectives, ability to observe, willingness to learn. These men of the past were no less intelligent, no less alert, no less ingenious and imaginative than our contemporaries. Starting from nothing, they gave the original impetus to the snowballing of modern scientific progress which now proceeds at a dizzying pace not only in medicine, but in all branches of modern science.

These pioneers were not ashamed to consider the folklore of their time, to evaluate it in the light of their own knowledge and experience, to sift the true from the false. As we shall see, many established modern practices grew out of folklore, just as much folklore has persisted without foundation. It is our challenge to scrutinize the traditional beliefs, to keep what is good and reject the remainder. In so doing, we should not forget the pioneers who first pointed the way to the paths which we now tread so confidently.

Chapter Two

FOLKLORE, RELIGION, MEDICINE

When you were young, did your family, or neighbors or friends, believe one or more of the following ideas handed down from times past? Do you believe them now? Do you know where they began? Do you know how much truth there is in them, if any?

Eating between meals is harmful;
Bowels must act daily to keep one healthy;
Food will become poisonous if kept in an open can;
Wearing rubbers in the house is bad for your eyes;
Pimples and boils indicate bad blood;
Never eat fish and ice cream at the same meal;
Fat people are always jolly;
Marriages between cousins mean defective children;
Expectant mothers should eat little to assure a small baby;
Strenuous exercise can damage the heart even if it is normal.

These are just random samples. There are so many such traditional ideas that a complete list of them, even if one could be obtained, would fill many books the size of this one. The explanations would fill many more. We shall examine some of these beliefs later. Here, we are concerned with how and why they came into existence.

All folklore, including that pertaining to medicine, shows certain underlying influences or philosophies. These are the instinctive reactions against dangers which menace life and health, plus the impulse to be helpful to the sick and injured, and to prevent misfortune of any kind. These same motives dictate human behavior today; presumably and hopefully they always will.

In earlier times, religion and medicine were more closely allied than later, though an evidence of closer ties for the future has appeared in recent years. The earliest physicians were priests, and many were magicians as well. They mingled a reliance upon the supernatural with a shrewd understanding of human nature, and made use of the medicinal qualities observed in plants and believed to reside also in some animals.

A fundamental concept underlying many folklore beliefs was that the Creator of the universe as they knew it, had provided a remedy for every human ill. This thinking was applied to the sun, moon, stars, weather, and above all, nature with a capital N. Plants and trees were clothed with a multitude of beneficent and some malignant attributes. Belief in a Creator varied from adherence to one God, as exemplified in the Israelite theology, to the Greek belief in many gods, goddesses, sprites and demons.

This multiplicity of deities, as in the Greek and Roman myths, was characterized by personifying natural phenomena, human emotions, dangers and benefits; thus:

Greek   (Roman)

- Zeus (Jove or Jupiter) was the supreme and ruling deity;

- Hera (Juno) was the queen goddess and consort of Zeus;

- Athena or Pallas Athena (Minerva) was goddess of thunder and lightning, war, peace, arts and intelligence;

- Apollo (Apollo) was a god of many attributes—a sun-god (but not the sun itself), symbol of masculine beauty, protector of crops, sender and controller of epidemics, prophet, shepherd, musician, builder and many more;

- Artemis (Diana), goddess of the moon, huntress, somewhat like the feminine counterpart of Apollo. Although she shunned the society of men, she was the goddess of childbirth;

- Hermes (Mercury), messenger of the gods and god of the wind (indicated by winged heels). Although he was said to be a protector of travelers, he was also known to be the god of thieves! He was god of commerce, of athletics and health;

- Ares (Mars), god of war, personification of "brutal rage," more hated and feared than venerated, except, of course, by Venus;

- Hephaestus (Vulcan), god of fire, of the hearth, possibly related to lightning; divine blacksmith and artisan;

- Aphrodite (Venus), goddess of beauty and a dual personality:
  1) inspiring pure and ideal love, marriage;
  2) fostering prostitution and allied concepts;

- Eros (Cupid), son of Jupiter and Venus, and Psyche (soul) —typified erotic love;

- Charities (Gratiae)—the familiar three Graces:
  Aglaia, the brilliant, beautiful and good goddess;
  Thalia personified perpetual freshness;
  Euphrosyne rejoiced the heart with her cheerfulness.
  They presided over nature, and were related to gratitude. Perhaps because gratitude was quickly forgotten, the Graces were regarded as the daughters of Lethe, who represented oblivion!

- Poseidon (Neptune), god of the sea, of horse racing and of fertility;

- Hestia (Vesta), goddess of the hearth, a fire divinity; protector of homes and cities;

- Hecate, goddess of the underworld, sweetheart of Hermes, gave men prosperity in many activities of earth, but did send demons to torment others; men made images of her with three faces and placed the statues at important crossroads to lay gifts at her feet;

- Demeter (Ceres), goddess of agriculture and harvest;

- Dionysus (Bacchus), god of revelry, of wine and sex; with a retinue of related characters, many of them akin to sex;

- Asklepios (Aesculapius), god of medicine, whose sons were Machaon and Podaleirius, also skilled in medicine; his daughters were Hygeia, patroness of health and hygiene, and Panacea, concerned with "cures"; Zeus, afraid that Asklepios might render men immortal, finally slew him with a thunderbolt;

- Hades (Pluto), king of the underworld, feared as a symbol of evil, mystery and inexorable fate; revered as Pluto, a benevolent deity associated with Demeter;

- Nike, the winged goddess of victory, whose name is more familiar today as that of a modern missile, but was a descriptive word used in conjunction with Athena's name on a temple on the Acropolis (not the Parthenon).

The pantheon of ancient deities is almost without limit. In addition, the Graeco-Roman, here cited as a typical example, has many minor deities, besides sprites, nymphs, wood spirits and the spirits of individual trees, flowers, springs, winds, clouds, rain and almost any other concept that comes to mind. Some myths tell of human beings transformed into gods—Hercules and some of the Roman emperors, for example. Much of this mythology is frankly sexual, though it is taught in the schools in a greatly expurgated form. The gods are constantly represented as seducing mortal women or other gods; the genealogies attributed to some are complicated and often contradictory, depending on what authority is quoted.

This typical mythology has many parallels in that of Egypt, Sumer (Mesopotamia), the Norse countries, Teutonic legend and the worship rituals of the Orient. Savage tribes in many parts of the world have comparable beliefs and customs. Each is flavored by the human experience of its adherents; all have a basic origin in the belief in supernatural control and sponsorship of human affairs.

The Judaic-Christian theology differs from many others in its firm adherence to one God rather than a galaxy of major and minor deities. This belief in one Creative Force is evident also in Mohammedanism; in the Stoic philosophy of ancient Greece; in Buddhism to a limited extent; and in the Indian (Vedic) philosophy. The American Indian also postulated one Great Spirit, but had room for lesser deities. Although the connection is not always clear, it would appear that most folklore goes back ultimately to the supernatural or observable natural phenomena. It has, of course, often been considerably modified or even corrupted in its transmission, frequently by word of mouth through many generations.

Belief in the supernatural is evident in the idea that nothing in the plant world grows without a purpose. This is interpreted to mean that all is planned for man's welfare, health and happiness. It is expressed in Shakespeare's *Romeo and Juliet*:

> "O! Fickle is the powerful grace that lies
> In herbs, plants, stones and their true qualities:
> For naught so vile that on the earth doth live
> But to the earth some special good doth give."

Following this reasoning, one is better able to understand some of the bizarre and often repulsive measures advised in folklore for the treatment of disease, (see Chapter Five).

Another alleged manifestation of the Creator's seeming desire to help man in every possible way is the so-called "doctrine of signatures." If plants, animals and stones were created to contribute to human welfare, then man must have means of recognizing the beneficent objects and applying them to his purpose. The doctrine of signatures was not unlike the religious doctrine of an inward and spiritual grace manifested in outward signs (Krutch). Here it is sufficient to mention such analogies as the hepatica, so named because the shape of its leaves resembled, or seemed to, the human liver (hepar). This doctrine was not prominent among the ancients. It flourished in the middle ages, and vestiges remain in the almost extinct philosophy of homeopathy, "like cures like," and the far from obsolete reliance of the drinker on the efficacy of "hair of the dog that bit me" for treating a hang-over.

NUMBERS

Numbers play an important part in folklore. The principle magic numbers are seven, nine and twelve.

A Turkoman ceremony for curing fever employs a string with seven knots, worn on the wrist by the patient; one knot is untied each day. Untying the seventh knot is followed by throwing the string, rolled into a ball, into a river—and the fever with it! The Athenians were required to send seven youths and seven maidens every eight years to Minos (Crete) where they were supposedly devoured by the Minotaur (the half-human, half-bull god).

The seventh day is the Sabbath of Jewish and Christian Scriptures. It is also the day of the great festival fires customary in Europe in the spring, when flocks are driven through fires to protect men against evil, while men, women and children used to leap over the fires to purify themselves. These took place in the Lenten season, at midsummer and in midwinter.

Even the sophisticated modern clings to the number seven in his shooting of craps! Otherwise he scoffs at these numbers superstitions, from which he regards himself as emancipated. He is concerned only with numbers of another kind—street address, zip code, telephone, driver's license, credit cards (by the dozen), bank accounts, Social Security, stocks and bonds (if lucky enough to have any), voters' registration, car keys (and others), batting averages, sweepstakes, bingo, bridge "slams," poker hands and the racketeers' numbers game!

True, belief that things happen in threes remains prevalent today even among the most enlightened persons, as does a firm belief in seven as a lucky number, and thirteen as a signal of danger. Yet the number three, strangely enough, does not appear as often as might be expected, and then only in combinations of three times three making nine. Virgil tells of the maid trying to draw her lover to her by tying three knots on three strings of three different colors. If a rival succeeded in untying the knots, the magic failed.

The number nine appears in many fire rituals: in Scotland in the Beltane fires of May Day; in the Balder's fires of Norway; in St. John's fires in Sweden, Austria, Germany and elsewhere in central Europe and Russia. Space forbids detailed description of these festivals beyond saying that they were concerned with agriculture and the harvest.

Number nine appears in a procedure practiced on the isle of Nias near Sumatra. When a wild pig falls into a pittrap, it is taken out and its back rubbed with nine leaves to make nine more pigs fall in.

In Lithuania, farmers take nine handfuls of each kind of crop, before the grain is used for any other purpose, and divide each handful into three parts. The twenty-seven portions are then mixed and used to make bread and beer, which are ceremonially consumed by the family.

Twelve is recognized today in the number of months in the year, the signs of the Zodiac, the Apostles of Jesus Christ, the tribes of Israel, the twelve days of Christmas, twelve units to a dozen, the twelve steps of Alcoholics Anonymous, and in many ceremonies and customs, both ancient and modern.

One of these is the driving out of witches during the Twelve Days of Christmas, when peasants burned pine resin to smoke them out or fired shots over the fields to scare them, and wrapped straw around the fruit trees as a protection against evil spirits. Twelve is associated also with the fire festivals mentioned above, particularly those of the Twelfth-night (or day) made familiar in the Shakespearean play of that name.

Friday the thirteenth is faced with apprehension by many who sneer at other peoples' "superstitions." Many will not sit down to a meal if there are thirteen persons at table, nor take three lights from one match, and so on and on!

Finally, the modern scientist relies heavily on mathematics (numbers!), though not in terms of superstition. There was a glimmer of scientific truth in the belief in numbers. Many evidences exist of periodicity or cycles in nature and disease. Before immunizations and other preventives were developed, epidemics of communicable diseases were fairly predictable on a basis of:

measles every twenty-seven months, spring and fall,

German measles every two years in winter,

whooping cough every other summer,

diphtheria every five years,

scarlet fever every seven years,

typhoid fever every fall,

severe influenza every thirty years, and milder forms during most winters.

Before the advent of antibiotics and the sulfonamides, the doctor expected a crisis in pneumonia on the seventh or eighth day; typhoid fever had a normal cycle of seven days growing worse, seven days holding even and seven days of slow improvement—subject, of course, to variations influenced by complications or individual differences in resistance among patients.

The ordered sequence of the seasons, determined by the motion of the earth around the sun, the phenomena of astronomy and especially the positions of the moon and of the stars, are all expressed in mathematical terms. Small wonder then that man pinned his faith on numbers.

COLORS

A man and his wife, window shopping, stopped in front of an art-goods store and looked at a landscape on display.

"I like that," he said.

"Yes, it's nice," she replied, "but I couldn't live with it."

"Why not?"

"It's too cold."

The picture was indeed done in what artists and decorators call cold or cool colors—predominantly blue and green. These, in the more delicate tints, are soothing; in darker shades, they may be depressing, especially when predominant in a room or a picture. Yellow and orange are classed as warm colors, stimulating and, if overdone, perhaps irritating. Red is the color of flame, fire and passion. Grays can be warm or cool, depending on the amount of the warm or cool primary color which enters into their mixing.

White is the symbol of purity and innocence, but in certain cultures it is also the color of mourning, contrary to our custom of wearing black to denote our sorrow. Here's an old verse:

> "When Christmas is white
> The graveyard is lean.
> But fat is the graveyard
> When Christmas is green."

In everyday life we express our moods in colors—bright gay prints and weaves for women's clothes, or color accents for so-called basic dresses. Men have a more limited scope, but ties, socks, blazers, shirts and vests give considerable chance for display of temperament and preference. And nowadays, among the really adventurous males, one sees bright green, orange and blue slacks. Wow!

Room décor too may be light and airy or dull and somber, depending on color choices. Even the office has departed from its monotonous tones and we now see color in draperies, rugs and the upholstery of chairs and settees, as well as paintings and other accessories. Files and other office equipment are now often seen in many colors.

The influence of color on individual reactions is given consideration in the newer hospital décor, which has departed from the white sameness of the past in favor of colorful walls, draperies and spreads, and the hanging of pictures in patients' rooms. Operating arenas are now painted in less dazzling hues than white; often gray, beige, or soft green, which is much easier on the eyes. Surgical drapes and gowns too may be of pastel shades rather than white.

Color has always played a large part in commonly used expressions such as:

green with envy; *green*-eyed with jealousy,
> true *blue*,
>> *yellow* to signify cowardice, jealousy or sickliness,
>>> a real *white* guy,
>>>> born to the *purple*, or *purple* with rage,
>>>> *black*-hearted villain,
>>>>> *pink* haze of romance,
>>>>>> *rose-colored* glasses,
>>>>>>> *orange* for simplicity,
>>>>>>>> *brown* study, indicating deep thought,
>>>>>>>>> seeing *red* . . .

Red, the most significant color, has had different meanings attributed even to its several shadings:

scarlet . . . anger or other emotional reaction,
crimson . . . animal passion,
bright red . . . courage and confidence.

The old-time weather prophet used to quote the verse:

> "Evening red, morning gray,
>> Will set the traveler on his way.
> Evening gray, morning red,
>> Will pour down rain on the traveler's head."

Then he would call attention to patches of blue sky—Dutchman's britches—a sure indication of clearing weather.

These color associations go back a long way into history. Red has been regarded in China and New Zealand as hateful to evil spirits. It is commonly recognized as the color of inflammation. The medical historian, Garrison, mentions bands of red silk, strings of red-coral beads, red pills and red fire, all with medicinal associations of various kinds. Red-coral rings and bells have been used for babies to help them cut their teeth. The red flannel around the neck for sore throats, still commonly used, was not regarded as effective because of the warmth of the flannel, but because of its red color.

In relatively modern times, red (Finsen) light was used in the treatment of smallpox to prevent pitting. But this was nothing new; smallpox patients in Japan were surrounded with drapes of red cloth in ancient times, and the red-light treatment for smallpox was used to treat the son of King Edward II of England early in the fourteenth century.

The reasoning behind these beliefs in color virtues was part of the doctrine of signatures, "like cures like," already mentioned. Eruptions and inflammation are red, and so red is the logical treatment.

Color of the eyes is supposedly indicative of character:

> green eyes . . . untrustworthy and jealous
> gray eyes . . . greedy
> blue eyes . . . beauty
> black eyes . . . "sure to tell lies."

We still look to color today, for its influence on our lives. Gray days depress us, bright ones stimulate. The dark hours of night are often peopled with fears and forebodings, and the biological clock which regulates our lives is sensitive to light, which is the essence of color.

TABOOS

Taboos loomed large in folklore. A taboo or tabu is a prohibition of actions believed to have adverse influence, often, but not always, when no valid proof of such relation exists. Their pattern varies, but there is an underlying sameness in all—that the doing of certain acts under certain circumstances will bring failure, disappointment or disaster up to and including not only death, but evil effects in the hereafter. This is the reverse of the belief in efficacy of rituals for accomplishing desired ends.

Taboos existed on the following subjects, and perhaps many more:

- food: items prohibited, manner of preparation;

- eating and drinking circumstances, time and manner of eating;

- against becoming parents of twins;

- time and manner of quitting one's habitation;

- conduct of mourning for the dead;

- behavior of warriors, hunters and fishermen;

- relating to use of iron (not to be used to cut mistletoe);

- against contacts with blood, animal or human;

- complicated lore about knots and rings;

- against addressing people by name (in some circles; some wives still address their husbands as "Mr. . . .");

- against use of personal names of friends;

- against using names of the dead, of relatives, kings, gods or sacred persons, for fear of offending evil spirits or disturbing the spirits of the deceased;

- governing royal or priestly conduct;

- about how to meet strangers;

- against showing the face (this is still in effect in parts of Arabia);

- against leaving food uneaten (children are still admonished to clean up their plates);

- about menstruating women, supposedly causing food to spoil or having unfavorable influence on progress of the sick if they act as nurses;

- about sharp weapons (this persists in the custom of demanding a penny in exchange for a gift of any sharp object, to avoid "cutting" the ties of friendship).

These taboos vary in different cultures, but they have an underlying pattern; they are either protective against unfavorable influences, or intended to induce beneficial outcomes. Many of the old taboos remain as custom or etiquette, such as leaving food on the plate to assure against future want. Others must be regarded as superstitions that have refused to die; among these is the taboo against menstruating women being engaged in food canning or nursing services.

HOW MEDICAL FOLKLORE SPREADS

Before the days of modern transportation and communications, folklore spread around the world through travel, migrations, explorations, wars and conquests. An excellent example of this is the common belief still held in Mexico that the cause of illnesses lies in evil winds or spirits, the evil eye or black magic. Naturally then, diagnosis and treatment had to originate in magic too. As late as 1947, Frances Toor reported personal observations of folklore "curers" at work. These are a mixture of traditional Mexican methods plus those introduced by the Spanish conquest and quite likely added to by the later French adventure. Among the methods used are bleeding, cupping, massage, sucking of wounds, and application of spittle, plus prayers addressed to the good and evil spirits, pagan gods and Christian saints. In common use are herbs, minerals and other substances which, coupled with the appropriate incantations, are held to be endowed with magical powers.

The Mexicans have an advanced knowledge of botanical properties. Thousands of herbs and plants and their medicinal values are known to practitioners of herb medicine. Herbs and simples are still sold in markets and from baskets along the streets, with full instructions as to their preparation and use. The stocks include numerous medicinal herbs, wild flowers, twigs, roots, branches and minerals, and the vendors know their wares.

A leading herb doctor in Mexico City was Doña Refugio. Frances Toor reports the case of a man whom she observed being treated by Doña Refugio. He was supposed to have been sickened by a witch hired by an angry neighbor. He was lying on a straw mat, and was badly in need of a bath. He was rubbed with a mixture of yellow daisies, violets, poppies and rosemary in alcohol. The next step was to slit the throat of a black hen—it had to be black if its magic were to be potent against the evil spirits. The hen's blood, mixed with grated pineapple and sherry wine and sweetened with sugar, was given to the patient to drink slowly, meanwhile making supplications to the Virgin of Guadalupe, who would certainly cure him. The hen was then cooked and eaten by the patient. After several weekly treatments of this nature, the patient seemed to be recovering. With tender loving care and good food, this could hardly be surprising, assuming the illness was one of the more common ones not requiring specific medical or surgical treatment.

Frances Toor also reports having been treated herself by Doña Juana, an herb doctor in the village of Tepoztlán, State of Morelos. The diagnosis was made by "cleaning" the whole body with an egg, which *afterward* was broken into a dish, and the form it assumed compared by the *curandera* to a snake. This was a sure indication of having been bitten by the Aztec air spirits, the *aquajque*. The treatment consisted in vigorous massage with herbs in warm oil on two days in succession; on the third day she was given a sweat bath in a low chamber or *tanazcal* into which she had to crawl. Here she was given a vigorous scrubbing with maguey (century plant) fibers and a beating with a branch of moist leaves. When she departed, the curandera gave her the branch to throw into a stream which she had to cross. She also was instructed to pray to the Virgin to be delivered of the aquajque. These spirits were supposed to frequent streams and hills.

The Mexican curanderas believe that when such spirits as the aquajque are stubborn about getting out of the patient, they have to be bribed with tiny clay-and-dough toys in the form of toads, snakes, and other reptiles and dolls. These gifts must be accompanied by a pair of candles, some tamales and a meat dish with gravy and raisins, pumpkin seeds, eggs, chilies and other ingredients. Everything is arranged tastefully in a basket trimmed with bright-colored paper because the spirits like gay colors. The patient takes all this to the place where the spirits have supposedly attacked him, and begs them to leave him in peace. In some places the offerings are buried; in others they are simply left for the spirits who, some unbelievers suggest, materialize in the form of the curandera who takes the food home for herself.

Some of the "cures" are offensive to the patient, such as the spraying of medicaments from the mouth of the curandera. Some of the treatments seem reasonable, but others do not. Many diseases are diagnosed by taking the patient's pulse while the "doctor" takes liberal drinks of *chicha* (brandy). The pulse-takers do not charge the patient, but the chicha they consume is expensive. In serious cases two or more, up to eight, pulse-takers may be called.

In order to help find out why the patient has been afflicted by witchcraft, he must confess what sins he has committed such as:

- quarrels with his spouse;
- revealing family secrets to neighbors;
- denying favors or services to relatives or friends;
- failing to invite to his fiestas all who are entitled to be invited;
- insulting or beating a friend.

Other members of the patient's family may also be questioned on these and related matters. Parents answer for sick children.

SEEING STARS

It was probably inevitable that ancient observers should link the heavenly bodies with earthly creatures and creations, since both were the work of the same Creator. Early concepts of man's relationship to the stars were erroneous, but even so, there are still many who seem to believe in astrological influences under the twelve signs of the Zodiac which refer to the twelve constellations encircling the earth and the sun. The sun, moon and planets are said to be "in" a constellation when they appear to pass by its area of sky. Each sign or phase, is called a "house." Each "house" is said to be ruled by a planet. The house just below the horizon when a person is born is believed to be *ascendant,* and to influence the life of that individual in

specific ways. This is the horoscope. For example, by knowing the
date and the hour of a person's birth, the astrologer claims to
be able to forecast the person's character, his activities and his
future life. This implies the ability to advise about decisions
relating to business affairs, marriage and other vital matters. The
horoscopes, which are still being published, are usually phrased
in so general a manner that there is little likelihood of predicting anything with certainty. This vagueness carries with it
the advantage—to the prognosticator—of seldom being wrong.
The gullible believer usually remembers best the prediction he
most wishes to realize. He retains the memory of the chance
"accuracy" of predictions which "came true," and conveniently
forgets those which did not.

The signs of the Zodiac are as follows:

Name and Meaning	Beginning	Ending
Aries, the Ram		
House of life	21 March	19 April
Taurus, the Bull		
House of riches	20 April	20 May
Gemini, the Twins		
House of brethren	21 May	21 June
Cancer, the Crab		
House of parents	22 June	22 July
Leo, the Lion		
House of children	23 July	22 August
Virgo, the Virgin		
House of health	23 August	22 September
Libra, the Scales		
House of marriage	23 September	23 October
Scorpio, the Scorpion		
House of death	24 October	21 November
Sagittarius, the Archer		
House of religion	22 November	21 December
Capricornus, the Goat		
House of dignities	22 December	19 January
Aquarius, the Water Bearer		
House of friends	20 January	18 February
Pisces, the Fishes		
House of enemies	19 February	20 March

Astrology was based on the mistaken theory of Ptolemy who held that the sun revolved around the earth rather than the actual fact, which is that the earth revolves around the sun. Not until Copernicus set the matter straight in 1543, did the modern science of astronomy displace the fallacious beliefs of the astrologers.

Modern science rejects astrology as based on a wrong concept of the stars, and considers horoscopes unsupported by scientific evidence. Yet as one considers the differences in disease occurrence at different times of the year, and other evidences of seasonal periodicity, one can understand how a belief in the influence of the stars could come about. And astrology was the forerunner of astronomy, a true science.

MAGICAL HEALERS

The ancient priest, like the modern clergyman, found man a difficult and often perverse individual, who could be led only through a shrewd understanding of his psychology. It is scarcely to be wondered, then, that priests, healers and magicians cultivated the same aptitudes at leadership which have been found successful in all ages. They used charms, incantations, and the power of suggestion, as will be shown in more detail in specific instances. They appealed to the emotions, with which many human beings do more thinking than with their intellect.

The magician-priest-healer was well versed in such drug lore as existed in his day. The use of drugs in religious rituals is still in vogue in the American Southwest, where mescal and peyote remain legal when used in established religious worship.

The ancient healers had their due percentage of cures, mainly in self-limited diseases. These still account for the majority of recoveries today, usually with little or no medical treatment, or merely the exercise of homespun methods and good nursing. Folk medicine is still being practiced today. The modern doctor has begun to recognize the importance of the emotions in the treatment of disease, as did his distant predecessor, and terms it psychosomatic medicine. Doctor and clergy, now separate entities, nevertheless are learning the value of collaboration.

Along with the doctor-priest-magician, the olden times had

their knowledgeable women ("Grannies"), who gathered herbs and prepared them for use in teas, powders, and poultices. Some of these remedies, like foxglove leaves from which digitalis sprang and bread mold which contained, all unknown to its users, the modern penicillin, were forerunners of the drugs we use today in more refined form. Rest, encouragement and hope, together with the natural resistance of the body, accounted for many cures. These were remembered and talked about, until they became accepted tradition. The failures, which occurred in the case of serious diseases or poor resistance in the patient, or perhaps the unskillful use of drugs or inadvertent administration of toxic substances, were conveniently forgotten, or plausibly explained away. In a generation or so the apparently successful procedures became traditional.

The role of the female herb doctor, practiced mainly by older women, was not always a rewarding one. In some instances these grannies became known as witches, which was all right so long as their ministrations were successful. But in the face of failure, the wrath of the community was likely to be visited upon them, whether the fault lay with them or not. The modern doctor, often the victim of character assassination over the bridge table, in the barroom or the launderette, may well feel a kinship with these unfortunates. It is not so many centuries since the witch burnings of our own Salem. A belief in the supernatural easily translates itself into fear of witches and demons as well as reverence for a benign God.

Psychology, belief, credulity and faith played a large part in folklore in all generations. It still does. Modern medicine, never averse to accepting valuable ideas from many sources, has adopted the basic philosophy of folk medicine, even while rejecting its erroneous specifics.

What else is the psychosomatic medicine of our enlightened age, if not a composite of the ingredients of folklore, plus the evaluation standards of scientific inquiry? Never, since the most ancient days of medical history, has so much attention been paid to man's mind and spirit—his psyche—as today.

All this puts us in a very poor position to scoff at those who originally pointed out the paths of progress, even though they may have wandered from time to time into the byways of error. We, too, are fallible.

Against this background, we may now look at another phase of medical folklore and practice, witchcraft, and the witch doctor.

Chapter Three

WITCHES, WITCHCRAFT AND WITCH DOCTORING

Folk medicine leads naturally into a consideration of witches, witchcraft and witch doctors.

The Encyclopedia Britannica relates witchcraft to "the art or the craft of the *wise*, as the word witch is allied with wit, *to know*." The older form *wist* clarifies this significance. But this is far from the popular concept, although knowledge is included in the attributes of the witch, as commonly accepted.

Witches were supposed to be persons, usually women, who possessed supernatural powers by reason of selling their souls to the devil. Male "witches" were occasionally believed to exist, and they were called wizards, warlocks or sorcerers, but they were rare, and less likely to be regarded with the superstitious fear attached to the witch. The Wizard of Oz is a typically likable character. As a character in children's stories, the wicked witch portrays pretty well the adult(!) concept prevalent among rich and poor, educated and ignorant, throughout the Middle Ages and even into the modern era.

Witches were believed to be endowed with the power of sorcery, and of foretelling the future. Usually pictured as old, ugly, ill-tempered and unkempt, they were frightening apparitions to the superstitious minds of believers in supernatural beings and powers, many of them evil. Add to this the reputed power of witches to ride in the air on broomsticks, to pass through keyholes, to change themselves into animals and back again, to cast evil spells upon human beings and animals, and it is easy to see how they inspired great fear among the people. Fear is easily transmuted into hate, and hate into persecution.

Elderly women living alone tend to have pets, and often these pets are cats. Many an unfortunate, poverty stricken, forsaken old woman who possessed one or more cats, was accused of witchcraft, and thousands of alleged witches were killed after conviction on the flimsiest evidence. Young children sometimes testified that they had seen such women visited by the devil in the form of a black dog, or a black cat, or in one instance, a spotted cat. Psychiatrists today recognize the occasional occurrence of a malevolent child who carries mischief to incredible and often sadistic lengths.

Occasionally a young and attractive woman was accused of witchcraft; a colloquialism common even today applies the term "bewitching" to a charming woman, and Shakespeare pays tribute to the witchery in a woman's weeping:

> "Oh, Father, what a heel of witchcraft lies,
> In the small orb of one particular tear."

In harmony with the belief in malignant powers of gods, spirits and demons, natural catastrophes such as wars, famines, epidemics among human beings, crop failures, sickening of domestic animals, or any other calamity which was not fully understood, were attributed to witchcraft, and blamed on individuals accused of the power to "witch," or bewitch. Accusation was as good as conviction, the temper of the times being what it was.

We read of witchcraft in the Old Testament, where the witch of Endor, consulted by Saul contrary to Hebrew law, prophesied to him that his kingdom would be wrested from him by David. The Egyptians believed in witches, and the Romans worshiped the goddess Hecate as patroness of witchcraft and sorcery.

Shakespeare, in Act IV of *Macbeth*, portrays the current concept of witches and witchcraft in his time; the scene is a forbidding cavern, in the midst of which a caldron is boiling; the three witches speak:

> First Witch: Thrice the brinded cat hath mew'd.
> Second Witch: Thrice and once the hedge-pig whined.
> Third Witch: Harpier cries " 'Tis time, 'tis time."
> First Witch: Round about the cauldron go:
> In the poison'd entrails throw.
> Toad, that under cold stone

> Days and nights has thirty one
> Swelter'd venom sleeping got,
> Boil thou first i' the charmed pot.
All: Double, double toil and trouble;
> Fire burn and cauldron bubble.

And so, speaking by turns, they add the sinister ingredients of their sorcery; the second witch starts with a fillet from a fenny snake, the eye of a newt and toe of a frog, the wool of a bat and the tongue of a dog, the forked tongue of an adder and the sting of a blindworm (lizard), a lizard's leg and the wing of a young owl. And then the refrain:

> Double, double toil and . . .

Now the third witch adds the scale of a dragon, tooth of a wolf, a witch's mummy, portions from the carcass of a shark, root of the poisonous hemlock, liver of a Jew, the gall (bladder) of a goat and slips of yew, nose of a Turk and lips of a Tartar, the finger of an illegitimate child of a prostitute strangled after being born in a ditch, some portion of a tiger called *chaudron*, "For the ingredients of our cauldron."

> Fire burn and cauldron bubble. . . . And finally,
Second Witch: Cool it with a baboon's blood,
> Then the charm is firm and good.
> By the pricking o' my thumbs,
> Something wicked this way comes . . .

In this masterly passage we find a summing up of the common belief about witches and witchcraft. They were believed to brew trouble by wicked incantations, and to use such repulsive materials for sorcery as are enumerated in the chants. We see here the belief that toads were poisonous, and they were either the familiar spirits of witches or witches in disguise. We meet the nonexistent but dreaded dragon, the superstitious fear of mummies and the dead, a poisonous herb and the rapacious shark. We encounter the evil of racial prejudice, specifically anti-Semitism. Included are the bitter organ (gall bladder) of a goat, and another poisonous plant, the yew. . . . But why go on? Here is a fearsome concentration of malice, wickedness and hatred which can explain if not justify the insane fear and hate for alleged witches which fanned the flames of persecution as late as the eighteenth century.

The practice of witchcraft was not confined to such evil purposes as those portrayed in Macbeth's murder of the king. Petitions for good fishing, a bountiful harvest, a favorable wind or safety at sea, success in love, political preferment, or victory in war could be the subject of charms, spells and incantations.

Spells, a Teutonic word meaning *spoken*, are combinations of words, used according to a formula, intended to bring about a desired result, or prevent one not desired. In Australia, a tribe of the "witchetty-grub totem," desiring a plentiful harvest of these grubs, organize a procession to certain stones shaped somewhat like the grubs, and rub their stomachs with the stones. This procedure is accompanied by a positive statement that they have had plenty to eat—one way of persuading the god in advance that their spell is potent.

Or the prayer for rain used by the Masai, whose chief god's name is the word for rain; they simply chant "Rain, rain, rain!" in chorus. Sometimes it actually does rain.

In Melanesia and elsewhere, a man may possess a ritual and sell it or bequeath it to an heir—the money is paid for the words or spell. Such spells degenerate into merely mysterious or nonsensical sound sequences like *abracadabra*.

Charms, like spells, are songs—the word comes from the Latin *carmen*, a song. They are used in connection with amulets and the teeth or claws of animals on chains or strings, or on bracelets. The charm bracelet, devoid of its traditional significance, is a favorite adornment of the modern woman. In the days of witchcraft, charms might have had sinister implications, or they might have been worn as a defense against evil. The pieces of skull removed during ancient trephining operations were often used as amulets, perhaps to forestall further need for surgery. Many other objects and substances were incorporated into amulets or worn as such, depending upon the culture from which the idea sprang. The amulet survives today in the form of religious medals, lockets containing hair of a loved one or the individual's picture; and in some quarters, the asafetida bag is worn to ward off communicable diseases. The latter purpose is accomplished by warding off people who carry the contagion, and is not as ridiculous as it may seem. The amber beads worn to ward off goiters, even today, are another form of the amulet.

What is the truth about witches? The light of modern knowledge exposes many of the fallacies by which suspected witches were tested and then accused. Any lonely old woman, or even a studious person of either sex with too great an interest in science, might be accused of witchcraft. It seems virtually certain that such accusations may not infrequently have been made for the purpose of removing rivals or of avenging fancied (or real) grievances, especially since belief in witchcraft was not limited to the ignorant. It extended into the ranks of scientists and rulers.

The only references to withcraft I could find in Sumerian laws are probably "repeats" in the Code of Hammurabi:

> "If a man weave a spell and put a ban on a man, and has not justified himself, he that wove the spell upon him shall be put to death."
>
> "If a man has put a spell upon a man, and has not justified himself, he upon whom the spell is laid shall go to the holy river, (Euphrates, then known as the Purattu) he shall plunge into the holy river, and if the holy river overcome him, he who wove the spell upon him shall take to himself his house. If the holy river makes that man to be innocent, and has saved him, he who laid the spell upon him shall be put to death. He who plunged into the holy river shall take to himself the house of him who wove the spell upon him."

—"The Oldest Code of Laws" Trans. by C. H. W. Johns, M.A. Pub. by T. & T. Clark, Edinburgh, eight printings to 1926.

Another test was performed with large brass pins, which were thrust into the body to test its sensitivity to pain; this was done by official or self-appointed *witch-prickers*. If the accused did not feel pain, she was considered guilty; no one understood at that time the insensitive areas which appear in the skin of hysterical persons. (*Hysterical* does not mean the laughing jag commonly so called; hysteria is a psychological disturbance in which varied symptoms may occur, such as paralysis, blindness, and many other manifestations, all from emotional causes.) Still another test method, practiced by one of the notorious witch-prickers, Matthew Hopkins of East Anglia, in the seventeenth century, was to keep the accused awake for several days and nights, and to starve her at the same time, until in desperation a confession of witchcraft was offered.

Hemorrhages under the skin, another indication sometimes found in hysteria, were regarded as proof against a suspected witch. Witchcraft was connected also with the persistence of the superstition about the *incubus*, a supposed evil spirit which preyed sexually upon women and was related to nightmares; and the female version of the same, the *succubus*, which attacked sleeping men in similar fashion. Both are now satisfactorily explained by the erotic dream. But such experience could readily be made the occasion of an accusation against someone feared or disliked. The motivation might be genuine or selfishly conceived—who was to say which?

Before we scoff at such "way out" ideas, we may well consider the type of individual who believed in witchcraft in its heyday, during the seventeenth and early eighteenth centuries. One was King James VI of Scotland, later James I of England, who wrote a book on demonology in 1597. The king believed that a storm at sea, in which he almost lost his Danish bride en route from Norway to Scotland, had been conjured up by a schoolmaster named Fian, who was reputed to be a leader in witchcraft. Fian was tried by torture and executed in 1590. The manner in which he was supposed to have caused the storm was by throwing cats into the sea! In his later years, the king changed his views, but Fian had already paid the penalty of superstitious royal malice.

Martin Luther declared that he would burn all witches. The medieval church made a strong stand against witchcraft. Pope Innocent VIII authorized the burning of witches in 1484.

Many physicians believed in witches and in pacts with the devil, including one of the most eminent clinicians of the seventeenth century, Daniel Sennert. Sennert, who contributed important treatises on scurvy, was one of the first to recognize scarlet fever, and gave an early description of the consequences of alcoholism. Still, he believed in witches.

Sir Thomas Browne, author of *Religio Medici*, one of medicine's great inspirational classics, nevertheless stated in that work, "I have ever believed, and do now know, that there are witches." He testified at a witchcraft trial in Bury St. Edmunds in 1664 when two women were tried on charges of causing fits in a child, stating that while the fits were natural, they were "heightened to a great excess by the devil co-operating." He stated also that there had been a "great discovery of witches" in Denmark shortly before the trial.

A few able physicians tried to stem the malignant tide of witch-hunting. Among them was the great Dutch surgeon, Johann Weyer, who led in the rationalization of magic and opposition to witchcraft in the early fifteenth century. Weyer declared that witches "are poor ignorant creatures, old and power-less, *who imagine themselves* to be the cause of the evils which God sends to man and beast." The italics are mine, because I want to emphasize that these imaginings, now known as halluci-nations, are well recognized psychotic manifestations.

Turning oneself into an animal and back again is one of the oldest forms of superstition. An early illustration of animal dis-guise is found in the Arlege cave paintings in southern France, where a man is portrayed clothed in a deerskin with antlers on his head. It is not hard to trace an analogy from this to the numerous uses of hides, horns, teeth, feathers, claws, bones, skins and hoofs in worship rituals, ceremonials, war-dress and medicine-man costuming. These were all based on a belief in the magic residing in gods masquerading as animals.* Witches accused of becoming black cats are said to have borne on their persons, in human form, the wounds or scars corresponding to injuries received in their animal impersonations. If the supposed transformation was effected by donning the skin of the animal, it certainly would follow that wounds inflicted would appear in corresponding locations on the body. The facts were right, but the reasoning was faulty.

Ancient foretelling, predicting or divining was often done by the use of animal entrails, as indicated by the witches in Mac-beth. The internal organs of sheep, pigs and poultry were be-lieved to contain the prophecies of future events, especially if they differed in any way from the familiar normal observed at slaughter. Witches also used animals somewhat after the fashion of the spiritualistic "control." This was considered legitimate in Rome, and known as an augury; in Greece the oracles were revered as sources of wisdom. But in later centuries the witches of Europe were constrained to foretell only favorable events, and hope that they came about reasonably soon. Unfavorable divining or failure to make good were certain to bring trouble to the foreteller. The animal, or "familiar spirit," might be a dog, a cat or a toad; in France it was always a toad.

The famous English physician William Harvey, discoverer of the circulation of the blood, used one of these familiars to demonstrate his conviction that witchcraft was a superstition without foundation in fact. Harvey unmasked an alleged witch at Newmarket through her familiar, a toad to which she attributed her divining power. He induced her to coax the toad with an offer of milk, then declared that he too was a sorcerer, and that it would be fine for the two magicians to have a drink of ale together. While she went for the ale, he took advantage of her absence to kill and dissect the toad, which he found just like any other toad. He had some difficulty escaping her wrath upon her return.

Harvey was a confirmed skeptic about witches. He testified at one of the witchcraft trials at Lancaster, after examining four of the persons accused of witchcraft, and found no evidence to confirm the charges; they were acquitted.

The English witchcraft trials were typical of persecutions which occurred in many parts of the world. In 1612, during the reign of James I, two old women who lived in a forest in miserable poverty, were arrested, accused of witchcraft. Their daughters were arrested, too, and so were about a dozen other persons. They were held in prison until brought to trial at Lancaster. The evidence on which the convictions were based included that of a child who "saw" the devil visit one of the "witches" in the form of a black dog. Ten persons were convicted and hanged, including one of the two old women; the other died in prison. At the second Lancaster trials in 1633, where Dr. William Harvey testified, seventeen persons were convicted, mainly on the evidence of an eleven-year-old boy, who had achieved a reputation as a detector of witches. What a ball that brat must have had!

The witchcraft delusion came to the American colonies in the

1692 arrest of hundreds of suspects in Salem, Massachusetts. The trials which followed caused nineteen persons to be hanged; one other was pressed to death for refusing to enter a plea. It began with accusations by ten young girls that an Indian slave of the Reverend Samuel Parris, and two old women, had bewitched them. Early in 1693 the governor ordered the release of all those charged who were still living.

Prominent in this episode was the Reverend Cotton Mather, son of a minister and described as a man of great learning. He was the first American elected to the British Royal Society, and a person of considerable courage. Against strong opposition and threats of mob violence, he advocated inoculation against small-pox, which in his day was the best hope for prevention. Vaccination was still a century in the future. Unfortunately, his writings against witchcraft were influential in stirring up popular feeling. Although he warned against putting faith in "spectral" evidence, he nevertheless defended some of the verdicts. Later, like King James, he changed his views and acknowledged the unfairness of the persecutions.

The history of witchcraft is a frightening example of how inconsistent even the most distinguished thinkers can be when panic possesses a populace. To this day, the term "witch-hunting" is used to designate social or political mistreatment of innocent persons. Sometimes a world leader like Churchill or Hoover lives long enough to see his justification by later events, but many a good man or woman is ruined by the witch-hunters of the twentieth century just as were the victims of the persecutions in the past.

Medicine and religion eventually became somewhat emancipated from the superstitious thrall of witchcraft, but traces remain even now. In many areas of the world, belief in black magic persists. There are still people who believe that some individuals have the power to "hex" others. *Hexe* is the German word for witch. Some ethnic groups of Teutonic origin still believe in hexing an enemy or rival, and live in fear of being hexed.

Voodoo, practiced among some of the people of the West Indies, notably Haiti, and in some parts of the United States, bears a strong resemblance to medieval witchcraft. Believers become "possessed" of their gods, speak in strange tongues and participate in frenzied dancing and in rituals involving snakes, chickens and other animals, some of which may be sacrificed. Prayers, incantations and charms are used to procure favors for the suppliants or to bring harm to others. They have been accused of obscene rituals and human blood sacrifices. The ancient device of inflicting damage upon a doll or image supposedly representing the person they wish to injure or kill, has caused death from fright, or suicide, after such rituals.

A belief in the "evil eye" also persists among credulous people. This is the supposed power to bring disease, misfortune or death upon a person by casting a spell through the power of the eyes. The exercise of hypnotic power may have been used by some folk before this influence was fully understood. The evil eye was not uncommonly attributed to unfortunate persons who had some defect or abnormality which gave their eyes an unusual appearance.

WITCH DOCTORS

An understanding of witchcraft provides a ready explanation for the witch doctor or medicine man, who appears in various forms in many parts of the world. He naturally falls under the sway of customs, beliefs and environment of the tribe from which he springs. He will appeal to the accepted gods for benefits or for protection against evils, using the symbols and rituals to which his contemporaries are accustomed. The witch doctor must be distinguished from the witch or the evil spirits, whose enemy he is. His function is to protect his people from the adverse influences of black magic or bad medicine by invoking favorable magic or making good medicine.

In order to frighten the evil spirits, the witch doctor must render his appearance as alarming as he can, and his charms and incantations as dramatic and impressive as possible. To offset the horrors of the witches' caldrons, he must interpose an effective barrier of his own devising.

The witch doctor's strongest weapon is psychological. How much he himself believes in superstitions which haunt his tribesmen and women is beside the point; his job is to make them believe in him. So he wears the weird and fantastic garb he considers best suited to scare away the boogies, paints his face and body, and dons the various animal parts already mentioned, as symbols of gods masquerading as beasts. He tries his best to outhex the hexes. He may also be aware of the advantages to himself when he is successful.

Often he does succeed. Fear, stress and apprehension are potent causes of many symptoms, and the state of mind of any ill person is a significant factor in his recovery. The witch doctor must necessarily be among the more intelligent members of the tribe, with more than average capacity for leadership. He must be acquainted with whatever knowledge exists of plant remedies and skilled in primitive first aid and surgery. In many instances he may also be the chief of the tribe, perhaps as a result of his success in keeping his people safe and well. So long as events beyond his control go well, his fame and security increase. When events go badly, he often has to exercise great ingenuity to survive.

The belief in and reliance upon witch doctors by primitive peoples is explained by the simple if not profound old cliché that nothing succeeds like success. The principle is still manifest today. The talented individual, shrewd enough to influence events as much as he can, and to roll with the punches when he cannot, still comes to the top in business, politics, the arts or any other human activity. People are still impressed by the person who shows leadership, just as they have always followed the strong man, and probably always will.

SUGGESTION AND HYPNOTISM

The power of suggestion has been known to leaders of public opinion for many centuries. Statesmen, clergy, professional persons and the military have recognized the potency of psychic influences. Many have used this knowledge for the betterment of mankind; others for their own advancement; some to the detriment of gullible people. Among the important uses of suggestion has been hypnotism, popularized by Franz Anton Mesmer (1734–1815), an Austrian doctor and mystic. It would have been strange indeed if the primitive witch doctors had not, wittingly or otherwise, used this potent device, since the technique is readily mastered, and superstitious persons are particularly susceptible to suggestion.

Mesmer believed that he could cure disease by a magnetic power in his hands, which he called animal magnetism. He did indeed appear to benefit many patients, particularly those whose illnesses were psychological, what we today would recognize as psychosomatic symptoms due to emotional maladjustment. Ordered to leave Austria, Mesmer settled in Paris and practiced his method, which became known as mesmerism.

While he achieved great popularity, some physicians regarded him as a charlatan while other observers regarded his belief in his "magnetic" powers as sincere. Eventually, a French Government commission, of which Benjamin Franklin was a member, investigated his alleged cures. The report of the investigators was unfavorable and his successes were attributed, not to animal magnetism, but to unknown physiological causes. As a result, Mesmer lost his practice and was forced to retire.

Mesmerism was adopted by unscrupulous operators for medical quackery and by entertainers for the amusement of audiences, and so the concept fell into serious disrepute. Today, under the name of hypnotism, it has a recognized, although limited, place in medicine, being used occasionally in treatment of the emotionally ill and the mentally disturbed. It has also been recommended as an anesthesia in surgery and obstetrics, but there are definite limitations. Some persons should never be hypnotized, and by no means do all who are, derive the desired benefits.

Hypnotism should be limited to use by qualified and experienced physicians, because it can be dangerous in the hands of an amateur. It is not a proper parlor or platform stunt and, unfortunately, it is too easy to learn. The common belief that a person under hypnotic influence can be compelled to commit crimes and otherwise act out of character with his normal state, is without foundation.

Before we grow too supercilious about the bizarre and fantastic beliefs which produced witchcraft and brought forth the witch doctor, we might well consider the modern manifestations of similar factors. Beneficent exercise of psychological approaches to the sick was the principal weapon of the beloved old family doctor who had few of the resources of modern medicine. Efforts are currently being made to restore to medicine some of the old-time relationship between doctors and patients which has been obscured in too many instances by the glamour of modern medical progress. In times of illness or stress, the sympathetic understanding and support of a relative, a good friend, or a trusted spiritual adviser, may be as important as the medicine prescribed or the surgery performed.

Half the beds in all our hospitals are occupied by persons with mental or emotional disturbances; many other patients with physical illnesses are haunted by psychological problems. And many, many more are struggling along day after day by dogged determination, figuratively looking behind for disaster to overtake them. Mental and emotional health is the greatest need of modern man. His fears are not the same as those of his primitive ancestors, but they do have a comparable basis—the necessity for security, love and hope.

The modern doctor finds his patients require reassurance as much as the tribesmen who looked to the witch doctor for protection against imaginary devils supposedly lurking in trees and rocks, in sky and earth, in wind and water. The scene has changed, and so have the methods, but there is no real challenge to the truth of the French proverb, *"Plus ça change, plus c'est la même chose."*

The more things change, the more they are the same!

Much attention was paid in remote times to the supposed power of divination, manifested in prophecies of coming events, as already mentioned. Observations of the stars, and the study of the entrails of animals and fowls were the basis, not only of forecasts of future events, but of medical diagnoses. The finding of water underground with the aid of a forked hickory branch has been practiced with varying success for many years. It is still not satisfactorily explained why some can and some cannot "find" these sources by this means. I had always been skeptical of this alleged power until a recent experience in England shook my confident opinion.

In a country lane near Taunton, Somerset, my host and I were wandering about more or less aimlessly, when he cut a forked branch and demonstrated his ability to locate a hidden stream. I accused him of knowing where it was. He in turn cut a proper stick for me, and showed me how to hold it upright by grasping it firmly with both hands. Then he asked me to walk across his front lawn. To my astonishment, at a certain point, and without any volition on my part, the stick moved slowly but definitely toward me until it lay against my chest. I had no prior knowledge of any underground waters. He then asked me to try again in several different directions, until it became apparent that I was tracing a line leading toward his home. He told me that I was following the water main which supplied his dwelling. When my wife tried it, nothing happened; our hostess had no luck either. Don't ask me to explain.

Annually we observe the often astoundingly accurate long-range weather forecasts of the *Farmer's Almanac*. We smile at the predictions of winter weather by the Illinois fisherman who observes the perch in Lake Michigan, and are amazed at correct forecasts of historical events by Jeane Pinckert Dixon.*

How do they do it?

Still another modern development which makes us wonder about the perception of the ancients, is the serious scientific attention being given to ESP (extrasensory perception). Innumerable examples of apparent thought transference have existed in fiction and in supposedly factual claims for many centuries. Many have come from sources which demanded serious consideration, although as a rule such incidents have been discounted by scientists. They have been attributed to coincidence, to reconstruction of submerged memories, to confused and wishful thinking, and other explanations which ruled out the concept of genuine thought transference. Yet the idea persisted. Circumstantial stories were related of what appeared to be actual thought transference, sometimes over long distances and under circumstances difficult to ignore. A typical experience of this kind is that of the mother who awakes from deep sleep with a sensation of nameless dread at the very hour when her son is killed in battle or dies in a wrecked automobile.

Today these matters are receiving intensive study at Duke University, Durham, N.C., under the leadership of Professor Joseph B. Rhine and his wife, Louisa, and elsewhere. Their conclusions are not fully accepted at this time, but they are not being ignored either. These repeated experiences of many kinds of people call for some sort of explanation, if any is possible.

Despite all the misinformation, misunderstanding, superstition,

* A *Gift of Prophecy: The Phenomenal Jeane Dixon*, by Ruth Montgomery.

groping and charlatanism which has dogged man's efforts to relieve suffering and distress and to achieve better health, he has been slowly but surely gaining an improved knowledge of how his body is made, and to some extent how it functions. Now he is turning his attention to the more difficult problem of exploring the mysteries of the human mind and soul. An emerging image of himself is necessary as a basis for further progress toward better patterns of living, necessary in order to endure a longer life.

Chapter Four

MAN'S EMERGING IMAGE OF HIMSELF

"The proper study of mankind is man"

Alexander Pope made that observation in the eighteenth century, cribbing it from the French. Ancient man seems to have sensed it much earlier, as numerous relics and other archeological evidences show. Curious about the world around him, as he is today, it is plain that early man evidenced a lively interest in what he himself was like. In the caves and excavations of Stone Age sites are found many paintings and sculptures showing man and animals. Museums around the world display carvings and line drawings or engravings as well as large and small statues derived from many ancient cultures. These show keen observation of the human figure, both normal and abnormal.

The oldest-known replica of the human form was discovered in Austria in 1908 in the loam strata of a period estimated at 22,000 years B.C.* It is known as the Venus of Willendorf. It is four and one-half inches high, carved of limestone, and represents a typical figure of female obesity, possibly due to sedentary cave living and overfeeding. Many such figurines exist in Egyptian bas-reliefs and those of Assyria and Babylonia. The male figure, on the contrary, is usually portrayed as an athletic type, with well-developed muscles, narrow hips and thin flanks, reflecting his active life as a warrior and hunter.

The observations of sculptors and painters have furnished the earliest evidences that man knew at least the external charac-

* This, and other dates and data, are based largely on *History of Medicine*, Fielding H. Garrison, W. B. Saunders & Company, Philadelphia, 1961.

teristics of his body, and could portray through these media some very realistic impressions of diseases still recognizable today. Arthritis and polio are notable examples.

At the height of Greece's cultural ascendancy, the knowledge of anatomy was favored by the common practice of engaging in athletics in the nude, or attempting to correct body defects by exercises. Statues of such figures as the god Apollo can still be seen in both Italy and Greece. The Farnese Bull, the Laocoön group, the Venus de Milo and numerous other famous statues exhibit an ability to observe details which, Garrison points out, have escaped the attention of modern artistic anatomists. Statues from many other ancient cultures in widely scattered parts of the world show similar familiarity with the human form.

Through experience of war, hunting and other accidents, and the effects of injury or disease, early man observed the dangers which affected him. He recognized bleeding, pain, fever, "stinking and festering," and he was intimately acquainted with fear, especially fear of the unknown. We shall see later how he tried, by magic and through herbs and other devices such as warm springs, to overcome these dangers. Here we are interested mainly in how man came, by slow and painful stages, to his present extensive but still incomplete knowledge of how he is made and how he functions.

Observing the bodies of the dead, often mutilated, an early knowledge of the internal organs was established. At least their structure was known, if not their function. Ancient marble or terra-cotta images of various parts of the body exist, showing three-dimensional representations of intestinal coils, the chest and other anatomical features.

But it was not until the Ptolemies ruled Egypt that real progress was made in anatomical knowledge. By government permission, vivisection of the bodies of criminals was allowed in the university of Alexandria, founded some two hundred years before by Darius the Great of Persia. Egyptian physicians had earlier discovered facts that served as an excellent foundation for systematic dissection of the human body. Herophilus, the greatest of the Alexandrian anatomists, found the optic nerve's connection with the brain, and thus was disclosed the system of sensation and control which we today know as the nervous system.

It is to the Alexandrian University that we owe gratitude for the collection of writings attributed to the Greek physician Hippocrates (400 B.C.) of whom we know little else. We do know that he studied at the temple of Aesculapius (god of medicine) on the island of Cos and that he traveled widely in the world of his day; he must have been a dedicated man, for travel in his day required endurance of ass and cart over poor roads and no private staterooms aboard ship.

In his time the doctrine of the four humors was introduced, of which more later. Hippocrates himself taught his system of careful observation of the patient, resulting in some descriptions of disease which have not been improved on even to the present time. Included among these are facial appearance, temperature, pulse, respiration, location of pains, nature of sputum and other excreta, and above all the classical description of impending death—picking at the bedcovers and *facies Hippocraticus* or face of dissolution.

Hippocrates also, together with his contemporary school, had knowledge of the valves of the heart, the heart's chambers and the principal vessels, and of the special sense organs. They studied the embryology of plants, animals and man, believed in survival of the fittest, and observed hereditary factors. They were influenced, however, by the supposed potency of numbers, tending to describe parts of the body in systems of sevens. Yet they understood dislocations, fractures, bandaging, and opening of the skull (trephining) for relief of pressure on the brain after head wounds or skull fractures.

THE DOCTRINE OF HUMORS

Despite surprisingly accurate knowledge of body structure, the ancient ideas about how organs worked were complicated and somewhat fantastic. The Greek poet Empedocles (c.495–c.435 B.C.) introduced the idea that certain elements—*earth, air, fire* and *water*—were the "fourfold root" of all things. Mingled with this was the philosophy of Pythagoras (c.582–c.507 B.C.), who held to the Chaldean doctrine that the essence of all things was numbers, plus a belief that the earth as a planet revolved around a fixed point, known as "the hearth of the universe."

A complicated scheme was evolved, supposedly descriptive of

disease processes which combined the *elements* with four abstract *qualities*—*dry, cold, hot,* and *moist*—and a third quartet of *humors*—*blood, phlegm* (mucus), *yellow bile* and *black bile*. Out of this came such combinations as:

First: hot and dry equals fire   cold and dry equals earth
      hot and moist equals air   cold and moist equals water
Second: hot and moist equals blood   cold and moist equals phlegm
      hot and dry equals yellow   cold and dry equals black bile
      bile

On these factors and their several combinations rested the explanations for the various manifestations of disease. Garrison sees in these a foreshadowing of the complex modern science of physiology and pathology with endocrine gland and chemical factors which even today are not perfectly understood. We have, however, discarded some of the ancient concepts, such as one held by the Arabians that sugar is cold in the first degree, warm in the second, dry in the second degree and moist in the first. Some substances were graded even in terms of half a degree.

It was about this time that eugenic procreation was compulsory, and crippled or deformed infants were exposed to die or otherwise disposed of, in the interest of improving the race.

From the Hippocratic era up to the time of William Harvey's demonstration of the circulation of the blood in 1628, the liver was regarded as the source of the blood and of the veins; the arteries stemming from the heart originally were considered to be filled with air, perhaps because their more elastic walls did not collapse after a hemorrhage, as did the flaccid walls of the veins.

Despite their limitations, the ancient philosophers and physicians—the terms are virtually synonymous—had the sense to see that the patient is more important than the disease, an idea stressed by the great modern physician, Sir William Osler. This approach is in current danger of being lost in a wilderness of scientific preoccupation with research, tests and specialization, plus a focus on diseases rather than on patients.

After Hippocrates, the next great name is that of Aristotle (384–322 B.C.), who introduced the study of plants and animals into medicine, and based his anatomical teachings on the dissection of animals. Yet Aristotle was weak on physiology, despite great keenness of observation and a special flair for classification of facts. He also added a great deal of botanical knowledge to ancient medicine. Much of this became part of the beliefs later known as folklore.

In the second and third centuries A.D., an outstanding name is Aretaeus of Cappadocia, who was familiar with empyema (pus in the chest), diabetes, the premonitory aura of epilepsy, lockjaw, diphtheria, various types of mental disease, and the limb swellings known as elephantiasis. He also knew of the important crossing from side to side of the nerve pathways from the brain, which causes paralytic symptoms other than those of the head to appear on the side of the body opposite the involved area of the brain.

Rufus of Ephesus, who lived at the end of the first century A.D. described the crystalline lens, the eye membrane and a portion of the optic nerves, as well as the duct which carried the ova to the uterus in sheep. But he erred in his description of the liver, an error which was not corrected for centuries. Yet he recognized the relationship of the pulse to the heart muscle contraction. He also described, for the first time, wound erysipelas, certain skin cancers and bubonic plague, and wrote a treatise on gout. He knew how to control hemorrhage by pressure, styptic drugs, cautery, tying the vessel or twisting it.

Among medicine's great personalities was Galen, also living in the second century A.D. He wrote voluminously, leaving much valuable information, but also perpetuating some colossal errors which took a long time to correct. He introduced a principle which he called *pneuma*, or spirit, penetrating all parts of the body. He attributed all disease manifestations to this spirit. When one observes the profound influence of psychological factors on health and disease, one wonders whether Galen had some glimmering of the modern concepts of emotional health, but perhaps this is stretching conjecture too far.

Whatever disservices Galen may have done to medical progress and the furtherance of man's image of himself, his contributions were great and lasting. Merely to list the scope of his works would be far beyond the purpose of this discussion. His additions to the knowledge of anatomy alone were voluminous. He fell into errors because he based his descriptions on dissections of apes, swine and oxen, and only occasionally had the good fortune to find a human body which he could study. The church of his time frowned on such dissection.

Galen recognized the principles of muscular action. He described the membranes which cover the brain, and many of its internal structures, as well as seven of the twelve cranial nerves. Despite the faults in his anatomical studies, he was the first experimental physiologist. Among his demonstrations were studies of the nerves governing respiration and speech; and experimental paralyses produced by cutting the spinal cords of animals at various levels. He proved that the arteries contained blood and not air; and that the heart will beat for a time outside the body. In these and other experiments, Galen led the way in asking himself and others about the how and the why as well as the what of the human body; questions that scientists continue to ask today, for the end of knowledge is not yet.

Galen held and promoted three fallacious ideas that tended to delay medical progress. He believed that:

1) the blood carried "natural spirits" in the liver; "vital spirits" in the left side of the heart; and that vital spirits become "animal spirits" in the brain; this continues the *pneuma* theory mentioned above;

2) the blood passed from the right side of the heart to the left through invisible pores in the dividing wall; and,

3) suppuration of a wound or "coction" is essential to healing, thus creating the concept of "laudable pus," which was not overcome until the nineteenth century.

These fallacies influenced many a follower of Galen into dead ends of medical research. And yet, it is astonishing how much Galen contributed to the extensive knowledge of man many centuries ago.

Innumerable details could be cited in the long, sometimes slow, and often erratic progress of man's understanding of himself. A few highlights will suffice to indicate the contributions from many sources which make up the mass of information existing today:

Eleventh Century: Avicenna or ibn Sina (980–1037), court

physician to Moslem caliphs of Bagdad, recognized the cattle disease anthrax as "Persian Fire," gave a good account of diabetes and is reputed to be the first to recognize the sweet taste of diabetic urine;

Albucasis of Andalusia (c. 936–1013) published a surgical treatise with descriptions of kidney-stone operations, amputations of gangrenous limbs, fractures of the pelvis and paralysis from spinal fracture;

Thirteenth Century: Gulielmus de Saliceto of Bologna (1201–1277) was the first to assign sexual contacts as the source of venereal infections, and gave a description of dropsy due to kidney disease;

Fifteenth Century: The Bologna and Padua schools in Italy observed gallstones and noted dizziness due to digestive disturbances; one anatomist dissected as many as fourteen bodies, a prodigious feat in those times; they noted the uses of foot baths, operated on the tear duct and extracted decayed teeth;

Sixteenth Century: Numerous treatises were published with anatomical plates showing the bodily systems, often overlaid with signs of the Zodiac or the planets themselves, or tattooed to show the best sites for bleeding in conjunction with the signs of the Zodiac, or surrounded with names of diseases and indefinite indications of the regions affected, or the so-called "wound-man" pierced with arrows, spears, swords or stones to show the best places to tie arteries for the control of hemorrhage; or the diagrammatic figure of a crouching, pregnant woman showing the fetus in the uterus; among these depictions are the early versions of the anatomical artistry of Leonardo da Vinci and Vesalius.

Andreas Vesalius (1514–1564), born in Flanders of German parentage, was the first of the modern anatomists and remains among the greatest today. His original anatomical plates are collector's items of great value. The plates are clear, detailed and accurate, showing bones, joints and articulated skeletons in various postures against symbolic backgrounds; figures with muscles seen in action poses; surgical instruments; animal dissections; blood-vessel and nerve distribution; the brain; the breathing tubes and lungs; the abdominal viscera; the heart and the reproductive organs.

A typical figure is that of a skeleton standing before a tomb in a contemplative pose, one hand resting on a skull. The head is pressed against the back of the other hand, and one leg is crossed over the other, its toes touching the ground, its heel uplifted. On the panel of the tomb is a Latin phrase which reads:

> All splendor is dissolved by death, and through
> The snow-white limbs steals Stygian hue to spoil
> The grace of form.

The old-time scientists were philosophers, too, as are the best ones even in this utilitarian age!

Seventeenth Century: Marcello Malpighi (1628–1694), the Italian anatomist and pioneer microscopist, completed proof of blood circulation by his observations of the capillaries.

Dissecting as a means of studying the human body became more common, though it was still looked upon with horror by the populace and disapproved by the clergy. People often watched the graves of their dead to guard against the grave robbing by which many bodies were obtained. At the same time, there was occasionally the display of a grim kind of humor, as in a painting in Amsterdam of a physician tickling the ribs of a laughing skeleton for the amusement of the onlookers. Dissections were practiced rather frequently in Holland, Italy and France; one French anatomist is credited with five hundred! They were less common in England and Germany.

In 1674 a Dutch biologist, Anton van Leeuwenhoek, after constructing various microscopes, gave the first accurate description of red blood corpuscles, and later described the capillary action of the blood. He was the first man to observe bacteria and protozoa.

Upon his work and the observations of Malpighi, William Harvey (1578–1657) was able to destroy, once and for all time, Galen's theory that pores in the heart walls allowed blood to pass from one side to the other. He discovered that blood circulates continuously due to the pumping action of the heart, and that it comes to that organ by way of the veins and leaves it by way of the arteries, being interchanged through the capillaries.

The ability to observe microscopic structures, normal and abnormal, gave great impetus to better understanding of the life process in health and disease. More and more, accurate knowledge could replace conjecture and tradition, the common ingredients of folklore.

Eighteenth Century: A Swiss anatomist, Albrecht von Haller, classed by Garrison as the "master physiologist of his time," gave us an early insight into the nature of muscular contraction in response to nerve stimuli. Such an idea had merely been postulated previously but not proved. He also made extensive studies of the heart and of the brain, and recognized the role of bile in the digestion of fats.

Nineteenth Century: These years witnessed the development of knowledge about the microscopic cells which constitute and determine the character and function of living tissues. This branch of medical knowledge had been made possible by van Leeuwenhoek's work with the microscope.

Surgery, dating far back into primitive times, gained great impetus from broader anatomical knowledge, the development of anesthesia and the dramatic new science of bacteriology.

The story of anesthesia has been told so often that a mere summary here, to round out this pageant of progress, will suffice:

Crawford W. Long of Georgia, who observed the young dandies of his day indulging in ether jags, decided to try this gas as a means of saving pain during some minor surgery in 1842, and then neglected to report his success until he almost lost the historical credit for his priority in the use of ether;

William Thomas Green Morton, who demonstrated the use of ether before the surgeons at the Harvard Medical School in 1846, engaged in bitter controversy with Long over who was first;

Horace Wells, dentist, who watched itinerant entertainers using "laughing gas" for kicks in 1844, and tried it in his practice, fell upon misfortune and died a suicide;

Sir James Young Simpson, who almost killed himself as well as his experimental rabbits by inhaling chloroform, went on from there to introduce it into obstetrics in 1847, and finally triumphed over the objections of the clergy by persuading Queen Victoria to be anesthetized during the birth of one of her children;

Arno Luckhardt, who observed in 1922 the anesthetic qualities of ethylene gas, a modification of ether, when noting that its presence in the air of a greenhouse caused the flowers to wilt.

From these beginnings, which supplanted the crude, earlier methods, refinements came thick and fast, including local anesthesia with cocaine and later with procaine (novocaine) and its modifications given by tissue infiltration, nerve blocking or spinal injection. Hypnosis, practiced first by Mesmer and from his name called mesmerism, had been a combination of science, charlatanism and entertainment; it was not placed upon a sound scientific basis for limited use until well after the middle of the twentieth century.

These refinements in anesthetics and the development of specially trained medical anesthesiologists, played a large part in the modern practice of advanced surgical procedures.

In bacteriology, advances were so rapid that progress was accelerated at an unprecedented rate. The outstanding pioneer, of course, was Pasteur, whose studies in the spoiling of wine and of epidemics among silkworms saved two basic industries for France in the second half of the nineteenth century. Even more important, he brought into medicine the establishment of the germ origin of many diseases together with the means for preventing or treating them. Among the great names in this dramatic sequence of events are:

Pasteur, himself, with his conquest of rabies in animals and man; and of anthrax; and many other basic bacteriological techniques;

von Behring and Kitasato, and later Ramon, in the discovery of the diphtheria bacillus, its toxin, an antitoxin and a toxoid for immunization;

Schaudinn's demonstration of the spirillum of syphilis through a special microscopic technique, the dark-field microscope;

Robert Koch's researches in tuberculosis, the cultivation of the bacillus, the tuberculin test; and the establishment of principles upon which proof of bacterial causation of a disease must rest:

a) the germ must be found where the disease exists;

b) the germ must not be universally present where the disease does not exist;

c) the germ must be capable of producing the disease experimentally in animals; and,

d) the germ must be recoverable from the experimental animal in recognizable and identifiable form.

Such criteria are a long step forward from the vague and formless speculations by which earlier observers tried to attribute disease to vital spirits, animal spirits, humors and other philosophical postulates.

The germ "theory" of disease was hotly disputed, and Pasteur, who was a scrappy character, led a tempestuous life. Today no reputable scientist considers germs in any way theoretical. They are very real; and they explain many diseases, but not all.

Surgery which had been limited by inability to guard the patient against intolerable pain, had also been handicapped by infection of wounds, causing suppuration or gangrene ("laudable pus"!). Surgeons, notably the British Quaker physician, Lord Lister, made use of the new bacteriological knowledge to develop first antisepsis, and then asepsis in the operating rooms. Antisepsis is a technique for *destroying* germs, by chemicals or heat; asepsis consists in preventing their presence by creating as nearly a sterilized environment as possible.

Twentieth Century: This is the great age of research and of specialization; perhaps the most outstanding features are:

X ray, radium and their application to the advancement of man's image of himself, and the diagnosis and treatment of disease, particularly the malignant tumors;

the tremendous growth in laboratory knowledge and its use in the study of normal physiology, variations from normal, and evaluation of treatment measures;

the growth and development of community-health measures: water purification, sewage disposal, epidemic controls through sanitary measures, and immunizations;

stepped-up research through public and private channels;

participation of millions of people through membership in, and contributions to voluntary medico-lay health organizations devoted to specific ailments, such as tuberculosis, venereal diseases, diabetes, heart and blood-vessel diseases, cancer, polio, mental illness and many others.

In the twentieth century, too, we have witnessed the growth of many varieties of technology, which have aided in exploring the mysteries of human health and disease:

electricity and electronics have given us directly or indirectly such tools as the X ray, the electric cautery, a variety of "scopes" for exploring the internal organs, diagnostic devices like the electrocardiograph, monitoring appliances, motor-driven apparatus and recording procedures, including such "idea-storage" devices as the electronic computer;

other branches of physical science have contributed the laser beam; the manipulation of body temperatures for therapeutic purposes; the uses as well as the dangers of ultraviolet rays from the sun or artificially produced; and infrared photography, to name but a few.

Medicine's debt to chemistry has always been great, but never more so than in this century when we have witnessed an unprecedented burgeoning of knowledge and the use of synthetic drugs. Many of these have helped to shorten illness, prevent severe suffering and to save lives; among these are the antibiotics, the hormones, the tranquilizers, those which prevent coagulation of blood, and many, many more.

Perhaps the most significant twentieth-century development, at least for the purposes of our discussion here, is the growth in man's awareness of himself through health education. It is no longer necessary for the nonmedical person to remain in ignorance about himself. He need not rely for "information" on neighbors no better informed than himself, or "medicine men," witch doctors, grannies or idolatrous priests.

In the schools, patterns of healthful living are being taught from the earliest grades through advanced college education. The voluntary health agencies make accurate materials available at nominal prices, or often free. Public health departments have special divisions for health education. The professional societies related to health—medical, dental, nursing, nutritional—have programs for the enlightenment of anyone interested. Youth groups, adult organizations and organizations for the aged concern themselves with providing health information. Reliable material is available from business-supported organizations interested in useful products such as meat, milk, fruits, nuts and other nutrients; admittedly promotional, these materials are scientifically authenticated and free from exaggerated claims for special products. Magazines and newspapers carry health articles, columns, and news, prepared by doctors or by specially qualified medical writers. Reliable books on many phases of healthful living, and prevention of disease and accidents are available in libraries, and new ones are constantly being produced.

The growth in medical and related knowledge and the efficiency of modern means of communication, have provided the best opportunity ever available for correct orientation in matters of health. Unfortunately, these same channels are open to the ignorant, the misguided, the opinionated, and the unscrupulous. They can be used to confuse as well as to clarify man's image of himself. Evidence that they are being so used is all about us.

Most people sincerely wish to be healthy. Being human, they also wish to accomplish this goal with a minimum of effort, inconvenience, expense or self-denial. This makes them sitting ducks for the slick promoter with a cynical knowledge of human frailties, a minimum of ethical principles or no conscience at all, and an abiding yen for living without working. For example, in 1967, *Harvest Years* magazine, a publication dedicated to the interests of the elderly, devoted almost one entire issue to warning its readers how to guard against frauds and quacks. Not all quackery is medical, of course, but most quackery has an impact on health. This may be directly physical or emotional. It may inflict financial losses which result in deprivations detrimental to health or in great mental anguish. It may even cause loss of life through delay in effective medical treatment or devotion to actually harmful practices, such as the Zen diet which has resulted in deaths from starvation (Chapter Six).

The mere headings of the *Harvest Years* exposé are revealing. Reprints of the articles are available for twenty-five cents from *Harvest Years* magazine, 104 East 40th Street, New York, New York 10016. Following is a list of the topics covered (the parenthetic comments are mine):

"Bait advertising" (to catch suckers);

"Lucky Winner" rackets (one sure winner, the promoter);

Dance Studio rackets (one dance "free," the rest expensive);

"Lonely Hearts" clubs (may be traps for the unwary);

Phony investigators (ask any stranger for his credentials);

Work-at-Home plans (if they sound too good to be true, maybe they are);

Phony franchises to make big money selling something or other (if it's that good, why give away the agency?);

Home Repair frauds (stick to known, reputable contractors);

Vanity publishers (they'll print your books and you try to sell them);

Burial Insurance (good idea if you deal with the right people);

Cemetery Lot frauds (see comment on burial insurance);

Medical and health frauds:
    Nutritional nonsense
    Fake "electronic" devices
    Cancer "cures"
    Hearing-aid rackets
    Reducing without diet, exercise or drugs
    Any "secret" or "exclusive" remedy or method.

I have included the apparently nonmedical rackets in this list because some of them, like the fake investigators, repairmen or meter readers, are used to provide access to the home for the purpose of rape, or robbery and physical harm. And, in the larger sense, any loss or waste has indirect effects on healthful living, especially for those who have to count their pennies—and who doesn't?

These flimflams require two kinds of people, the schemer and the victim. The victim may be either ignorant, inexperienced, stupid or gullible; scarcely an admirable image, but understandable. One feels sympathy for such persons. But there is another class of victim; the grasping individual whose vulnerability to exploitation is due to his own crafty greed; he tries to get something for nothing; he deserves what he gets.

These modern rackets lack the sincerity of genuine folklore, but they have become confused with it, and have replaced it in the minds of persons not alerted to the dangers of being hoaxed. True folklore, while often in error, had at least the virtues of honesty and the motive of helpfulness in the search for cause, effect, prevention and cure. Even so, there is no longer any valid reason for anyone to be deceived, or to entertain a blurred and faulty image of himself in his physical, mental, emotional and social aspects.

And let's not forget that we owe much of our modern knowledge to the probing after truth which is the basis for folklore. Observation of plants, herbs, foods and animals has been built into a world-wide network of confused ideas about the health and medical implications of these everyday factors from which modern science is gradually winnowing out the truth, and modern education is endeavoring to aid in separating the truth from the fallacies.

Chapter Five

MEDICINAL PLANTS AND HERBS

When you were young, did your grandmother, like mine:

- feed you camomile tea as a "physic"?

- rub mustard on your chest for a cough?

- give you hot lemonade for a cold?

- feed you sulphur and molasses as a "tonic"?

- use a linseed poultice to "draw" a boil?

If she did, she was recalling the home-remedy experiences of generations of her ancestry and yours.

Interest in the healing potential of plants and herbs dates back into man's earliest history. Out of his search for food, and the inevitable catastrophes from eating unrecognized poisons, there has evolved a bewildering, complex and fascinating herb lore which is now undergoing a renewal of interest.

A clay document lay buried for more than four thousand years in the ruins of Nippur, about one hundred miles south of modern Bagdad in Iraq. Nippur had been the spiritual and cultural center of ancient Sumer, and during its excavation by an American expedition the oldest medical handbook known to man, according to Samuel Noah Kramer, came to light. For some years it lay untouched because its phraseology seemed highly specialized. Then a chemist of Philadelphia, Martin Levey, and Dr. Kramer went to work on it.

They learned that, like the modern physician, the ancient one, who had put a reed stylus to work on a moist clay rectangle, used botanical, zoological and mineralogical sources in his healing practice:

> Sodium chloride (salt),
> Potassium nitrate (saltpeter),
> Milk,
> Snake skin,
> Turtle shell,
> Cassia,
> Myrtle,
> Asafoetida,
> Thyme,
> Willow, ⎫ preparing from these sources, salves
> Pear,   ⎪ for external use, and liquids for in-
> Fir,   ⎬ ternal prescriptions. After pulveriz-
> Fig,   ⎪ ing the seeds, roots, branches, bark
> Date   ⎭ (dried, of course), the powder was
>   mixed with various oils or wine,
>   depending on use.

And this physician lived nearly five thousand years ago! Incidentally, not one god or demon is mentioned in the text, so he did not give his medicines with any magic spells and incantations. Ahead of his day? Perhaps by centuries, for the common folk around him believed that their ailments were caused by demons invading their bodies.

In 1965 a magnificent Herbal by Joseph Wood Krutch was published, and in it are woodcuts from Pier Andrea Mattioli's *Commentaries on the Six Books of Dioscorides*, published in 1563 and 1565. This work was first published with smaller plates in 1544. Much information in this chapter is based upon Krutch's summaries of herbal lore.

The first English herbal was published by Banckes in 1525, named after its printer, whose name is the only one known to be connected with the work. Other important herb books include:

• *Adam in Eden* (1657) by William Coles of New College, Oxford.

- A treatise by Nicholas Culpepper, astrologer and physician of London about 1640, whom Krutch regarded as unreliable in that he was able to "prove" by astrology almost anything he wanted to.

- Pedanius Dioscorides of Greece (c.50 A.D.) was the source of much of the herbal lore of ancient and medieval times and is regarded as the "fountainhead" by Krutch.

- *The Herbal* or *General History of Plants*, (1597) by John Gerard of London, a barber-surgeon deeply interested in plant lore; a handsome hand-illustrated edition partly in color, which owes much to the work of a Belgian botanist, Rembert Dodoens.

- *Natural History* by Gaius Plinius Secundus (Pliny, the elder) about A.D. 50 to 70 in Rome, who gathered enormous amounts of material in an uncritical manner and passed it on, claiming as sources some two thousand books by one hundred authors. It is full of tall tales which make delightful reading but it must be taken with more than the proverbial grain of salt.

- Many other authors have contributed to and sometimes confused the subject of medicinal herbs, and of course much material has been passed down through word of mouth against many different cultural backgrounds.

Certain important concepts, some of which have been mentioned before, must precede the limited listing of medicinal herbs presented in this chapter, in order to indicate the underlying philosophies and theories which guided and sometimes misguided the thinking of students of herbal lore, and the uncritical observations of the uneducated citizenry.

Mention has already been made (Chapter II) of two important influences, which are mentioned here in specific reference to the following listing of herbs and their alleged medicinal properties.

The belief, religious in origin, that nothing grows on this earth in vain, no matter how obnoxious it may seem, but everything is meant for the benefit of man through the wisdom of the Creator;

The doctrine of "signatures," which in essence is the belief that the shape, structure or other quality of a plant is a clue or *signature* telling mankind what its uses and purposes are (see Saxifrage, page 97).

An outgrowth of the doctrine of signatures is the further belief that plants and animals indigenous to a given region, would always be those which were most useful for the feeding and medication of the inhabitants.

The multiplicity of herbs and the numerous claims made for many of them illustrate the fact that when many remedies were advocated, it is a reasonable assumption that none of them was really effective. A modern example would be the case of diphtheria, for which many palliative treatments existed until 1895 when von Behring produced antitoxin by immunizing horses and using their serum for the treatment of patients. The refinements which followed have led to the complete eradication of this disease *where preventive measures are adequately practiced.* All other diphtheria treatments, except routine nursing measures, or occasional emergency procedures, have disappeared. This illustrates a common experience in medicine, namely that when there are many alleged remedies, it is a reasonable assumption that none of them is much good.

Ineffective herbs, used when no more potent remedy was available, had at least the virtue of doing no harm; they may even have helped the patient's outlook by inspiring hope, in the same manner that the modern physician uses the so-called "sugar pills" (placebos) with a psychological purpose.

Relationship between time sequence and cause and effect is often confused. The mere fact that one event follows another does not necessarily establish a causal relationship. One has only to observe the "testimonials" given by good but misguided people in behalf of remedies which they took, and to which they credit their recovery, without the slightest valid proof.

Remembering the favorable course of events and forgetting the failures have given a false reputation for effectiveness, not only to herbal claims, but in many other areas of experience.

An understanding and constant remembrance of these basic

patterns of thought is essential for a sympathetic comprehension of the origins of popular ideas which, when taken out of context, may seem merely ridiculous and fantastic. Actually, the large number of modern remedies based on traditional methods and beliefs (Chapter Ten) indicates that the ancients were often on the right track, even though it was for the wrong reasons.

The tender, loving care and solicitude which accompanied home treatment and use of folk remedies, was no small factor in the reputation for potency acquired by many drugs of small actual value. The persistence of folk medicine in the face of modern science is due in large part to the growing complexity of medical treatment, the delegation of many medical duties to nurses and technicians and the consequent loss of the personal touch between physician and patient.

Hope, which springs eternal, and faith, also contribute to the spontaneous recovery which is the course of most illness, regardless of treatment. The strength of the old-time physician, and the "granny," neither of whom knew much medicine as we know it today, lay in their ability to inspire hope and nourish faith in the sick to whom they ministered.

Another reason for the successes and the persistence of folk medicine into the era of science is its direct approach to the patient's wants. He comes to the doctor for relief of his distress, and he has little interest in abstract scientific considerations as long as he hurts, itches or suffers other discomforts or disabilities. It is reported, perhaps facetiously, that an irate doctor, annoyed by a patient who insisted on immediate treatment and refused to answer the doctor's probing questions, finally said:

"Well, if you don't want to answer questions, I suggest you go to the doctor across the street—he won't ask you any. He's a horse doctor."

A typical patient is the American Indian woman who was critical of her hospital experience because she had not been relieved of her hemorrhoids. When she was asked why she had not mentioned them to her doctor, she replied, "He's a doctor, isn't he—he ought to know!" The doctor of today agrees—he ought to know. So he asks questions, makes a complete examination, and calls for laboratory tests. This does not necessarily please the patient, who may prefer a quicker relief for his symptoms.

The direct approach, with a minimum of diagnosis, is the forte of the witch doctor and the herbalists, and of certain modern cultists. However, the herbalists often made more sense than the pseudo-scientific cults of this day and age, and they had, at least, the virtue of sincerity, and were motivated by kindness rather than profit.

Beginning with the Greek herbalist Dioscorides of the first century A.D., and supplemented by the traditional writings of other cultures, a vast list of herbs, plants and other charms has been accumulated. A few of the more important ones are reported here.

The many unfamiliar names—to the modern—in these lists indicate the attitude of the modern physician to such concepts as the "alterative," defined as a substance bringing about a gradual change for the better, and the "tonic," intended to exert a more immediate effect. Better diet and living conditions plus more specific drugs, and the elimination of many preventable diseases, have consigned the alterative and the tonic to the past.

In similar manner, more scientific approaches have replaced many of the plants and herbs, despite the fact that many possessed, and still do, useful and valuable properties. Perhaps most of all, synthetic chemistry has been responsible for the diminished need for plants and herbs. And yet, *researchers* are now turning into searchers, combing remote places, the jungles and swamps and mountains, for plant sources of new drugs (Chapter Thirteen).

Other common symptoms calling for remedies were the disorders of the menstrual function, including the days of uncertainty when a period was delayed and pregnancy was either greatly desired or awaited with apprehension. So we have:

EMMENAGOGUES (to stimulate menstruation): wormseed (Mexican epazote) tea; garden rue; shepherd's-purse; pennyroyal; wild sunflower; lion's-ear; arbor vitae; the well-known tansy, and a dozen others.

Worm infestation is rarer today. It was a common problem before the days of improved sanitation, and so worm medicines naturally appeared:

ANTHELMINTICS: wormwood; wormseed (Mexican tea); shellflower; male fern; buck bean; fire pink; pomegranate roots.

HERBS REGARDED AS ALTERATIVES OR TONICS*

Alterative Properties	Tonic Properties	Alterative and Tonic
sarsaparilla	star grass	cocklebur
butterfly weed	camomile	bittersweet
wintergreen	snakeroot	barberry
black snakeroot	wild licorice	flowering ash
boneset	gentian	trumpetweed
blue flag	shellflower	American white ash
moonseed	wormseed	goldenseal
buck bean	chicory	Indian cup
pokeweed	blessed thistle	dandelion
Jacob's-ladder	lily of the valley	red clover
scarlet sumac	goldthread	lamb's-quarter
yellow dock	flowering dogwood	rattlesnake root
queen's-delight	horseweed	coneflower
lion's-ear (or tail)	burning bush	Indian lettuce
silverweed	teaberry	quaking aspen
bloodroot	creeping Charlie	swamp dogwood
star anise	wild sunflower	sneezeweed
	wild camomile	
	chokecherry	
	horse balm	
	umbrella tree	

Only the male fern has retained a place in modern therapeutics. The prevalence of constipation naturally called forth a wide variety of laxatives and, happily, a smaller number of purgatives.

LAXATIVES: dogbane; butterfly weed; wild senna; flowering dogwood; burning bush; boneset; white ash; blue flag; buck bean; May apple; queen's-delight; prickly ash; leopard's-bane; field bindweed; sow thistle; and veronica.

PURGATIVES: butterfly weed; celandine; white pine; thorn apple; wild indigo; and field bindweed.

Both purgatives and laxatives are now used sparingly in medicine, but their use by the general public continues despite medical insistence that constipation is better controlled by other means,

* Coon, Nelson: *Using Plants for Healing*, Hearthside Press, N.Y., 1963.

and that the laxative habit actually complicates the problem rather than solving it.

> At this point it becomes apparent, and will be more so as this listing proceeds, that few of the plants and herbs mentioned seem to have only one attribute. The same names reappear in many categories.

The symptom commonly described as indigestion was long regarded as one disease, rather than an indication of many, as is now understood. We find a multiplicity of "stomach remedies" under such titles as *carminatives* and *stomachics*. Carminatives were intended to redden the stomach lining and promote digestion; stomachics to "excite the action of the stomach by stimulating secretions"; something in the nature of a cordial (Coon *op. cit.*). Among the fifteen carminatives and twenty-two stomachics listed by Coon are the following, which may strike a familiar note on the memories of older readers:

CARMINATIVES: jack-in-the-pulpit; wild ginger; black birch; pennyroyal; wild (German) camomile; spearmint; catnip; sage; goldenrod; garden heliotrope; feather geranium.

STOMACHICS: angelica; true camomile; wormwood; butterfly weed; chicory; rosinweed; goldenseal; spearmint; buck bean (again!); chokecherry; swamp dogwood; tansy; dandelion; southern white cedar; "cure-all"; magnolia; and others.

Indigestion is no longer treated symptomatically; instead, a search is made for the cause, which may be due to such serious conditions as appendicitis, gall-bladder disease, pernicious anemia and cancer. Folklore remedies doubtless helped many cases of overindulgence in food or drink, or of stress situations producing digestive symptoms.

The removal of warts was, and is, a challenge to the home healer. Warts have the quality, never adequately explained, of coming and going without apparent cause. They are now known to be virus infections, and so some folklore remedies may have worked through antiseptic action. Such remedies were always accompanied by psychotherapy, as illustrated by the injunction to massage the wart with a stone gathered in a graveyard in the dark of the moon; or by tying knots in a string equal to the number of warts and then leaving the string by a path where someone might pick it up and thus acquire your warts. It has never been adequately explained why anyone versed in folklore would be so foolish as to pick up a knotted string. Be that as it may, the removal of warts was one of the attributes ascribed to plants:

WART REMOVERS: celandine; sunflower; balsam; dandelion; hemlock.

ASTRINGENTS: These are drugs used to shrink or contract the tissues, and are useful in bleeding, swellings, and formerly much recommended for dysentery (a common term for all diarrheas regardless of cause). The tannin in oak bark was used as an astringent. Willow bark, source of salicylic acid and a forerunner of aspirin (Chapter Ten) was another. Burdock seeds, rose leaves, raspberry leaves and ginger are among the more popular astringents, and so is blackberry brandy, which may have owed part of its popularity to other than its astringent qualities. Many of these herbs, at least fifty in number, have now been superseded by synthetic drugs.

Astringents were also used to control bleeding, and here we encounter an interesting experience with a method not related to plants, namely the successful control of hemorrhage by application of spider webs (see also *puffballs*, page 97).

ANTISEPTICS: *wormwood*, containing a volatile oil that is poisonous; *black birch*, yielding an oil similar to oil of wintergreen; *sassafras*, another oil-bearing plant widely employed; *peat moss*, probably more useful as an absorbent and a bandaging material than as an antiseptic; *woundwort* or *allheal*: got its reputation from its odor, but did not live up to it; *wild indigo*, *portulacca* (purslane), *Indian lettuce*, and others have been classified as antiseptics. And let's not overlook moldybread poultices which, all unsuspected, were the prophecy of penicillin, a modern "miracle" drug (Chapter Ten).

The melancholy truth is that before Pasteur and his contemporaries unveiled the causes of infection, and numerous researchers found ways to curb it, an infected wound either recovered or grew worse, depending largely upon the patient's natural resistance and little, if at all, upon the supposed antiseptic properties of plants and herbs. There was some virtue in poultices made from seeds or leaves, often because of their warmth rather than their composition.

Coughs and colds would naturally be expected to call for a varied display of folk remedies, and the records do not disappoint in this regard, though the results should often be attributed to time and the patient's natural resistance. This has not changed much; we still say that a cold will be over in seven days under skilled treatment; untreated it lasts a week. The painstaking care, the solicitude and the reassurance which accompany the cold remedies, probably do a lot for the patient, like the hot rum punch given me by the Yorkshire-inn hostess. Was she embarrassed to discover later that she had prescribed for a doctor! Her contribution didn't affect the cold, but it made me feel much, much better.

In addition to the common groups just mentioned, there are many other herb classifications which received the attention of the herb doctors and the knowledgeable "grannies" to whom their families and neighbors turned for aid:

Antiperiodics were herbs supposedly capable of preventing the return of recurring diseases such as fevers; in this class quinine (Peruvian bark) is the classic example of a genuinely useful folklore remedy (Chapter Ten).

Antipyretics are supposed to reduce fever; much of their reputation is based on the gradual recovery which takes place in most of the minor diseases; genuine antipyretics tend to be damaging to the heart.

Antiscorbutics (scurvy preventives) served a real purpose in times when diets were likely to be lean and lacking in variety, especially in fruits and vegetables during the winter months; the number of such plants is legion in the folklore of medicine, and we now realize that fresh foods contain the ascorbic acid (vitamin C) which guards against scurvy.

Antispasmodics were intended to reduce cramps and involuntary muscle contraction or spasms.

Aperients are gentle laxatives; many foods were quite correctly recognized to have aperient qualities; a much more sensible approach than the present-day reliance on laxative drugs to promote "regularity."

Aromatics, such as spices, are closely allied to the carminatives and stomachics already mentioned.

Cholagogues are agents intended to stimulate the flow of bile; often the gall of the ox was used, and bile salts still play a part in modern medicine.

Demulcents, such as glycerine or bland oils like olive oil, are soothing to the digestive tract; their value is still recognized.

Deobstruents, as their name implies, are supposed to be able to remove obstructions such as stones, from passages like the gall ducts and ureters, which carry urine from the kidneys to the bladder. Gallstones cannot be dissolved; some kidney stones can.

Diaphoretics are something to make you sweat; the hot teas commonly used for this purpose may have been useful in minor illnesses.

Diarrhea remedies were important in times when epidemics of typhoid fever, cholera and dysentery swept the land; unfortunately, the mere treatment of a symptom did not influence the more serious aspects of the disease. Still, out of the use of ipecac for coughs and to induce vomiting for the treatment of poisoning, has come a drug, emetine, useful as a specific for the amoebic form of true dysentery (Chapter Ten).

Diuretics stimulate the flow of urine and help remove excess water (dropsy) from the tissues; they retain great importance today in instances of heart and kidney disease. Folklore supplies many teas for this purpose, and they probably had a limited value, simply because they were hot liquids.

Hallocinogens, now the center of controversy, were known to the ancients as hashish (cannabis indica—marijuana), peyote from a cactus, and the active property of Mexican sacred mushrooms. The modern addiction is LSD, derived from ergot, the rye fungus, which is also the source of a drug useful in obstetrical practice (Chapter Ten).

Miscellaneous drugs include:

Nervines: tonics for the nerves,

Rubefacients: skin reddeners,

Refrigerants: supposed to cool the blood (obsolete term),

Vulneraries: agents to heal wounds.

The accumulated lore of medicinal plants and herbs (simples) provided explicit instructions for recognizing the plants (pharmacognosy). The best time for gathering each variety was specified, in order to get the most effective concentration of the potent principle. The active ingredients in plants vary quantitatively according to season. Different parts of the same plant might have different properties. Uses were often specified separately for flowers, seeds, leaves, stems, roots, bark and juices or sap. Preparation methods too were prescribed.

Plants and herbs might be used in:

Dried and powdered form,

Teas or decoctions; usually made with boiling water, or infusions by steeping in cold water,

Tinctures—water-alcohol infusions,

Pills,

Ointments or liniments,

Poultices,

Electuaries (dried or powdered herbs suspended in honey, and worked into a mass easily taken from a spoon).

Add to our list of individual herbs and plants, limited but selective and significant, alphabetized for convenient reference:

ALMOND: Bitter almonds were once believed to help some twenty-nine different diseases, and were esteemed then as now as a luxury food. A so-called almond milk used during the Renaissance, included a round dozen or more herbs mixed with powdered almonds. Twin almond meats in one shell were regarded as good-luck omens in my childhood; they were called "filipinos"—don't ask me why! Five bitter almonds were supposed to prevent intoxication. The bitter almond contains prussic acid, not in sufficient quantities to be poisonous to adults in ordinary use, but may poison children.

ALOE: This herb was known in ancient China. It was a component of most laxative pills until less irritating substances became available (see *cascara sagrada*). Aloes were also said to expel worms if mixed with honey and rubbed on the navel. Herbalists differ as to whether it will cure hemorrhoids or make them worse. The active principle, *aloin*, is often used in so-called liver pills even today, but has no real effect upon the liver.

ARUM: Various members of this plant family are known in America as jack-in-the-pulpit and skunk cabbage; in England as wake-robin or cuckoopint. Perhaps because of resemblances to the male organ, the arums were regarded as sexual stimulants, though not until the so-called doctrine of signatures, previously mentioned, came into being. The skunk cabbage has also been used for asthma and as an emetic. It resembles the swamp hellebore, which is poisonous if taken internally. The roots are poisonous when eaten fresh, but in powdered form they have been recommended for headache. Applying the irritating, grated root of jack-in-the-pulpit to the sweating forehead was intended to cause such pain that the headache would be forgotten! It was used also as a urinary disinfectant, and for "thrush" sore throats in children.

ASPHODEL: see Bog Asphodel.

BANANA: Generally regarded as a food, the banana is so useful as a dietary item in treating certain varieties of digestive and nutritional conditions, that it rates a place as one of the genuinely useful medicinal plants. Ironically, it was dismissed by Mediterranean ancients as virtually useless, at the very time when it was the principal food in the then "undiscovered" parts of the world.

BOG ASPHODEL: This plant has been famous since the Greek poet, Homer, described it as flourishing in the (imaginary) Elysian fields. It is one of the lily family, and its botanical name is Narthecium. It has been believed to cure many disorders; Pliny mentions fifty-one, not including its reputed ability to scare off evil spirits and drive rats out of their holes. The roots, flowers and leaves are all regarded as potent, either alone or mixed together, or taken with wine. Among the diseases supposedly "cured" by this herb are snakebites, coughs, hernias, and toothaches. It was also used to grow hair, and for reducing men's appetite for "venery." It is "good" also for inflamed breasts and testicles. Its modern counterpart may be the daffodil or the narcissus. It does not appear in modern pharmaceutical formulas. Both narcissus and daffodil bulbs are poisonous.

CABBAGE: This humble vegetable and its many relatives—kale, cauliflower, broccoli, kohlrabi, turnips, and rutabagas—were used before Captain James Lind employed lemons to prevent scurvy among sailors of the British Navy on long sea voyages in 1754. Along with other low-calorie green vegetables the cabbage family remains a valuable dietary item, rich in vitamins and minerals, for those who can tolerate a bit of roughage. One can hardly credit it, however, with the ancient virtues assigned it—removal of the effects of too much wine, improving eyesight, and overcoming carbuncles. It will not grow hair, either, any better than the best modern methods!

CAPSICUM is familiar as the "red and green peppers," although neither is a true pepper. In Mexico and adjacent American states, capsicum is valued medicinally to arrest diarrhea, to cure a cold (by swallowing small peppers whole), and to act as a sexual stimulant. One will scarcely disagree with Pier Andrea Mattioli who in 1544 said, "They are hot to the fourth degree; as a result of which they burn and ulcerate." (Krutch)

CASCARA SAGRADA, which in Spanish means the sacred cascara, comes from the bark of the tree of that name, which grows in the Pacific States, and from the cascara amarga, bitter-bark or Honduras bark, a South American tree. It is a laxative and cathartic, a common ingredient of commercial laxative preparations.

CLOVE: Named for its nail-like shape by the Romans, who called it *clavus*, the clove has always been a favorite spice; the modern cook who sticks cloves in his ham and other baked meats has centuries of precedent behind him. There were also many medicinal uses claimed for cloves, and some of them have come down to the present. What grown person today does not remember oil of cloves for toothache? It was also once believed to "stay" the plague, make the breath sweet after too much wine—and relieve vomiting, as well as to remedy "wind" in the intestines.

CORK: The cork oak has given its name to any kind of bottle stopper no matter what the more modern material may be. On the theory that nothing that grows is without its usefulness, the ancient naturalists pointed to the oak as an example of how everything in existence is for man's benefit. This oak is unlike other trees in that its bark can be removed without killing it. After a variable number of years, the debarking can be repeated. (See also Chapter One for worship of the oak.) Medicinally, the tannin from oak bark had a brief modern vogue as a treatment for burns, but is now in disfavor for that purpose. It is still useful in "tanning" leather. Tannin is also a principal ingredient in tea, and tea leaves were used as emergency treatment for burns within this century, but are no longer recommended.

CUMIN: If you enjoy curries, sauerkraut, and the European cordial, kümmel, you'll know what cumin is, even if you never heard of it by that name. It was, and is, a favorite spice, but has little medicinal reputation, though it was formerly believed to cause the skin to assume a scholarly pallor without the intellectual effort otherwise involved. It was also used to overcome gas formation in the intestines, as were other aromatics. The doctor today proceeds in somewhat different manner to overcome the "wicked winds and other evils in a man's stomach" (Bancke's Herbal). It was formerly believed that one had to curse the seeds when sowing them if a good crop was desired; people who like curry but find it dislikes them, curse their luck!

FLAX: The fibers of the flax plant have been used by man since the Stone Age for making cloth; linen has been found in Egyptian tombs. There are more than eighty references to linen in the Old Testament and many more in the New. The ancient VIPs were often described as robed in "purple and fine linen." Grandma knew the virtues of linseed poultices for relieving all kinds of inflammation and bringing boils "to a head." The modern physician employs other methods, but the principle of hot wet dressings is as sound as it ever was in certain circumstances.

GARDEN HELIOTROPE: Valerian, also known as "phu" because of its strong odor, is virtually obsolete today; it was once regarded as a nerve sedative and "nervine." Its popular name "allheal" is a reflection of the high value once placed upon it, even for so serious a condition as epilepsy. Valerian affects cats in a manner similar to catnip, and has the same action on rats—the latter has been mentioned as a possible explanation for the Pied Piper of Hamelin, who is said to have carried heliotrope on his person. It would hardly explain why the children followed him.

HAWKWEED or devil's-paintbrush is an example of how an ordinary plant can be imbued with many virtues. Krutch lists the following:

sharpens the eyesight of hawks (hence the name),
good for a burning stomach,
helps scorpion bites if applied to the puncture,
helps eye maladies when mixed with human milk,
induces sleep,
facilitates urination,
diminishes sexual desire,
increases supply of blood,
eases the stomach after a hearty meal,
aids digestion without "crudities" in the stomach,
encourages appetite if one eats little,
tempers steel when dissolved in hot water,
counteracts all poisons except those of the bladder or those which suffocate.

Quite a record for a weed! The steel tempering, of course, works just as well without the herb.

HELLEBORE: Plants of the lily family, confusingly similar to skunk cabbage (cf. above). The root of white hellebore is cathartic, promotes nasal discharge and causes vomiting. The root of the green hellebore is poisonous. Several active principles have been isolated from these roots and have been used medically, but they are drastic and not in great favor today.

HOLLYHOCK: (See Mallow.)

HORSE CHESTNUTS: These are not chestnuts at all; they are the buckeyes after which the state of Ohio is nicknamed. Many an American still carries one in his pocket for good luck and to ward off rheumatism, a use to which they were put by the Chinese for many centuries. They are said to have received the "horse" appellation because of their use in Constantinople to cure "broken-winded" horses.

HOUSELEEK: Sempervivum or hen-and-chickens is not highly regarded medicinally, but its magic repute includes such supposed powers as ability to protect against fire and lightning. It also is said that if the juice of this plant is mixed with the milk of a woman nursing a boy about twelve weeks old, just a drop of this mixture will restore hearing when dropped into a deaf ear.

IRIS is named after the Greek goddess of the rainbow, who was also a messenger between the gods and humankind, and who waited on the gods and sometimes helped to alleviate their sufferings. This flower and plant are credited with usefulness in treating fractures and head wounds, and removing imbedded weapons from the body without pain. As a pessary, it was used to cause abortion—as might any pessary, regardless of composition. The iris is one of the many common flowering plants which is too seldom recognized as poisonous. When roots are powdered, they can be used in the manufacture of medicines, perfumes and tooth powder, according to the New Standard Encyclopedia. (Chapter Twelve.)

JUNIPER: This plant is most familiar to moderns as an ingredient of gin, which is still esteemed in some quarters as a remedy "for the kidneys." The ancients attributed a long list of virtues to it, including the cure of coughs, cramps, "consumption," hemorrhoids, fevers, gout, difficult labors, "falling sickness" (Remember, Julius Caesar had it—epilepsy), ruptures and convulsions, besides helping the brain, the eyesight and the memory. Possibly the juniper-flavored wine, predecessor of the modern martini or bloody mary, had something to do with improving the sufferer's outlook.

KERMES OAK "BERRIES" are not berries at all, but galls—the bodies of scale insects known since the time of Moses, when they were used for dyes as, later, the American cochineal bug was used. Both are now outmoded. Kermes oak was listed for a time in the London pharmacopoeia as an astringent. It has disappeared from among modern medical remedies.

LETTUCE: Our common salad stand-by was valued by the ancients for saving the life of the Roman Emperor Augustus, and was used for treating burns (mixed with human milk), and as a means of overcoming sleeplessness. So highly was it regarded that a means of preserving it was devised—the so-called Oxmel, a mixture of vinegar and honey which has had a rebirth of a sort in some modern writings on folk medicine. Neither lettuce nor the preservative is regarded by physicians today in the drug category, though all three ingredients still enjoy usefulness and well-deserved popularity in the kitchen. "White lettuce" is a perennial leafy plant otherwise known as rattlesnake root or gall of the earth, and is said to have value in dysentery and in treating insect and snakebites.

LILY: All sorts of legends surround the lily from the most remote times, and it is not surprising that some of them are related to medicine; for example, that smelling lilies, especially tiger lilies, will cause freckles. The lily family is a big one, and not all are beautiful flowers:

Star grass is recommended for all varieties of "female trouble," and for colic, rheumatism and flatulence. Oh yes—and for hysteria!

Garlic, supposedly beneficial in asthma, bronchitis, rheumatism, coughs, colds, hoarseness, worms and ivy poisoning. Garlic-eating peoples were said to be healthy, as a rule, and the garlic got the credit, perhaps because it was difficult to avoid noting its presence. In modern times it has been peddled commercially as a remedy for high blood pressure; its benefits were enjoyed exclusively by the promoters.

Asparagus is credited with being gently laxative, probably because of its fibrous nature, and also with stimulating the kidneys; the latter deduction may hinge upon its tendency to impart a strong odor to the urine.

Lily of the valley produces a drug closely resembling the heart stimulant, digitalis, derived from the foxglove, but much less potent. However, fresh preparations of this flower taken internally are poisonous (Chapter Twelve). Distilled water infusions of the flowers are said to remove freckles and sun tan and, since many of these tend to vanish when sun exposure ceases, there were probably few disappointments.

Dogtooth violet is listed as an emetic and emollient—a paradox—and the American Indians used it for "breast complaints."

Smilax or greenbrier has an edible root to which "alterative" and "depurant"—itch-relieving—properties were imputed.

Trillium erectum or wake-robin has been regarded as an "alterative," astringent and tonic; also for menstrual disturbances and as an aid in childbirth. One of its common names is birthroot.

Comment: the occurrence of the name "wake-robin" applied to this lily and also to the arum, a quite different plant, shows the overlapping and confusing variation in popular names from one locality to another.

Yucca, or Spanish bayonet root, is supposed to be good for rheumatism or gonorrhea!

LICORICE: Sweetroot is well known to anybody who hasn't forgotten his childhood—strings, whips and stalks of the black, sweet, sticky confection which had the additional virtue of being cheap even in the days when pennies were still money. Some of us even now retain a sneaking liking for the stuff. It is still used for the same purpose as the ancients used it, to soothe an irritated throat or to add flavor to medical mixtures as well as to "chawin' tobacca."

MALLOW: The mallow root was formerly the source of a gummy juice which was used in confections. (Who doesn't know and like marshmallows?) It has been succeeded by the cheaper substitute, gum arabic, and still later by gelatin. The substance is a mild demulcent and was much used for poultices, coughs, bronchitis and urinary complaints.

MANDRAKE: Several perennial herbs are known by this name in Europe, Africa, Asia and North America. It grows about a foot in height and has a juicy, orange-colored berry. Superstitious people believe that eating the fruit (which has a sickening taste) brings health and wealth. It has long been known to be poisonous, yet has earned respect for its emetic and narcotic qualities. In ancient times it served to dull the senses during surgery.

Because of its forked root, it was thought to be demon-possessed in ancient times. In medieval days people believed it could not be uprooted, except by prayer and incantations in the moonlight, because at any other time it shrieked to high heaven and deranged the minds of all who heard it. However, in Shakespeare's lifetime, mandrake was believed to be—once freed from the earth, that is!—a valuable aid to physicians as a laxative, to lovers who had quarreled, to the restless to gain sleep and to ladies who wanted children. Quite a plant! But not much in use today for any but the first virtue.

MEADOWSWEET was valued mainly for its fragrance—a valuable quality in the Middle Ages when sanitation and personal cleanliness left much to be desired. It was celebrated in Chaucer's *Canterbury Tales* as an ingredient in ointments for healing wounds by local application, and protecting knights in combat when taken internally in a "concoction."

MOUNTAIN ASH: Here is another in the long list of anti-snake charms; the story goes that if a snake is enclosed in a circle made partly of fire and partly of ash branches, the serpent will go through the fire in preference to crossing the ash. Naturally then, it was also recommended as a remedy for snake-bites. Lameness in horses was said to be curable by gentle rubbing with the branches of the ash. The bark is supposed to have virtues as a cathartic, a tonic, febrifuge, alterative and diuretic, and to be useful in arthritis and to induce sweating, as well as for treating dizziness and headache.

FLOWERING OR POISON ASH: Also called fringe tree or old-man's-beard, is recommended for about the usual general list, but warnings are issued that an overdose is poisonous, as the name suggests.

WAFER OR STINKING ASH is related to the edible orange, and is mainly noted for its odor, and as a bitter tonic.

PRICKLY ASH or devil's-walking-stick is used as an emetic and cathartic and the oil of the seeds for earache and deafness. (Any warm oil has a soothing effect in earache, and none helps deafness.)

NARCISSUS: see *bog asphodel* (also see Chapter Twelve on poisons).

NASTURTIUM, meaning nose-twister, is one of the pungent members of the mustard family, but if you are thinking of the peppery-tasting garden flower, think again. This *nasturtium* is the well-known watercress, prized as a salad ingredient. In less sophisticated days, it was esteemed for its lime content required by children with soft teeth; for more iron than spinach; and good for diabetics because of its low carbohydrate content. Other vitamin claims, such as vitamin A for night blindness, were also made. Actually, this excellent herb shares these constituents with many another green vegetable, so we must love the cress for its flavor alone.

PLANTAIN: This enemy of the suburban lawn is connected with an interesting superstition:

"Three roots will cure one grief, four another disease, six hanged about the neck are good for another malady, etc., all of which are but ridiculous toys" (John Gerard, 1597, quoted by Krutch). Thus does one medieval herbalist save us the trouble of denying the multiplicity of virtues claimed for this nuisance herb.

PUFFBALL: An edible fungus; it forms a large ball containing spores which when ripe can be made to "puff" by applying external force. These spores form a fine powder which is genuinely useful in stopping hemorrhage and is medicinally employed as a powder for its absorbent and "dusting" virtues (on "sweaty" feet), and as a coating for pills. The powder is highly flammable and should not be used near open flames.

SAGE: For many centuries, as today, this has been a favorite spice, but despite its name *salvia*, from the Latin *salveo*, "I save," it has had little medical reputation. It was revered in religious circles because of its reputed part in sheltering the Virgin Mary from Herod's troops during her flight into Egypt.

SCABIOSA: A lovely flower with an unpleasant name, but one derived directly from its reputed usefulness as a treatment for skin diseases. (And, of course, snakebite!) (And the plague!) In hot water, it was recommended as a bath to relieve itching.

SAXIFRAGE: Sometimes known as a rock breaker because it grows among rocks and its roots penetrate into their crevices; this large group of garden plants was advocated—naturally— for breaking up kidney stones, stimulating urination and protecting against the plague.

Comment: Diuresis, increasing the flow of urine, is mentioned as a virtue of many herbs; perhaps this may be explained in part by the fact that most were used in infusions or teas, with plenty of water, which in itself would increase urinary output, and might well help to prevent or even to dissolve some stones.

Protection against the plague is also mentioned frequently in herbals. This disease, the Black Death of the Middle Ages, was a great source of fear as it ravaged whole nations. It was natural that many herbs were tried, and if the plague abated or the individual escaped or recovered, the herb got the credit. It was not until the nineteenth century that the plague was traced to bacterial infection spread by rats and by the rat flea.

THYME: This aromatic was the ancient source of the best honey, from the slopes of Mount Hymettus in Greece. It was always a favorite spice, and medicinally advocated for inducing urination and menstruation and bring about abortion, among some twenty-eight other disorders. Epileptics were advised to sniff it and sleep on it, and girls who wore it in their wreaths were considered irresistibly kissable. (See also Chapter Ten on Thymol.)

WATERCRESS: See Nasturtium (page 96).

WORMWOOD (*Artimesia*): This herb gets its name from its genuine ability to expel worms. It is also an ingredient of absinthe, which had a bad reputation even in ancient China and in Roman times, and is still held capable of causing nervous disorders. Wormwood is related to the kitchen herb, tarragon, and to the sagebrush of our western deserts.

PLANTS AND FLOWERS OF SMALL MEDICINAL VALUE

LAVENDER: A pleasant fragrance, nostalgically associated with old lace and gracious living, and useful as an ingredient in aromatic spirits of ammonia (smelling salts), perfumed soap, and sachets.

MYRRH: One of the gifts of the Magi to the Babe of Bethlehem as a symbol of healing. The Bible lists 128 varieties of plants, many of them with healing qualities. Among them are some still familiar today:

Balm	Cucumber
Bitter herbs (Passover)	Desire (caper)
Endive	Dove's dung (star-of-Bethlehem)
Chicory	Fig
Lettuce	Frankincense
Dandelion	Flax
Cedars of Lebanon	Garlick (with the "k")

Green bay tree
Hemlock
Juniper
Lentils
Lilies
Locust tree pods (St.
  John's bread)
Myrtle

Olive
Onion
  Palm
Rose of Sharon
Turpentine
Willow
Wormwood
Thistles
Tares (weeds) (rye grass)

WATER LILY, of the same family as the fabled lotus which so
  narcotized sailors that they did not want to return home, but
  probably not the true lotus.

ERGOT, the fungus which infests rye, belongs in the category of
  dangerous poisons as well as useful drugs (Chapter Ten).

LEEKS are charged with the death of the Roman Emperor,
  Tiberius. They are said to dull the sight and produce nightmares, besides being very bad for the stomach. They are also
  considered good for "hardness of the womb" when boiled with
  sea water, and capable of stopping nosebleed when mixed with
  frankincense. Not only can they provoke to "venery," but they
  are good for chest diseases including "consumption." To top
  all these virtues, they are good eating, as any Welshman knows,
  since they are the national emblem of Wales.

BINDWEED, which looks like a morning glory—and one species
  really is—ranks low in popularity with gardeners, since it
  twines itself around everything in sight and is hard to get rid
  of. One variety contains a violent purgative called jalap, which
  used to be an ingredient of the so-called "thunderbolt" purgatives which were popular at one time. Of course they did
  more harm than good. Modern therapists say the jalap and
  related resinous purgatives should be abandoned—they include
  colocynth (bitter apple), elaterin (squirting cucumber), gamboge (from Asian trees) and podophyllum (mandrake root).

CATTAIL was valued for its down, useful for stuffing pillows;
  it was also accused of causing deafness if it fell on a person's
  ear—a queer combination of ideas indeed!

ROSES, strange to relate, are given little medicinal significance,
  though greatly admired for their beauty, their fragrant oil, and

their symbolism—of love, of mystic vision, of the female organs, and of the Virgin Mary! In the days of my youth, a bottle of rose water and glycerine always stood on our kitchen sink and another in the bathroom in the interest of avoiding dishpan hands. The ladies of medieval days washed their hands in rose water and ate rose-petal candy. The modern entrepreneur offers you rose hips for vitamins, if you are gullible enough. A bouquet of red roses is still the bashful swain's most eloquent proposal.

This is admittedly a brief and superficial survey of the enormous amount of material available in the sources listed at the back of the book, but perhaps it will lead to some worthwhile conclusions:

- Observations of plants, trees and herbs have been an interesting and, in general, a useful pursuit for many centuries all over the world.

- Many plants do have definite medicinal qualities.

- Many plants have been credited with qualities which they do not possess.

- Modern medicine is indebted to herbal lore for many of its most potent drugs (Chapter Ten).

- Many of the basic principles of herbal lore have been proved to be sound by centuries of experience, plus the validation of modern scientific research. This includes the use of teas, poultices, powders, oils, resins, and of active principles of herbs identified by chemical research, followed by synthesis.

- It is not sensible nor realistic either to accept or to reject herbal lore *in toto*.

- Herbal lore should be evaluated objectively to preserve what is valid and eliminate what is mistaken or outmoded.

Chapter Six

MEDICINAL PROPERTIES IN FOODS

Medicinal virtues were attributed by our ancestors not only to plants and flowers, trees and weeds, but to foods. These were over and above the nutrient functions. Some of them had a certain validity. Vegetables with considerable roughage are still recognized as having laxative qualities. Some of those formerly valued as remedies for scurvy have been shown chemically to be rich sources of ascorbic acid (vitamin C), the antiscurvy factor. In other instances, however, the idea was a mistaken one, as in the case of asparagus, which was regarded as a powerful diuretic, probably because of the strong odor it imparts to the urine. Its active principle, asparagine, is still listed in medical dictionaries as derived from many varieties of seeds, but is not found in therapeutic recommendations. Taken in hot water, as recommended by herbalists, almost any herb naturally has a diuretic effect from the water alone.

Black currant juice mixed with honey has been used for easing sore throats. This is one of the many uses recommended for honey, which was the universal sweetener in the old world before cane sugar was introduced from America. Honey remains today just a sweetener.

Carrots are properly regarded as useful for their contribution of vitamin A, which is essential for good vision. Its lack or deficiency is noted first as night blindness, and so a popular idea has grown up that carrots are remedies for other forms of eye trouble, such as near- or farsightedness, astigmatism, and eye diseases. However, this is not so. Eating carrots will not help any eye malady except deficiency in vitamin A. Overeating of carrots may cause the skin and membranes to turn yellow from the carotene, which is the substance from which vitamin A is derived.

Cucumbers found their way not only into the diet, where they belong, but to the cosmetic shelf in the form of skin lotions, often combined with Irish moss. They seem to have given enough satisfaction to become popular, and it is quite likely that they are just as good as some of the expensive preparations now marketed for softening the skin you love to touch.

Figs, of course, are a staple food in the Orient, though somewhat of a luxury with us. They are esteemed as a laxative, and rightly so.

Grapes have been exploited in one way or another for many years. As probably the best sources of good wine, one cannot deny their value. But the promotion of diets limited to grapes, even to the extent of claiming a cure for syphilis, as was done in this country a few decades ago, is ridiculous. The diuretic action of grapes is also commonly accepted, but not in scientific circles.

Horse-radish, which gets the "horse" portion of its name because it is strong "like a horse," is popular as a condiment, but has also been recommended for "dropsy." This symptom is now treated more effectively in other ways.

Strong vegetables other than horse-radish include *onions* and *garlic*. These are admittedly excellent flavorings, when employed with judgment, but they are also touted for many medicinal uses. The onion has been used as a poultice, and has been tied to the soles of the feet to "draw out" fever—when the onion turned dark, as onions will, this was regarded as the sign of effectiveness. Garlic is still sold for high blood pressure, for which it has no demonstrable value; it was formerly recommended for toothache, and as an antibiotic. Whatever one may say about these estimable vegetables, there is certainly no mistaking their presence in strength.

Older people who have good memories will recall the times when they were young and had colds—they got a dose of hot lemonade. As a cold drink this is excellent, but hot—I'll settle for the cold! The modern folklore includes a glass of *lemon juice* before breakfast for prolonging life, or for preserving your bowel function, whichever need is most acute at the moment.

Dentists say that undiluted lemon juice is bad for the tooth enamel, especially around the gum margins.

Tropical dwellers wrapped their meat in *papaya* leaves to tenderize it. We still use this method in the form of commercial preparations. Here is an instance where experience alone proved a good guide, for the natives knew nothing of the enzymes which we now recognize as the source of papaya juice activity.

The *banana*, too, has genuine medical usefulness in bland diets, and for its specific place in the treatment of cystic fibrosis of the pancreas, a congenital disease of infants.

Fruits of the *apple family—peaches, pears, plums, apples themselves,* and the lowly but invaluable *prune*—are useful sources of fruit sugar, vitamins, minerals and roughage. Thus they are natural preventives for vitamin and mineral shortages which so many moderns fear without just cause. Fruits are useful too in favoring good bowel function.

Before the days of modern cosmetic magic, the lady with hair-setting problems was advised to simmer a tablespoonful of *quince seeds* in a pint of hot water until the mixture was thick, strain it, add some cologne and bottle it (Coon). A drop or so on the hairbrush was probably just about as prone to foster romantic admiration as the commercial products of today are supposed to do. Quince-seed preparations were also recommended as soothing applications for burns, or as mouthwashes.

Rhubarb is the rival of the prune and the fig as a laxative in folklore. Certainly a rhubarb stew or pie would be preferable, as a spring tonic, to the sulphur and molasses which used to be foisted upon the helpless young. Only the stems are suitable for food; the leaves contain oxalic acid and are not palatable; in large amounts they may prove poisonous (Chapter Twelve).

Many spices such as *pepper, sage, curry, cayenne* (chili), *ginger, mustard* have long been used, not only as flavoring agents but for their supposed medicinal value as "carminatives" and for their aid to digestion and avoidance of flatulence. That they have limited value in this regard is true, but the modern doctor recognizes digestive symptoms as signals of some deeper and perhaps more serious trouble than appears at first glance. He does not care to rely on mere temporary relief of symptoms. Mustard appears also in poultices or plaster, as does pepper, especially for chest infection or asthma.

Perhaps the most deflated vegetable in the list is *spinach*. Once celebrated as a source of strength by Popeye the Sailorman, it has now been basely deserted by him in favor of a cereal product. Valued for its iron and mineral content, it was fed to children whether they liked it or not. Now it is recognized that the iron in spinach is often poorly absorbed, and is, therefore, less nutritionally available than that in eggs, liver and meats. Spinach is difficult for many persons to digest and its roughage often causes severe abdominal distress. But for those who like it, puréed spinach with croutons and a dash of wine vinegar, or spinach soufflé, remains a delectable treat. And that should be recommendation enough.

Almonds, like other nuts, are good sources of protein and fat, but the recommendation that they are particularly "good" for diabetics is too good to be true. The absence of appreciable amounts of carbohydrates in most nuts does make them useful in the diabetic diet as foods, but not as medicinal specifics.

Psyllium seeds and other starchy substances that absorb water and swell up have long been used to overcome constipation. They have a value in cases where lack of bulk is responsible, especially in persons who cannot tolerate the rougher vegetables. Of course, there are many other causes for constipation, and a folk remedy should not be relied upon without knowing what the underlying cause may be.

Arrowroot, barley, corn and other grains used as flour or in gruel, were former stand-bys in feeding convalescents. They have the virtue of being mild and nonirritating, but have no medicinal qualities otherwise. And there's not much food value in gruel, once convalescence begins.

Another favorite food for the sick is chicken broth or chicken meat. The broth is warm and perhaps comforting, as is the kind and neighborly impulse which brings it. There is, however, little nourishment in it. Chicken meat is another matter; it is a tasty, nutritious and easily digested meat when properly cooked. In the days when many families, even in cities, kept chickens, it was natural that this source of food should be highly valued. There is no longer a need for one of the traditional uses of the chicken, namely to employ the warm carcass of a freshly killed chicken in place of a poultice.

Bread is made to be eaten, of course, but it has also been put to other uses—as a poultice for small burns, and when it is moldy, as a treatment for infected wounds (see penicillin, Chapter X).

Burnt toast has been used as an antidote for poisons because it is charcoal, but modern usage demands a special kind of chemically activated charcoal. White of egg is a better and safer antidote against poisons, especially if one is not sure what poison has been taken. So is milk or sweet butter. As a dentifrice, burnt toast is no better or worse than dozens of other home remedies such as salt or baking soda.

Modern proponents of folk medicine have kept alive the reputation of honey for many uses:
- with vinegar for arthritis
  - for sleeplessness
    - for bed-wetting
      - for burns
        - for sore throats
          - for coughs
            - as a sugar for diabetics
              - for hay fever

It is a pity that so excellent and enjoyable a food should be saddled needlessly with so many attributes which it does not possess. Some of the recommendations are actually dangerous.

Diabetics who believe that honey is not a sugar may do themselves serious harm—honey *is* a sugar, and diabetics cannot tolerate it any better than they can any other sugar. Hay fever, which is caused by pollen allergies, may be made worse by use of honey, since it contains variable amounts of pollen. Indeed, honey itself may *cause* an allergy in persons with tendencies toward such sensitivities. It can, and should, be recommended as a delightful sweet and a useful ingredient in many kitchen recipes, without trying to give it medicinal virtues which are nonexistent.

Rice, in addition to being the staple food of the Orient, is a useful cereal anywhere. Brown or unpolished rice has more vitamins, but this is not important where the diet is not limited to rice. It is medicinally useful in bland, low-sodium diets. Otherwise, it is best regarded as a food rather than a medicine.

Salt is one of the basic chemicals necessary for metabolism. Too much salt is eliminated by the kidneys; in diseases of circulation or of the kidneys, salt restriction may have to be practiced. Medicinally, *iodized salt* is a preventive of simple goiter. Other medicinal claims for salt, especially sea salt, are without foundation. Aside from iodine, there are many better food-sources of minerals than sea salt: to be specific, all deep-sea fish and "sea food," and vegetables raised on soil close to salt water. Still, gullible people buy sea salt by the gallon at prices that must yield the seller profits out of all proportion to the benefits gained by the buyer.

Salt has a long and fascinating history. Domestic animals must be supplied with blocks of salt, and wild animals instinctively seek salt licks. Trails to these were followed by hunters in search of game. They may have become roads in the course of time, and helped to determine the locations of villages which grew into cities. Salt is mentioned frequently in the Bible, beginning with the self-answering question in Job, Chapter 6, Verse 6, "Can that which is unsavory be eaten without salt? Or is there any taste in the white of an egg?"

Salt was known as "the magic white sand." Because it was so important to man, governments taxed it. The early Greeks worshiped salt along with sun worship. All Hebrew babies were rubbed with salt as soon as they were born, and many babies of the Near East receive the same treatment today. Every child knows that a bird can be captured by sprinkling salt on its tail, but the birds don't seem to realize it! Throwing salt over the left shoulder when it has been spilled goes back to the tradition that spilling salt involves incurring the ill will of evil spirits. Da Vinci's painting of The Last Supper shows spilled salt before Judas, and what has been interpreted as a motion on his part of throwing some over his shoulder. It is certain that salt has always been an important factor in life and living, and valued accordingly.

Salt receptacles, preceding the modern shaker, were dishes, ranging in value from the simple sea shells of the peasants to the magnificent Cellini cup of gold, pearls and fine enamel inlays which may be seen in New York's Metropolitan Museum of Art. Salt was a symbol of friendship, and was regarded as inimical to evil spirits. Grimm's fairy tales relate that no salt was to be found in witches' kitchens nor at devils' feasts. Finnish mythology attributes salt in the oceans to a spark struck from a blaze kindled in the sky by the god Ukko, which fell into the sea and turned to salt. Every one is familiar with the Biblical story of Lot's wife, who disobeyed the command not to look behind her at the destruction of Sodom and Gomorrah, and was turned into a pillar of salt.

Salt has been used as money in many ways. The Roman legionnaires were provided with salt or the means of buying it as a part of their pay, giving rise to our modern term "salary." Salt was traded for slaves, who were defined as "not worth their salt" if they failed to satisfy their purchasers. Tablets of pure salt were used as coins in Ethiopia as late as 1900, and when Italian soldiers entered the country before World War II, they found salt held in the bank as part of the nation's financial reserve.

Archaeologists have found evidence that salt was used by cave dwellers in Western Europe more than 3000 years B.C., about the same time our Sumerian physician (mentioned in the last chapter) considered it a valued mineral in his medicine cabinet. The Trojans salted their fish 1000 years B.C., and the Egyptians used salt for embalming as well as for seasoning foods. There is also a record of a Chinese emperor in 2000 B.C., who required his servants to keep his court well supplied with salt.

Like many another good and useful substance, salt in excess can be destructive, as in the Dead Sea in Palestine and Great Salt Lake in Utah, where no living things can survive. The Romans knew this; when they conquered Carthage they salted the ground on which it had been built and plowed the earth.

In our time, salt is recognized as an essential of all living tissues. It is a necessary constituent of blood and body fluids. Its proper balance and utilization is vital to good health. Because of its universal use, salt has become a valuable vehicle for the prevention of simple goiter in regions where ground water and crops are deficient in iodine; an iodine compound is added during manufacture and packaging.

Salt is also involved in circulation and kidney function, and in the maintenance of proper fluid exchange in the body. It has from time to time been blamed for high blood pressure, but this is open to considerable doubt. Nevertheless, the idea has been misconstrued by some persons, like the one who wrote to me some years ago, saying that man should abandon the use of salt altogether because "you see, animals don't salt their food." I pointed out to him the well-known need for salt licks, to which he replied that these were for grazing animals only—beasts of prey did not require salt. He never replied to my reminder that the blood of the prey and the meat supplied salt for the carnivores.

When Jesus called His disciples "the salt of the earth," He paid them a very high compliment indeed.*

Seaweed (kelp) has been promoted as a valuable source of iodine. But those who can and do use iodized salt and who give deep-sea foods a place in their diet, need pay no attention to this advice.

Soap is not a food, as any youngster can attest after having his mouth washed out for using bad words—if that ancient and wholesome practice has not given way to modern, permissive child psychology. Soap is always ready at hand in the home, and a glassful of soapy water makes an excellent emetic for one who has taken a dose of some poison left carelessly about the premises.

Soap as a cleansing agent is also a great contributor to good health. Mixed with sunshine, elbow grease and enthusiastic application, it is as good and safe a germicide as we know anything about.

Soap is the best first aid for ivy and oak poisoning—applied as a liberal lather without hard rubbing, then rinsed and re-rinsed. Then repeated and rinsed again. It also has the virtue of being less irritating to most skins than are detergents. It does not, however, have any magic power to remove skin blemishes other than dirt and, in some instances, excessive oiliness.

* Some of this material has been adapted from *The History of Salt*, Morton Salt Company, Chicago, Illinois, 1956; and *Superstitions About Salt*, William B. Wilkinson, Cayuga Salt Company, Ithaca, N.Y., courtesy of The Salt Institute, Chicago, Illinois.

Baking soda is a common household chemical and cooking aid of real value. Aside from its culinary uses, which are many, it is valuable as a paste for relieving itching insect stings, or for soothing small, first-degree burns. It is a good mouthwash and dentifrice, and helpful for *occasional* use against stomach acidity and heartburn. Its continued use for treating "indigestion" is not advisable. Baking soda should not be added to green vegetables to preserve their color; it reduces their vitamin B values.

Yeast is such a busy agent that many medicinal virtues were naturally attributed to it. It is a good source of vitamins of the B-complex group, but indiscriminate taking of such an active ferment can cause, as well as occasionally remedy, bowel disturbances. The use of concentrated yeast as a sole diet is illogical. The virtues of brewers' yeast have been extolled by the food faddists beyond any rhyme or reason, except possibly for the reason they do it. Just because it pays! Except for baking or brewing, use of yeast should be governed by medical advice.

In any consideration of food and its possible medicinal value, there is surprisingly little mention in folklore of the *citrus fruits* and other fruits and vegetables containing ascorbic acid (vitamin C). Oranges, lemons, grapefruit and limes are the most important common sources of the nutrient. The Caribbean acerola berry is probably the richest but is not yet widely used. The tomato, once regarded as a poisonous plant, has now gained the status of the poor man's orange for its contribution of ascorbic acid, and the potato is another relatively inexpensive staple which adds a useful source of this vitamin.

The story of vitamin C is a real example of how experience and observation is the basis of science, and how folklore can show the way to the scientist. Discovery of the antiscurvy properties of fresh fruits and vegetables is generally credited to the Scottish Navy surgeon James Lind, who observed the disease in sailors in the Royal British Navy. They had bleeding gums and loosened teeth and hemorrhages into their flesh. Often they sickened and died. He published his treatise in 1754, but he was not really the first; he himself points out that the Dutch had used orange juice and lemon juice as early as 1564, and so had Sir Richard Hawkins in 1593.

A manual for naval surgeons recognized the need and recommended the orange- and lemon-juice diet in 1636. Admiral Watson employed lemon juice in 1774, and it became obligatory in the British Navy about that time. In addition to oranges and lemons, limes were employed, and British sailors are still called *limeys*. Actually the lime is the least rich in ascorbic acid (vitamin C), the citrus fruits ranking in the following order: lemons, oranges, grapefruit, limes. Melons and berries also provide important supplies of this vitamin, as do tomatoes and potatoes. As a vitamin source, these foods may legitimately be given medical (preventive) significance, and in cases of severe deficiencies, they also have curative potency.

Vitamin C has been synthesized in the laboratory and may be had medicinally. The vitamin is also being added to foods in which it does not naturally occur, mainly as a sales gimmick. This must be regarded as synthetic folklore, circa 1969.

Toast and tea are excellent food for the convalescent or one with acutely upset stomach, but not for too long. Their nutritive value is limited. As an antidote for poisons, their use should be restricted to occasions when there is nothing better available. The tannic acid in tea is a mild astringent, and the charcoal of the toast is supposed to absorb the poisons.

The medicinal significance of *water* is perhaps without limit. In fevers, plenty of fluid is usually advised; in constipation the same advice may be given. Water may have to be restricted in some instances of heart, kidney and circulatory diseases. Externally, water may be used to apply heat or cold, or with soap for cleansing.

Occasionally, it should be noted, there are skins to which water should not be applied, but oils used for cleansing. Here a common household product, olive oil, is useful, and very recently, the American Medical Association has suggested vegetable shortening for dry skins. Sweet butter but not salted butter is also useful.

Here is a brief list of additional popularly held ideas about foods and their medicinal significance. It is by no means complete, since these beliefs are universal, and vary from district to district and time to time, as they are influenced by national, tribal and perhaps religious considerations:

The Food Fallacy	*Why It Isn't So*
Cook cabbage for several hours to keep it from "acting up":	All vegetables should be cooked as briefly as possible to preserve their nutrient value.
Fish and milk should never be eaten together:	If that were so, fish chowders with milk, and oyster stews would be taboo; actually, if neither the fish nor the milk is spoiled, they may safely be combined.
Eat only proteins at one meal or only carbohydrates; never mix them; Only "natural" foods are wholesome:	These are contradictory and impossible; natural foods contain both proteins and carbohydrates, and mixing them does no harm.
A teaspoon of whiskey in which arborvitae has been soaked will cure cancer, if taken before meals:	This is a dangerous misconception, for which there is, of course, no shred of genuine evidence.
Ripe, sweet cherries prevent aging by removing "old age matter" from the body; Cherries are acid foods and therefore undesirable:	Well, we can't have it both ways. Cherries will not prevent aging, but they are good fruits (see following item).
Acid foods are bad for health:	There are so few acid foods that any reasonable diet will not contain too many; besides, the alkaline reaction of the body is maintained automatically except in starvation, and in certain metabolic (chemical) disturbances due to disease.
Milk-drinking people live longer; Older people don't need milk:	Again, we can't have it both ways; milk and its products are essential at any age, but no food assures long life.
Aspirin will preserve canned apples:	Salicylates do have preservative qualities, but proper sterilization is better than adding drugs.

The Food Fallacy	*Why It Isn't So*
Never eat rabbits because they are disease carriers:	Not all of them are; and what a lot of good *Hasenpfeffer* we would miss if we didn't eat properly cooked rabbit, which is quite safe.
Sauerkraut must be made in the light of the moon or the brine won't rise:	Fortunately the moon does not affect the pickling of sauerkraut or other preserving processes.
Sardines, frozen celery and kelp should be eaten every other day to preserve good health:	Sardines and celery (not necessarily frozen) are good foods, but they need not be eaten so often; kelp (seaweed) is sold for its iodine content. Fish, crabs, shrimp, lobster, scallops taste better and serve the same purpose.
Eat parsnips or asparagus often to cleanse the kidneys:	Kidneys don't need cleansing and vegetables wouldn't do it.
Beets build blood; Wine makes blood:	They contribute nutrients, but blood is built in the bone marrow.
Diabetes is caused by eating too many sweets; it can be cured by eating sour foods like lemon juice or sauerkraut:	Diabetes is due to a deficiency in the pancreas which interferes with proper use of starches and sweets. It cannot be cured, but can be managed so as to keep the person in good health.
Grape juice, honey, dried poke berries, carrot juice, vinegar, tomatoes, alfalfa tea and many other edible substances are recommended for treating arthritis (rheumatism):	No single food is curative of arthritis; arthritic persons need a good all-around diet.
Celery and fish are good food for the brain and nerves:	Nerves and all other body tissues are nourished by all foods.

The Food Fallacy	*Why It Isn't So*
Cooked cereals heat the blood:	The temperature of the blood and of the body as a whole is regulated by a nerve center in the brain, not by any foodstuffs.
Warm bread may cause a stroke:	If only it were as simple as that!
Tomato juice and ice water were blamed for causing heart disease:	There is no basis for this belief; the causes of heart disease are many and complex.
Eating watermelon or cucumbers, or using soft drinks, may cause polio:	Polio is an infection, not related to diet; it is caused by a virus.
Pork is indigestible:	Not if it is properly cooked, but like all foods with high fat content, it digests more slowly.
Sassafras, vinegar and many other foods were believed capable of thinning the blood:	The composition of the blood is governed by the body chemistry, and is influenced only indirectly by specific foods.
White sugar is not good for the health:	In proper amounts, as part of a well-planned diet, it is good and useful.
White bread is poisonous:	This is nonsense; white bread as it is baked today from enriched flour, is perfectly good food.
Raw vegetable juice contains important food values but cooked foods are "dead"; Raw foods are harmful to the expectant mother; Raw cucumbers without salt are poisonous:	Considering these three contradictory items together shows how inconsistent they are. Fresh, raw-vegetable juices are good, but the whole vegetable is better, for expectant mothers or anybody else. Properly cooked foods are not "dead."
An egg a day is harmful:	Normal persons can eat as many eggs as they like; eggs need not be restricted, except for specific medical reasons.

The Food Fallacy:	*Why It Isn't So:*
Putting cream in coffee makes the coffee more harmful:	This is a double fallacy; coffee in moderation is not harmful to normal persons, and adding cream does nothing but improve the flavor, if you like it that way —and can add calories!
Melba toast has no calories; Eat all you want before 4 P.M. to lose weight; Calories don't count; Honey is not fattening; Enriched candy is good for reducing:	All foods have some calories; Melba toast has as many as the bread had before it was toasted; calories *do* count; eating all you want may cause you to gain weight no matter what time of day you do so; honey has 100 calories per tablespoon; any candy made with sugar, 75–188 calories per piece.
Olives, oysters and raw eggs increase sexual potency:	Wishful thinking, pure and simple—accent on the *simple*.
Dried currants are poisonous:	Of course they are not; they're just one kind of raisin.
Food canned by menstruating women is sure to spoil:	This came from the days when women did not understand how to sterilize foods and jars; some of it spoiled; and much canning, of course, was done while menstruating, thus creating a deceptive coincidence.

The damage done by inadequate diets due to unwise choice of foods is not usually apparent at once. Some years ago, however, a grand jury in Passaic, New Jersey, held a so-called Zen diet responsible for the death of a young woman aged twenty-two, who dropped from 130 to 74 pounds in weight in nine months. She was following a diet based on food shortages in Japan during World War II; the promoter of the diet now lives in France. This diet has no relation to Zen Buddhism ("Zen" means meditation).

It consists of a vegetable concoction based on sesame seeds, and the progressive elimination of animal products, salads, fruits, and desserts, until at the seventh stage, the diet is 100 per cent cereal. At the same time, fluids are progressively restricted to "as little as possible." The result has been emaciation, and death from starvation for many people. Five other severe but nonfatal cases were reported to the same grand jury, and the New Jersey State Department of Health issued strong warnings about the dangers involved in this diet (*Public Health News,* August 1966). The grand jury cautioned the citizens: "*All people should be warned not to go on any type of diet without proper medical advice.*"

It should be apparent by this time that foods should be regarded as *foods* rather than medicines. The time has passed when the mild and often questionable medicinal values of foods are considered important or even useful. In primitive conditions, with doctors few and far between and medical knowledge in its infancy, medicinal herbs and their food properties had a place, even if their real value was much overrated. Today, we can rely on more accurate knowledge, purer and more active medicinal ingredients, and greater medical skills.

An objective and unprejudiced view of medicinal folklore in relation to herbs and food plants, gives no warrant for any supercilious attitude toward the beliefs held by many in the virtues of these sources. Newer knowledge has invalidated some of these traditional ideas, and confirmed others. Some have proved to be the forerunners of established, modern scientific remedies; many of them are indispensable in modern medicine. Our ancestors gave us a pretty good start on the road to medical knowledge, and while we have now progressed beyond some of their beliefs, we should give them credit for doing an intelligent job against the background of their times and the state of general knowledge in their day.

MODERN SYNTHETIC "FOLKLORE"

Before we raise our eyebrows too much at the ideas entertained by our ancestors, we might profitably take a look at our own views, in this enlightened age, about food, diets, and nutrition.

A hundred years from now the historians will be able to describe some very amusing ideas which we now entertain, and they will have the aid and encouragement of the mass media of communication, which spreads ideas faster than in any previous era. The bad ideas spread as fast as the good ones, and sometimes it seems faster.

If you look about you among your friends, or even your relatives, you may find many of the fallacious ideas which persist out of the past, plus many new ones which it is difficult to explain in view of the many opportunities which exist today for getting facts straight.

Our people exhibit an exaggerated fear of dietary deficiencies in the face of the world's most abundant food supply. In many parts of the world, deficient diets are common as a result of poverty and ignorance. In this country, there is no need for the person of average income, or better, to suffer a dietary inadequacy if he will learn and make use of a few simple facts about good nutrition. Even poverty, which exists among us, does not necessarily doom a family to serious nutritional problems. Relief allowances and limited budgets do not permit luxurious living, but they can, if wisely used, provide a diet that supplies all essential nutrients.

Despite these facts, people worry about their diets.

Vitamins, discovered and identified in the early years of the twentieth century, are recognized as essential for good nutrition and body chemistry. The manner of their discovery seems to have created unwarranted fears in many minds. Vitamins were first recognized through studies of deficiencies in human and animal nutrition, showing up as diseases like scurvy, beriberi, pellagra, night blindness and infantile rickets. How many of these diseases have you observed in your family and your circle of friends?

Scurvy is a disease due to absence or deficiency of vitamin C (ascorbic acid), occurring mainly in persons deprived of fresh fruits and vegetables. It was formerly prevalent among sailors and passengers on long ship voyages, in jails, and where poverty or ignorance prevented the use of a proper diet.

Beriberi, mainly an Oriental disease due to diets too much limited to polished rice, is seldom seen in this country today, since the B-vitamin, thiamine, is present in adequate quantities in any reasonable diet.

Pellagra, causing diarrhea, skin diseases, mental retardation, and in extreme cases, death, was formerly prevalent in our rural South where the main diet of the sharecropper was "hog and hominy" and without fresh foods containing the various vitamins of the B-complex. Pellagra has virtually disappeared in the face of a determined campaign to improve the diets of the victims.

Night blindness, resulting from a deficiency of vitamin A, was widely publicized during wartime when candidates for the Air Force were found afflicted with it; the result has been a near-panic in many quarters, as already mentioned in connection with carrots as a medicinal food.

Rickets, a bone disease in infants and children, has long since given way to fish-liver oil preparations supplementing the diet with vitamin D. Fortification of milk with this vitamin keeps adults supplied with the relatively small amounts they require.

All the vitamins needed by a normal person, except for infants, some pregnant women and some nursing mothers, are contained in a diet selected from the four food groups recommended by the Food and Nutrition Board of the National Research Council. These foods are easy to remember:

I. Meats, poultry, fish, seafood, eggs, cheese, and dried peas, beans, lentils, and soybeans; two three-ounce servings a day selected from these foods provide most of the protein needs for growth, maintenance and repair of body tissues;

II. Fruits and vegetables (fresh, frozen or canned) provide the necessary vitamins and minerals, as well as some of the energy needed, plus roughage to assist bowel function; four servings a day are needed, two of them raw, including a citrus fruit or juice;

III. Dairy products such as milk, cream, cheese, ice cream and butter supply protein, carbohydrates, fats, minerals, vitamins; two glasses of milk a day for adults and from three to four for children, or the equivalent in other dairy products (cheese, butter, ice cream) are suggested.

IV. Enriched cereals and breadstuffs supply carbohydrates for energy and heat, plus some protein and B-vitamins, and supplementary iron as well as other minerals; two servings a day recommended.

If you are not threatened with overweight, add sweets judiciously after the basic requirements above have been met.

That's simple, isn't it? It's scientific, too. And it is all you need to know. Yet it's a good bet that you know, as I do, many people who worry constantly for fear that they are not eating the right foods.

Why do they worry?

One reason is that distributors of legitimate food products, fighting for a place in a competitive market, are advertising with undue emphasis on vitamins and minerals, or on protein, thus creating the impression that danger of deficiency exists unless that particular product is purchased. In a well-chosen diet, for example, there is no good reason why one food product should supply all of a day's recommended vitamin or mineral needs. These should be met by the diet as a whole. Let's have variety in our menus!

Folklore, "modern" version, has it that vitamin and mineral deficiencies lurk in every corner, and they will "git you ef you don't watch out," like the goblins in the bedtime story that frightened the kids when you and I were young, Maggie. Folklore also spreads the belief that if a few vitamins are good, more must be better. That's an old-time concept about medicines too. Both are wrong.

Another come-on is the common practice among food advertisers of comparing their product in such terms as these:

more protein than a pound of steak,

more minerals than a glass of milk,

more energy than a buttered roll,

PLUS vitamin X (which doesn't belong in this particular food at all).

Let's take a good look at these claims. Is protein all there is to steak? Are minerals the whole story of milk? Is a roll with butter nothing more than a source of energy? And why the claim at all, when vitamins are amply supplied in other foods?

What you are expected to conclude—and I hope you don't—is that this advertised article *takes the place* of a pound of steak, a glass of milk, and a buttered roll, plus the vitamin. Of course, it does no such thing.

The vitamania from which the American people suffer reminds me of the old chestnut about the second lieutenant in the Army who brought a suggestion to the attention of an experienced and perhaps somewhat cynical general. After listening to the young man, the general replied in a kindly manner: "Son, that's an excellent idea, but it will never do for the Army—it's too simple and too sensible."

Maybe that's what's wrong with the scientific advice about nutrition. It *is* so simple and so sensible. All you need to know is that if you cultivate a taste for all kinds of good food, and vary your diet from day to day, choosing from the four food groups, you get all the nutrients a normal person needs. You can forget the vitamania, and the mineral madness that usually goes with it.

This does not mean that vitamins and minerals may not have to be supplied as medicines under certain conditions, for example:

- the infant needs added orange juice and fish-liver oil for vitamins C and D respectively, which his exclusive milk diet (human or animal) does not supply in sufficient amounts;

- the expectant mother may require vitamin or mineral supplements to protect her and her unborn child against deficiencies;

- fast-growing adolescents, especially girls as they begin to menstruate, may need supplementation with iron;

- older persons with diets limited by poor teeth or none, or ailing from various illnesses, may need food supplements;

- nursing mothers, by reason of the special drains on their body chemistry, may require extra vitamins or minerals;

- persons with allergies, who are denied certain foods;

- persons with digestive disturbances, whose diets are temporarily limited;

- those with metabolic disturbances like gout or diabetes;

- those with heart or kidney ailments that limit their diet;

- those on severely restricted reducing diets;

- convalescents from severe illnesses . . .

These are medical situations, and necessary vitamins or minerals should be prescribed, and their quantities regulated by their physician. This differs from the vitamin gulping which has become far too prevalent on the American scene.

Okay, I hear you thinking:

"What's wrong with vitamins?"

"When are we going to get pills to take instead of food?"

"You can't have too many vitamins, can you?"

The answers are: There's nothing wrong with vitamins; your foods are teeming with them. I hope we never substitute pills for food. Can you imagine inviting your wife, your date, your boss, or anybody else you want to impress or show a good time, to a fancy dinner consisting of four kinds of pills and a glass of water?

And you *can* have too many vitamins!

In excessive doses, vitamins can be toxic. Carrots, we have observed already, will turn you yellow if you eat too many, because of the carotene from which vitamin A is derived. Too much thiamine (vitamin B_1) may upset the digestion, causing diarrhea. Too much niacin (vitamin B_2) will turn you red as a beet. Too much vitamin C does no special harm, but excess is wasted. Too much vitamin D upsets the calcium metabolism and can prove toxic in large doses.

The taking of excess vitamins has given sufficient concern to nutritionists, doctors and public health officials to cause the Food and Drug Administration to consider regulations limiting the additions of vitamins, especially A and D, to foodstuffs, with the exception of milk and infant-feeding formulas.

Excessive vitamins are eliminated through the kidneys if they belong to the water-soluble groups (B and C); they are broken down in the liver if they are fat-soluble (A and D), but even then the end products are eliminated through the kidneys. It does not make sense to put needless extra work on any vital organ.

An English physician, attending a medical meeting in the United States, is credited with the following comment on a discussion of the American passion for vitamin consumption:

"The American people must excrete the most expensive urine in the world!"

In these days of skyrocketing food prices and generally tight budgets as inflation proceeds, who can afford to waste money on needless vitamins when the same expenditure would buy more foods and other necessities?

Except in special cases, vitamins are best found and taken in foodstuffs rather than as medicines.

Another modern (?) bit of folklore is that which creates fear of certain types of cooking utensils. Some fear aluminum because it might get into the food. This is a groundless fear. There are aluminum compounds in many vegetables, and they form a small part of human chemistry; the aluminum cooking utensils do not add more, because the compounds they form are not dissolved and, therefore, they are not absorbed.

There was a time when tankards, pitchers and other utensils were made from pewter, and it was a dangerous metal because it contained lead. Modern pewter contains no lead, and is quite safe. But watch out for antiques, especially where acid drinks like lemonade are involved.

The simple and sensible advice about cooking utensils is that whatever kind appeals to you is safe it it is a recognized modern brand. The manufacturer is not trying to kill off his customers. He needs 'em!

The fact that a few vegetables may be toxic (Chapter Twelve), has made many persons afraid of all of them, usually without warrant. I had a letter recently from a woman who wanted to know whether lettuce and cabbage leaves had laudanum in their veins, and whether she would have to cut out the veins to avoid this drug. If she had known that laudanum, an alcoholic solution made from gum opium, is a man-made chemical not found in nature, her question would have been answered. Where the baseless rumor which frightened her originated, I have not the faintest idea.

There is widespread fear that modern food processing in which chemicals are used, may be harmful. Specifically, the dread of cancer is entertained. This is based on the fact that some chemicals have been found to produce malignant tumors in animals. These are promptly excluded from processed foodstuffs by the Food and Drug Administration, which takes no chances, and would rather bar a substance on suspicion than take risks by waiting for positive proof. This very caution on the part of officials has been misinterpreted, and has created apprehension rather than the feeling of security which it should have engendered.

The distribution of food products required in an increasingly urbanized culture, where fewer people can grow and process their own food, has required the evolution of means to keep food safe, nutritious, attractive to look at, and good to the taste. For this, chemical additives are required.

Your grandmother and mine probably grew much of their own food or, at the very least, shopped for it in a nearby farmer's market. If it was to be kept for use out of season, it had to be canned, pickled, preserved, jellied, or salted, or maybe stored in a root cellar. Today's grandmother and all her descendants who live in cities, expect to buy their foods in the corner store or the supermarket. We seem to have forgotten that Grandma's jellies sometimes got moldy, her pickles turned rancid, her canned fruit soured, her vegetables occasionally developed the deadly botulinus toxin. If, as many did, she canned meat, some of that spoiled.

If she was a real old-fashioned lady, she may have blamed these spoilages on the presence, all unsuspected, of a menstruating woman at the canning or pickling or whatever. Mostly, however, she knew what had happened. Her foods had not been properly prepared, or the containers were not "scalded" sufficiently, or the seals were not tight.

Today, we expect to take down from the shelves at the store, foods that look good, taste good, keep well and supply us with the nourishment for which we pay. The only way this can be done is as it is being done, by the judicious use of safe chemical additives. The integrity of the great majority of processors is our safeguard; government supervision soon catches and controls the fellow who tries to cut corners.

As consumers, it is unfair and unrealistic for us to react as violently as we tend to do, toward the occasional mishap in the food processing business. The discovery of one can of tuna fish which had become contaminated nearly ruined the entire industry. You may say that it should not have happened. Right. But it did happen to only one batch out of millions, and is very unlikely to happen again. You and I are much more likely to poison ourselves in our homes with careless handling of toxic substances, than we are to be poisoned by the good foods waiting for us on the shelves of our favorite shopping area.

Right here might be a good place to note that even the best nutrition does not, of itself, insure good health. There are many other factors, such as heredity, infection, disease, metabolic abnormalities and psychological factors. Good health is impossible without good nutrition, but good nutrition alone is not always enough. This simply means that health claims for even the best of foods have only a limited validity.

Another common fear which I hope you do not entertain is that in the processing of our food, nutritional values have mysteriously disappeared. This begins with the carefully nourished theory of the food faddists who claim that our soils are depleted, and that chemical fertilizers are no substitute for "natural" fertilizers, namely manure. Well, tractors which have largely replaced horses, produce no manure, and cows and pigs cannot produce enough. What truth is there, then, in the claim that chemical fertilizers produce only deficient foods? Absolutely none! Yet we hear much about "natural foods," presumably grown without the use of "natural" fertilizers, but who knows but the grower? And what, may I ask, is an *unnatural* food?

The faddists are vocal, too, in their denunciation of devitalized foods—a term created to deceive. This goes back to Sylvester Graham, who invented the cracker named after him. He also concluded that cholera stemmed from eating chicken pie and indulging in too much "lewdness"! Dr. John Harvey Kellogg promulgated the theory that some foods carried poisons; he indicted meat and became a sort of patron saint of vegetarianism. He also fed his patients fourteen pounds of grapes a day and, not contented with these frontal assaults, he added the insult of the colonic irrigation—sixteen gallons of water forcibly injected into the bowel. These methods are still the forte of the so-called "nature healers" (naturopaths) who claim to heal whatever ails you without a medical education.*

The food faddists are models of inconsistency. They insist that foods have been robbed, but they resist every effort at proper restoration when processing has actually removed desirable nutrients or when the "natural" sources which they worship are actually deficient. Two examples will illustrate this point:

1. Graham was correct about the removal of the husks and the germ from grains, because these do contain important mineral and vitamin substances. It was not the millers or the bakers who wanted white flour; it was the consumers, because this refined flour made nicer-looking breads and pastries. During World War II under the leadership of the Food and Nutrition Board of the National Research Council and the American Medical Association, and with the co-operation of the milling and baking industries, enrichment of flour was begun, adding the vitamins thiamine, riboflavin, and niacin and the mineral, iron. The results have been spectacular from a health standpoint, and we still enjoy the refinements of white flour. But the food fanatics will have none of it. They continue to demand whole-wheat flour and its products.
2. Investigations into the cause of mottled enamel in the teeth of those living in certain areas disclosed two important facts:
   a) the mottled teeth were exceptionally resistant to decay;
   b) the water supply in the affected areas was exceptionally high in fluorides.

Out of this correlation arose a long series of comparative studies of dental decay in cities comparable in general, but differing in the amount of fluorides in their public water supplies. These studies confirmed the fact that where fluorides in the water are below one part per million parts of water, tooth decay is more prevalent. The logical next step was to add fluoride to the water where it was not present in adequate amounts.

This sensible measure in due course proved that it would prevent tooth decay in children up to as much as 60 per cent. But do you think that the food fanatics would accept

* *Nutritional Nonsense and Food Fanatics*, Ronald M. Deutch, Proceedings of the Third National Congress on Medical Quackery, American Medical Association, Chicago, 1966.

this? Not on your life! They fought it tooth and nail, and successfully, too. They called fluorides "rat poison," and scared many voters. Fluorides *can* poison rats, just as salt can poison babies, and has done so when it was accidentally misused. The "antis" screamed about mass medication, when they should know that fluoride added to water is not medication at all, but nutritional supplementation. Too often they have made their attitudes stick, to the detriment of the dental health of millions of children.

Milk, the nearest approach to a perfect food, has been improved by adding vitamin D, and in some instances has also been fortified with additional protein through adding dry milk to fluid milk. In short, the principle of food additives where necessary or desirable, is sound and correct, despite the opposition of the faddists.

Many sincere persons have been led astray by the false representations of these faddists—dare we say eccentrics?—to their own detriment. These good people do not realize that food faddism can be used, and is being used, to enrich its promoters at the expense of its victims. "Special health foods," so-called, are promoted and sold at fancy prices, though there is no such thing as a health food. Except that all foods are healthful contributions to a good diet.

Unfortunately, the erroneous impression that secret deficiencies may exist in the normal diet has been fostered, not only by faddists, fanatics and promoters, but in much of the "popular" educational material used in our schools and colleges. In an effort to inform about vitamins, for example, it is common practice to describe the effects of a deficiency in a certain vitamin, say vitamin A which is connected with night blindness. Then there follow descriptions of what happens when the diet is lacking in sufficient vitamins B, C, D, or B_{12}—all creating the impression that there is danger of such deficiencies in the ordinary American diet. This is not the case; despite spots of poverty and consequent deprivation, we are still the best-fed people in the history of the world, or we would be if we could persuade ourselves to accept simple and sensible advice about a varied diet, let the chemistry fall where it may.

While certain vitamins do have individual influences, ALL

the vitamins and all the required minerals must be present in order to assure adequate nutrition. "Taking" one or another, or a shotgun mixture, is not the answer. Eating a varied diet is.

Much ado is made over natural vitamins, derived from the plants which produce them. This doesn't make sense either, because if so-called "natural" vitamins are so important, what's wrong with eating them in their natural state? Again, the simple fact is that any vitamin which has been manufactured instead of grown, is chemically identical with the natural product, and nutritionally of equal value. Any other representation is nutritional nonsense.

Books on nutrition flood the market; a small minority is reliable enough to be worth reading. The sensational ones, which sell best, claim that you can eat your way to long life, radiant health, robust vigor, glorious romance, financial success, social triumphs and, most alluring of all, sexual satisfactions. Hogwash! And yet, even (otherwise) reliable publishers have issued such misleading books. Otherwise reliable magazines follow by advertising them. The wee, small voice of the scientist is lost in the welter of propaganda on the printed page, over radio and television and by word of mouth.

How much of what you "know" about nutrition have you "learned" over the bridge table, at the laundromat, in the checker's line at the supermart, at the nineteenth hole and while shooting the breeze at the coffee break? Don't be ashamed. You have lots of company. But wake up and quit being a gull; in other words, don't be gullible. You don't have to assume personal responsibility for proving the cynical crack that there's one born every minute—and two to take him.

Before we sniff and sneer at the strange notions of previous generations, it might be a good idea to take a long and critical look at our own current folklore, in this age when we have all the advantages of education and communication which previous generations lacked.

Surprising, isn't it, what a good start those old-timers gave us toward our own advanced knowledge? Most surprising of all is the acceptance gap between scientific progress and popular practices, and how many things we still "know," even when they aren't so.

Chapter Seven

ANIMALS IN FOLK MEDICINE

Animals and birds have their places in folklore, including folk medicine, as well as plants. We still speak of the qualities attributed to the birds and the beasts when we say:

brave as a lion,
  fierce as a tiger,
    gentle as a dove,
      ravenous as a wolf,
        cunning as a fox,
          strong as a horse,
            faithful as a dog,
              independent as "a hog on ice,"
                slimy as a snake,
                  dumb as an ox,
                    stubborn as a mule,
                      chipper as a bird.

Perhaps the first symbolic animal—a "beast of the field" (Genesis 3:1, 14)—was the serpent in the Garden of Eden, now synonymous with guile, temptation and transgression. He was beautiful and wily, and not a crawling reptile until after the banishment from Eden and the curse. Many snakes retain the beautiful colors, and some still have vestigial legs. Animals and birds are primary symbols used in ancient myths, like the half-man, half-bull Minotaur of Crete, the bull-god Apis of Egypt, the sacred cattle of the Hindus, and the eagle and the serpent of the Aztecs. In heraldry of ancient and medieval times, and in modern national coats of arms, we still see the lion and the unicorn of the United Kingdom, the double eagle of imperial

Germany, the American eagle and other variations of this theme. Most of these are, perhaps appropriately, birds of prey. The dove exemplifies peace, gentleness and spiritual grace.

The qualities attributed to animals are the basis of many, if not all, common allusions to them:

- the lion, king of beasts, is a symbol of the qualities supposedly, if not always actually, possessed by rulers: strength, dignity, nobility and power;

- closely allied to the lion is the leopard—lithe, lethal and graceful, also a symbol of royalty;

- (lions and leopards sometimes appeared with forked tails or two heads)

- pigs appeared in some coats of arms—Swinburne (swineburn) of Northumberland and, naturally, Bacon;

- bears are found in the arms of *Bar*lingham and *Bar*nard; in the municipal seal of Berlin and the name of the Swiss city, Berne;

- The *Lovett* crest has three running wolves and that of the Vide*lous* three wolves' heads; one may see here traces of the Spanish *lobo* and the French *loup* (wolf);

- Colfax, of course, has three foxes' heads.

The most common dogs in heraldry are the greyhound and the mastiff (talbot). Horses' heads, rearing goats, a white mule, and even fish and crows, are found in various crests, as are bats or flittermice (Fledermaus in German). In modern cartoon symbolism one finds the British bulldog, the French poodle and the Russian bear.

The dog, of course, has always borne the title of man's best friend. His place was by the fireside, in my lady's boudoir, in the cow pasture, on the sheep range, and by the side of the hunter in forest or blind. In some cultures, or in times of famine or siege, he has served as meat. Supernatural powers were often assigned to him, as when he howled or whined in the presence of impending death. Dogs were believed capable of seeing gods and ghosts invisible to men. Actually, an explanation for these beliefs lies in the hound's superior hearing ability and sense of smell, which enables him to detect signs hidden from human observation.

Garrison points out that "A dog licks his wounds, hides in holes if sick or injured, limps on three legs if maimed, tries to destroy parasites on his body, exercises, stretches, and warms himself in the sun, assumes a definite posture in sleeping and seeks out certain herbs and grasses when sick." These herbs belong to the wheat family, and dogs seek them in the same way that cats go for catnip and valerian. Garrison adds that primitive man may have had similar instinctive reactions, or have learned these processes from observing dogs.

Dogs are easy to train. They often perform astonishing feats, both on stage and in circus rings, in movies or television, and in everyday living. Their life-saving record is outstanding, and they often give warning of fire or other dangers not noticed by human beings. They are particularly faithful in watching over children. They display great courage in the face of danger. They often demonstrate their faithfulness by mourning over the grave of a dead master or mistress. In the frozen polar regions, they were once the principal motive power during the winter seasons, until partially displaced by the plane and the helicopter.

The dog's contribution to modern medicine stems from his similarity in structure and function to man. His diet is comparable to that of human beings. He has been the subject for scientific demonstrations to students and for experiments by research scientists, and continues in that role. Open-heart surgery has been made possible largely through experience with dogs, and these animals are loved and cherished by scientists and children alike. Often these same dogs become pets of those who work with them in the laboratory. Research on these animals, which has required the sacrifice of some, has repaid the species through safeguarding it from rabies, distemper and other diseases.

The wild deer, common in English heraldry, still flourishes in that country, though not as it did in the days of Robin Hood. The deer, or hart as it is commonly called, forms a device observable in the names and signboards of numerous inns and taverns, usually as a white hart with a golden chain around its neck. Other names for deer, such as stag, roe and buck, are reflected in the famous old families of Britain: Buckingham, Ro(e)therham, Hertford. The reindeer also appears on the banner of Bourbon of France, wearing a huge necklace and a pair of durable-looking wings. A fictitious creature resembling an antelope is represented with huge claws, a lion's tail, a boar's muzzle and tusks. Some designs had horns like the ibex, often shown with one horn pointed forward and the other backward.

Deer have always been valuable to man. In the forests of the Old World and the New, and in the northern areas bordering on the arctic, the reindeer, moose, elk and caribou, as well as the roe deer, have been sources of fresh and dried meat, of milk and cheese. Their hides provided clothing and tent material. The antlers were used for ceremonial symbols, and for such practical purposes as cups, horns for blowing, and for powder which, when burned, produced an aromatic chemical, ammonium carbonate, still used in smelling salts. Doctors used this to counteract the stench of putrefying wounds in hospitals before the days of asepsis. Some carried canes with snuff boxes in the heads to contain the smelling salts. Long known as spirits of hartshorn, they were the standby of the fainting ladies of the Victorian era. Oh, incidentally, the right horn was said to be the more useful!

Here in America, the elk and the moose have given their names to popular lodges. Their teeth continued to serve as identification emblems, as they did for the chiefs, the braves and the sorcerers of earlier days, until vests and watch fobs went out of fashion.

Why should a lodge be named after an animal? Organizers of the Elks, for example, deciding between the buffalo and the elk, may have been influenced by a fine antlered trophy which graced their meeting place. At any rate, they decided that the elk "possessed characteristics that were desirable to emulate. It lives in herds; it is fleet of foot and graceful of movement, quick and keen of perception and, while of a gentle disposition, it is strong and valiant in defense of its own."*

This seems a most admirable modern transmutation from the animal worship of ancient times. The Elks, and other fraternal

* Personal communication to the author: Otho DeVilbiss, Director of Public Relations, B.P.O.E. of the U.S.A., Chicago, Illinois, 1967.

orders, emphasize friendship, mutual assistance, public service and good fellowship.

The great forests are sadly diminished now, but where they persist, the deer still flourish. On the motor speedways which now traverse the glades where Robin Hood and his Merry Men held forth, or where the American Indian roamed, the motorist is warned about deer crossings, but too often one witnesses the tragic spectacle of an antlered stag who met his end head on with an automobile. In Britain, one may even occasionally find a reminder of happier days in the few remaining herds of deer in private parks. And everywhere in the world, children of all ages love to feed the deer.

Lions were even more popular than the forest animals, and they are pictured with enormous claws, many walking on their hind feet and flourishing swords in menacing style. A few hedgehogs, some fish, a trio of roosters and one gray goat attacking a red goat are other symbols of family shields, crests and banners.

Not content with real animals, the heraldic designers invented or at least used such creatures as the *griffin*. This figment of the imagination had the head and wings of an eagle and the body of a lion. Since the head alone was sometimes used in crests, it also had pointed ears and a goateelike tuft under the chin. Another mythical beast was the wivern, a two-legged dragon with wings. Still another was the dragon symbol, borrowed from the Chinese, which was the crest of the Tudor monarchs. It was a four-legged monster with wings and an arrow-tipped tail, sometimes depicted as breathing fire.

Perhaps the best known of these fictitious beasts is the unicorn, a creature with the body of a horse, the tail of a lion and a long, twisted horn in the middle of its forehead. Its origin was supposed to be a wild, white ass of India, reputed to possess a horn. There may have been some confusion here between animals with two horns, and the rhinoceros with its single horn. This is suggested by the fact that a cup made of rhinoceros horn was submitted to the British Royal Society, during the reign of Charles II, for experimentation on the ability of the unicorn to guard against poisoning. In ancient days, poison was a common weapon against enemies, or against relatives who stood in the way of inheritance or succession to power. The horn of the unicorn, when made into cups from which wine was drunk, was supposed to prevent poisoning. Since there never was a unicorn, some other horn must have been used. Meantime, the device of the mythical creature appeared on drinking cups as a decoration and a talisman against poison. It also was a symbol of purity in medieval paintings.

The rabbit, usually termed hare in times past, has also been endowed with medical value. Having a tremulous and easily frightened nature, it seems a bit illogical that roasted rabbit brain was recommended as a remedy for timidity and trembling. Nor is it clear why burning the hare's head and mixing the ashes with bear's grease should be regarded as a remedy for baldness. But so it was. The rabbit appeared in modern medicine for a time as an indicator for pregnancy tests; injection of urine from the woman being tested, caused characteristic changes in the ovaries or in the eyes of female rabbits. Other pregnancy tests involved mice, rats, fish and tadpoles.

Rabbits have also been connected with bad luck; they were reputed to be able to change themselves into witches. They were also said to suffer from depression, and those who ate rabbit meat were believed to become afflicted in like manner. "Mad as a March hare," a common expression, has been attributed to the fact that hares go somewhat mad in March, when they mate. This phrase probably should have contained the word "marsh," a place where rabbits could find no place to hide from their enemies, and became frantic. *Alice in Wonderland* not only gives us the great big rabbit, but the Mad Hatter, who was said to have been made mad by mercury poisoning from the chemicals used in making felt for hats out of rabbit hair.

So we come to perhaps the most bizarre relationship of all, the Easter rabbit and the Easter egg. Rabbits obviously lay no eggs, but the egg and the rabbit are both symbols of fertility, and Easter is the celebration of birth and regeneration with the coming of spring—a feast which far antedated Christianity. So much for bunny, except that he remains among the most useful animal subjects in the research laboratory, constantly helping scientists to add to medical knowledge.

"Fishes," specifically the electric ray fish, were suggested for the treatment of headaches in Rome in A.D. 47. Medicine is still studying the headache, which often baffles the best physicians, in spite of the explanations on television by nonmedical sufferers whose "minor pains" were relieved by the latest double-strength pill. The electric fish continued to interest scientists for several centuries, until 1768, when Galvani noticed muscle spasms in frogs' legs hanging from an iron railing on copper hooks. Out of these and numerous related observations and experiments grew modern techniques of electrochemical diagnosis and treatment—muscle and nerve testing, electrocardiography, electroencephalography and many other applications to medical and physiological research of the galvanic current and the galvanometer by which electrical impulses are measured.

In the meantime, of course, fishermen ranged the wide expanse of the oceans and followed the lakes and streams for some of the most delectable and useful food known to man. In so doing, they noted the beneficial effects of eating the livers of fish, and by gradual steps were led to a practical recognition of dietary requirements and deficiencies, notably the bone disease, rickets. This disorder was absent from children who had plenty of sunlight or whose diet contained oil from livers of deep-sea fishes—notably the cod. Similar oils from ocean perch, the halibut, the tuna and the shark were found equally effective, and so was the synthetic product made by irradiating ergosterol to create vitamin D. Ergosterol is an alcohol related to cholesterol; it is found in plant and animal tissues, and in milk. Its presence in the human skin explains the antirickets action of sunlight. Folk medicine did not include all this knowledge, but people close to the sea knew about cod-liver oil and its use.

In addition to enriching the protein content of diets containing too little meat, deep-sea fish and sea foods also conferred a benefit not realized until the early years of the present century: iodine. That nonmetallic element was discovered in 1811 by B. Courtois, who manufactured saltpeter. It is found in all known plants, and seems essential for normal growth of all animals with backbones. Lack of it in the diet can cause goiter. Users of fresh water, poor in iodine, and products of soils watered from such sources, can be plagued by goiter. These facts were not demonstrated until the early twentieth century when an observer of Japanese life realized that the people had little trouble with goiter and concluded it must be because they were eaters of kelp (seaweed).

Fish also had symbolic significance. They appear as one of the signs of the Zodiac (Pisces). Jesus used the fish in the parable when He told His disciples to follow Him and He would make them fishers of men. The ancient Christians used the fish, painted or scratched on the walls of the catacombs, as a sign to those who understood it and wanted to reach a secret meeting place made necessary by persecution. Until recently, it was the weekly symbol of an act of sacrifice by Roman Catholics, and is still so regarded by many. Fish is classed as a flesh food and is refused by some modern Christians.

The fisherman? He has been, is, and will be a philosopher who regards the world well lost if he can find a lake, stream or deep-sea fishing ground where he can catch his fish, or try to. He is also regarded as one to whom truth, at least in relation to size and ferocity of his prey, is relative.

The serpent, aside from its Biblical symbolism, has been a subject of medical interest for centuries. Susruta, the surgeon of ancient India, mentions antidotes for snakebites long before the Christian era. Studies of snake venom were advanced by British-Indian physicians and American workers in the eighteenth century, as well as by Brazilian observers in the twentieth century. In the meantime, the serpent became a world-wide embodiment of wisdom, often but not always combined with subtlety and guile, and frequently of evil. It has acquired a sexual (phallic) significance.

Man, and especially woman, instinctively fears snakes, and yet they have a strange fascination for people, and are not infrequently found as pets. Snake skins were used in sorcery. Most snakes are harmless, and useful in keeping down the population of rodents and other vermin. Antivenins are now available for the more important venoms, and are obtainable in emergency kits which can be carried by those venturing into territory where venomous snakes may be encountered.

In medicine, the serpent is found in various forms. In the true caduceus, official emblem of the medical profession, there is one serpent twined about a stout staff, and without wings.

Does the design come from the staff of the god who was physician to the Argonauts? In a shrine at Epidaurus in Greece, there was once the most famous statue of "the god of physic," Asklepios (Aesculapius), seated on a throne of gold and ivory. In one hand he is holding a knotty walking stick, in the other a staff entwined by a serpent. Did the official emblem of the medical profession come from so far back? One wonders.

The emblem of the United States Army medical personnel is not a caduceus, but a modification of the staff of Mercury, the Greek god related to medicine and it has wings. The Navy medical personnel is identified by an acorn. The Public Health Service emblem includes a caduceus and an anchor.

Folk medicine, which was often more intelligent than its practitioners knew, missed the boat in remedies for the bites of venomous snakes. Whiskey was recommended and this merely spreads the venom. Cutting the bites crosswise and sucking is still good medicine, provided one can be sure that there are no sores or cuts in the mouth through which venom can be absorbed. Swallowed venom is harmless, since the stomach destroys it. Quiet, a moderately tight bandage above the bite, and sedatives, if obtainable, are the best first aid, when no antivenin is available.

Another reptile which is found in folk medicine is the toad, commonly reputed to give warts to anyone who touches him. There is no truth in this. It is a manifestation of the belief in magic which relates like to like. The toad does secrete a milky, bitter substance from its skin glands, and also from the salivary apparatus, which acts to repel enemies. The skin of the toad, exonerated from the onus of causing warts, has been found to be the source of six alkaloidal principles, two of them poisonous, and one capable of constricting the blood vessels and strongly raising the blood pressure. Some of these alkaloids are found also in the skins of lizards. Their medical use, which is limited, is termed bufotherapy, from the Latin for the toad genus, which consists of many species. A further contribution of the toad to health and agriculture is his enormous appetite for insects, thus helping to keep these pests in check.

The frog, besides furnishing delectable leg muscles for the taste of the gourmet, shares with the toad the useful function of eating enormous numbers of insects. The frog was one of the first creatures to be dissected in the search for light on human physiology, and continues to be one of the common subjects in elementary biology courses. The frog's heart, which continues to beat even after being removed from the body, has been a valuable organ for research. The frog's legs, from which electric stimulation of muscles was first observed, remain useful adjuncts in more advanced research, especially about nerve and muscle interaction. Before exact chemical standards were possible, the frog served as a test animal for standardizing digitalis preparations.

Veneration for the cat goes far back into history. In Egypt, 2100 years B.C., cats were deified and worshiped; one of the principal goddesses, Pasht or Bast, was depicted with the head of a cat. Cats were held in sufficient esteem to be mummified; carvings as old as 4500 B.C. show domesticated cats in Egypt. Many superstitions have been attached to cats, some with medical significance, others without. Some of the more common expressions referring to cats, and their reputed origins, are as follows:*

- the nine lives of the cat are believed related to the "magic" of the number nine, which is three times three;

- "raining cats and dogs" may have been prompted by the finding of drowned strays of both species after floods;

- black cats were considered lucky in ancient Egypt, and the blacker the better;

- black cats were believed to be animal forms of witches, capable of transformations back and forth;

- the slang expression "having kittens" over something, may have originated in a Scottish belief that "cats in the bellie" could result from eating food contaminated with cat semen;

- the Cheshire cat grin has been explained by reference to a forest warden of county Cheshire in the time of Richard III, who was so determined to keep order in his domain that he fought many duels, making horrible grimaces as he battled; his name was Caterling;

* How Did It Begin?: Rabbi R. Brasch, David McKay Co., New York, 1966.

- "no room to swing a cat" has nothing to do with cats, but with the cat-o'-nine-tails. This brutal whip, which left skin wounds like cat scratches, was always used on deck, because below decks there wasn't room enough to swing it;

- and the Kilkenny cats, who fought until there was nothing left of them but their tails, are symbolic of the determined and indomitable nature of the cat, which is owned by no one but itself.

In modern medicine, the cat, the frog and the pigeon were used as test animals for standardizing digitalis preparations, used in treating heart disease, before knowledge of the active principles made accurate chemical determination possible. The cat is also a useful subject for medical research, especially brain-wave research on sleep, dreams and brain-localization studies. Cats also contribute to health and sanitation by their enmity to rats and mice, which may carry disease. Cats are valuable in storerooms where materials which attract rodents are kept, and of course in barns. They are always welcome on ships.

The pig appears very early in remote times, often in the role of a tabooed animal. The Mosaic injunction against the eating of flesh from animals that do not have cloven hoofs and chew the cud is still observed by Orthodox Jews and by Moslems, as well as by some Christians. The origin of the pig is not clearly established, but it is said to have been domesticated in China about 2900 B.C. Regarded as a scavenger for some time, its flesh was not used at first for food.

The discovery that pigs are subject to a parasitic worm which may infest man with painful and sometimes serious results, is often cited as a possible basis for the taboos against pork in the Old Testament and elsewhere. Certainly it is true that those who ate no pork escaped the pork worm (trichina), yet the worm is destroyed by adequate cooking. Taboos against pork no longer have a sanitary justification and it is among the best of meats when properly prepared.

The pig became the basis of ancient man's impressions of human body structure and was one of the animals commonly used for dissection. "Mutilation" of the human corpse was banned by religious and superstitious taboos. The idea that dissecting of the body would interfere with successful resurrection showed a strange lack of faith in a God Who could bring about the greater miracle of creating it in the first place. We still see a remnant of this old belief in the objections raised by many individuals, and supported by some religious groups, against post-mortem examinations.

This continues to be one of the needless brakes applied to medical progress. Galen, the Roman doctor who lived in the last seventy years of the second century A.D., based his voluminous works on anatomy largely on the dissection of apes and swine. In consequence he was led into many errors, and since he was regarded as the most authoritative physician for many centuries, his errors as well as his valuable contributions were perpetuated until the fifteenth century, when Andreas Vesalius of Padua placed anatomy on a firm scientific basis.

An amusing sidelight on the pig in folklore lies in the story of how "piggy" banks came to be. The story goes that when English potters received orders for a money receptacle of *pygg*, a popular and economical ceramic clay, the potters misinterpreted the term as "piggy bank" and shaped the product like a pig. However that may be, it is certain that pigs have been considerably maligned by such comparisons as a silk purse with a sow's ear, and the futility of casting pearls before swine. And it might be remembered that the Gadarene swine were presumably normal before Jesus cast the demons into them. Moreover, pigs are not dirty animals unless they have to be; if one expresses surprise on an English farm at the clean pastures where the pigs thrive, one is informed that pigs like to be clean. They can even be taught to use a limited portion of their enclosure for excretory purposes. Keeping prize pigs is a source of pride to many an English nobleman outside of popular fiction—and profitable, too.

Cattle have been of importance to man since the earliest times. Domesticated cattle existed in Europe as early as 3500 B.C. They were probably descended from a much earlier variety, the primitive aurochs. The term cattle is a corruption of chattel, which means property, and while it is sometimes used in reference to all livestock, it is now generally restricted to the breeds commonly included in the term *oxen*. Cattle were originally kept for the milk produced by the females and the work performed by the males and, sometimes, by the females as well. The meat was for some time regarded as unfit to eat; it is now a prime source of protein food. Cow's milk is the principal type for human consumption in many areas, so much so that the cow has been called the foster mother of the human race.

The milk cow is responsible for the prevention of smallpox, one of the greatest epidemic scourges. The development of smallpox vaccination (Chapter Nine) was a result of the experiences of dairy farmers and their milkers. Most of the smallpox vaccine in use today is composed of virus cultured on the skin of calves' bellies.

Home remedies on the farm included the repulsive practice of using manure for poultices, probably based on the fact that bacterial action keeps the manure pile warm. The danger of infecting wounds with lockjaw germs, which flourish in the intestines and the droppings of domestic animals was not recognized until late in the nineteenth century. The use of animal and human excrement was so common as to receive the name *Dreckapotheke*, which is German for *pharmacy of filth*.

For centuries milk has been the principal and probably the only good source of the calcium needed for the integrity of bones, teeth, blood, nerves and muscles. Only recently have questions been raised about the role of animal fats in causing heart and blood-vessel diseases, and too many normal persons have become afraid to use milk, butter, cheese and fat meats. The evidence thus far adduced has not been convincing to the two most important authoritative scientific bodies—on the medical side, the American Medical Association and, on the nutritional side, the Food and Nutrition Board of the National Research Council. But restriction of animal fats in selected individuals under medical care is another matter.

Rural man depended upon sheep as much as upon cattle, though the two interests were often incompatible, as in the American West where sheepmen and cattlemen waged bitter conflicts over grazing rights. The sheep is able to thrive where cattle cannot; it is a smaller and less costly chattel, and a good source of meat, milk and wool. Its place in folklore is that of a sacrificial animal. In primitive Ireland, the sick were clothed in the skins of sheep sacrificed for their recovery. In the New

Testament, the sheep symbolizes man's relationship to the Good Shepherd.

The sheep may very well have been included among "the higher animals" observed by William Harvey in his historic research to establish the circulation of the blood and the action of the heart. In modern medicine the fat of the sheep's fleece is the basis of lanolin, a valuable ingredient in emollient preparations for the skin.

In the early days of diphtheria immunization with mixtures of toxin and antitoxin, sheep's blood was the basis of some preparations and was preferred where there was allergy to horse serum, the common source of antitoxins. In the treatment of gout, lamb and mutton were often recommended as desirable "white" meats, though this has been somewhat de-emphasized more recently. The surgical suture most commonly used for many years, known as catgut, came actually from the intestines of sheep and is still used extensively.

Goats were known and domesticated in the Middle East as early as 3500 B.C. They have been a valuable source of milk and roasted kid, which was highly regarded as a delicacy in early times, and is still popular, especially in the Orient. Hides (for Morocco leather) and hair (for mohair) were valuable, and still are. The goat, closely related to the sheep, is at least as thrifty as the latter; certainly goats can thrive where cows cannot. Goats' milk differs in composition from cows' milk in its protein content, and therefore, may be very useful in infant feeding where there is allergy to cows' milk. The medicinal values attributed to goats' milk since very remote times, especially in the treatment of tuberculosis, are probably exaggerated, but are sound to the extent that any good milk is advantageous in treatment of the disease. Nutrition was a principal factor, along with rest, for many centuries and even today's surgical advances and new drugs do not obviate these needs. Goats' blood serum has also been used as an alternate to horse serum as a base for biological immunizing products.

The horse has been man's companion since earliest times, for we find him pictured on the walls of caves and tombs. The evolution of the beast is largely speculative, but it is believed that he preceded man by many ages. The zoological reconstruction of various stages of his development has been made possible by fossil skeletons unearthed in the trans-Mississippi region of the United States, and some of these are the earliest unearthed to the present time, but the source of its origin is still controversial.

Without the horse, such engineering marvels as the Pyramids and Stonehenge would have been even more difficult to erect than they were. By mounting the horse, man increased his stature, the limits of his environment and his warlike potential. A man on his steed became the symbol of power and conquest, striking fear into the vanquished. Dislike for mounted police, still evident today, may hark back to centuries of oppression by men astride horses. At the same period, a knight owned several horses, one for war, some for racing, still others for jousting while his lady had her mare, or palfrey. Primitive man is said to have hunted horses for food, and horseflesh is still commonly eaten in some countries of Europe and many in Asia. In the United States it serves mainly as cat and dog food.

Medicinally, the horse played a part in determining the measurement of blood pressure (Chapter Four) and as a source of blood for serums and antitoxins. It was on horses that von Behring in 1895 developed the serum used against diphtheria, by injecting into horses increasing doses of toxins until their blood built up a resistance. Such *anti*toxin helped cure diphtheria in human beings. A parallel procedure resulted in tetanus antitoxin from horses' blood, used in the disease commonly known as lockjaw.

Horsehairs, used for ornamental purposes and for weaving fabrics, have been useful for sewing and as surgical sutures. The horse has given his name, because of his great strength, to herbs such as horsemint and horse-radish (Chapter Five).

Many other animals have made their contributions to modern medicine, even though they may not be mentioned in medical folklore:

- The goose, valued by the ancients for its fat as an external application for colds and chest diseases, still supplies home-remedy material in the grease-and-pepper and other applications for bronchitis and asthma. These, an exasperated yet humorous doctor said, never helped the patient, but made the family feel useful. The real contribution of the goose includes its meat, eggs and feathers, and the nutritious delicacies based on its liver—the French pâté de foie gras and the German Leberwurst. For these the goose is confined in a cage that permits little or no motion and force fed until it is fat enough to kill;

- Mice and rats, whose parts or carcasses were common in the primitive *materia medica* for all sorts of purposes, have proved valuable in modern research, especially the white rats and mice. These animals are used in cancer research, genetic studies, drug testing, pregnancy tests, nutrition projects and psychological investigations;

- Hamsters and guinea pigs are valuable small animals in research and clinical laboratories. The guinea pig's name has become synonymous with any person who submits to any sort of evaluation or testing program;

- Apes and monkeys served in early days as subjects for dissection in place of the proscribed investigation of human anatomy by dissection of corpses. In modern times they have been of great value in research involving germs to which other animals are not susceptible, and in psychological studies and training experiments;

- The chicken has already been mentioned in several connections; these birds, along with ducks and pigeons, have been bred in China for more than three thousand years. Their eggs and flesh are fine foods, and their feathers have many uses. Medicinally they were believed to be excellent food for invalids, and their warm carcasses, split, formed primitive and somewhat gory poultices, a term strikingly similar to the generic *poultry*, to which genus they belong. In modern medicine, the study of the chick embryo has been very informative to geneticists, and eggs have served as culture media for vaccines to be used where allergies exist to other media. Experiments with chickens gave Christiaan Eijkman the clue to vitamin B_1 when he investigated limber-neck in poultry in the Dutch East Indies. Thus was disclosed the cause of beriberi, a nutritional deficiency disease in human beings.

Among other animals used in the laboratory we must include ferrets, eels, fish of various kinds and birds.

ANIMALS IN BIOLOGICAL RESEARCH

Of the many ways in which animals have served man, none is more important than their usefulness in biological and medical research. The earliest knowledge of man's body and its functions was derived from observing injuries and abnormalities in man, and by dissecting animal bodies. Direct study of the human body was forbidden for centuries; the dissection of corpses among Occidentals was discouraged well into the nineteenth century, and there are still some who look upon a post-mortem examination with disfavor. Respect for the dead, and a mistaken interpretation of the doctrine of resurrection and eternal life, invested the body with an aura of taboos difficult to overcome. Some persist to this day, including refusal of blood transfusions, surgery and particularly amputations. Ceremonial burial of amputated limbs is still practiced here and there, so that the body may arise complete.

Such taboos did not apply to animals until relatively modern times. Then they were expressed in terms of opposition to the use of animals in laboratory experiments by famous personages like George Bernard Shaw, the English actor George Arliss and the American dancer Irene Castle. They lent their names, and the publicity they commanded, to support those who objected to using animals for the advancement of medical knowledge. These groups used the graphic and misleading term *vivisection*, which means cutting up a living animal, to impress kindly but uninformed people in order to gain financial support and influence.

The arguments advanced against animal experimentation, and the counterarguments were roughly as follows:

The Charges	*The Facts*
Scientific investigators are motivated by curiosity and sadism:	To the contrary, they are dedicated physicians and scientists of good repute;
Animal experiments are not essential to medical progress:	Medical history shows innumerable examples of new knowledge derived from work done on animals or human beings;

The Charges	The Facts
Why don't the experimenters experiment on themselves?	They do, as witness the long list of scientists who died in so doing;
The final proof of any theory rests upon experience with human beings:	A half-truth; the safety of the final experience is enhanced by previous experience on animals;
Pet animals are stolen and sold to laboratories:	Reputable laboratories do not knowingly buy pets, and good pound laws help to cut down bootlegging of animals;
Useless experiments are done over and over again:	This was formerly necessary for teaching purposes; with modern aids such as movies and video tapes, repetitious experiments are no longer needed;
Laboratory animals are neglected, poorly fed and inadequately housed; some animals are actually starved:	To do this would defeat the purpose of the experiment, which must usually start with a healthy animal; sometimes dietary limitations may be necessary in nutritional experiments;
Animals are not properly anesthetized for painful procedures:	This is so only when anesthesia would defeat the purpose of the research;
Animals are neglected during convalescence from surgery:	This is simply not true;
Animal experimentation is unethical because it causes needless suffering to animals; and it is degrading to those who practice it:	Needless suffering is avoided; the world is full of more suffering than is ever inflicted in research laboratories; there can be no degradation in the motivation to save human suffering, and animal too.

In the early years of this century, the arguments were vehement and acrimonious. Scientists understandably resented harassment through false accusations of cruelty and sadism. They disliked wasting valuable time to defend themselves and to oppose drastic hampering legislation introduced into the Congress and the state legislatures. Such bills usually prohibited the use of dogs and cats in medical research, and their supporters made much of the alleged anguish suffered by children whose pets had supposedly been stolen. Cats and dogs are among the most valuable subjects for medical research.

Extremists among antivivisectionists went so far as to threaten bodily harm to investigators of medical problems. Threats were made to put the researchers "to the same agonies suffered by the animals." The alleged abuses listed above were published in journals and pamphlets and widely circulated. Researchers categorically denied these allegations, and their position was supported by educators other than medical or scientific, by public officials, and by leading clergymen. The latter pointed out the twenty-sixth verse of the first chapter of the Book of Genesis, which reads as follows in the King James version:

"And God said, Let us make man in our image, after our likeness: and let them have dominion over the fish of the sea, and over the fowl of the air, and over the cattle, and over all the earth, and over every creeping thing that creepeth upon the earth."

Support for an extensive campaign against the use of animals in the laboratory was mobilized through national and local antivivisection societies, publishing tracts and periodicals and lobbying for their bills before legislative bodies. Support from the public must have been liberal, at least for a time. The organizations had shrewd leaders, some of whom were not above the suspicion of self-seeking. One leader was indicted for misuse of donated funds; he became ill by a strange coincidence.

It is only fair to record that most of the supporters of antivivisectionism were sincere people who loved animals but had little understanding of medical research, or of the humane laws which adequately protect animals in laboratories as well as out, when they are properly invoked. This, the antivivisectionists failed to do, perhaps because of a lack of faith in the evidence they could produce. They preferred to shock kindly persons with lurid descriptions of alleged cruelties. Only on the rarest occasions did a laboratory mishap expose an animal to needless pain; no one regretted such an occurrence more than the laboratory personnel, many of whom treat the little creatures with real affection.

Some amusing incidents occurred during the battle over laboratory animals. Many community organizations gave the antivivisectionists an opportunity for a hearing, usually extending a similar invitation to a scientific investigator to attend and debate the issue. As a rule, these occasions degenerated into an exchange of accusations and insults, complaints and denials. Since a lie always outruns the truth, the scientists usually got the worst of the interchange. The audience went home in the state described by Omar Khayyam who "did eagerly frequent doctor and saint and heard great argument, but evermore came out by that same door wherein I went," or in more modern lingo, "This is where I came in."

On one occasion, the tactics of the antivivisectionists backfired. One of their advocates had appeared at a debate with two beautiful dogs, whom she allowed to run about while the doctor was speaking. Guess who won that debate! But the next time the lady appeared with her dogs, she was confronted by a scientist with a child on each knee.

Many inconsistencies of the antivivisectionists are highlighted by this incident. Advocates of banning the use of animals in laboratories have appeared garbed in luxurious furs and feathered hats. When challenged, the excuse was made that the animals had been humanely killed. The antivivisectionists eat meat, which requires the killing of animals, fish which must be caught and killed, eggs which deprive a chick of life; and they drink milk which is available because a calf has been slaughtered or deprived of its mother. And they wear leather shoes, too. On the other hand, Seventh-day Adventists, who do not eat any form of flesh, have been among the staunch defenders of the proper use of animals in medical research.

The antivivisectionists have defeated themselves. When scientists organized the National Society for Medical Research, and began a militant campaign to enlighten the public, antivivisectionism was doomed, at least in its cruder manifestations. The movement may be dead, or it may be sleeping. It may even be masquerading under the aegis of humanitarian concern for animals. Scientists are not sure which, but they can scarcely be blamed for keeping a skeptical eye open.

The most influential organizations currently concerning themselves with animal welfare in the laboratory are not opposing animal experimentation. There are no longer any violent personal attacks upon the reputations of scientists. Instead, there are efforts to insure the best conditions for animals in research institutions. Naturally this appeals to persons who desire to see such animals well treated and cared for.

The current approach is through federal legislation calling for the licensing of animal dealers operating across state boundaries, and institutions using cats or dogs so transported. Individual researchers are not required to have a personal license. The law provides standards for the size and character of animal quarters or cages, for sanitation and ventilation, and for avoidance of pain wherever possible. Scientists do not object to such reasonable regulations; they have been striving for years to get budgets which would make better animal quarters available. They are concerned that legal restraints shall not grow into burdensome interference with productive use of their time, and that the expense of complying with the law shall not cripple their work by pricing animals and animal care out of reach. Laws can be amended, and the general history of regulatory measures is that they tend to grow rather than to regress.

People who desire the continuance of the phenomenal growth in medical knowledge during the past half century, should be alert to prevent unreasonable interference with proper medical research. Scientists need public support before legislative bodies, when hearings are conducted on bills affecting medical education and research.

Many animal diseases are transmissible to man, which is in itself a justification for studying them. But animals themselves are spared much suffering as a result of the conquest of diseases peculiar to them:

- anthrax in cattle and other farm animals;
- blacktongue and distemper in dogs;
- rabies in many species;
- hoof and mouth disease, contagious abortion and tuberculosis in cattle;

and many others. Owners and lovers of pets should be the first to defend the researcher against needless restrictions. Finally, the stray animals which reach laboratories through municipal pounds "never had it so good" as when they get into the immaculate tile-and-chrome animal houses, heated and air-conditioned, with automatic water feed to every cage, regular and well-prepared food, and only a very small likelihood of being subjected to severe pain.

Anyone who opposes animal experiments should visit a hospital like Chicago Children's Memorial and many like it, where blue babies and other heart cases come in gasping for breath at the slightest exertion, and emerge from their heart surgery, pink and soon able to play about the wards with the very dogs on whom the doctors learned to perform the operation.

Irwin S. Cobb, the Kentucky humorist who spoke many a true word in jest, is credited with the remark, "I would rather that any white rabbit should have the Asiatic cholera twice, than that I should have it just once."

One last word. Don't confuse the antivivisectionists with the humane societies. They are not the same breed of cat.

In man's earliest history, the various parts of human and animal bodies were vested with special attributes. The skins of certain animals were believed to ward off evil spirits and protect against disease. In Babylon, fishskins were worn by the priests when they conducted their rites. A girdle of animal skin, a wolf's hide, or a necklace of animals' teeth was regarded as a talisman against misfortune. The skin was regarded as the "external soul." Eating of the internal organs was practiced as much for their ritual significance as for their food value, if not more. Blood was considered the best remedial agent of all, but liver, brain and heart were valued as well.

"The life of the flesh is in the blood . . . for it is the life of all flesh; the blood of it is for the life thereof; whosoever eateth it shall be cut off" (Leviticus 17).

Blood bore a dual significance from the very beginning. In addition to its physical and medicinal qualities, it carried important spiritual connotations. The pagan offered blood sacrifices to please his gods or appease the demons he feared.

The above quotation from the Mosaic Law shows the rigid rules against the eating of blood. "It is the blood that makes an atonement for the soul" (Leviticus 17). Severe penalties were prescribed for violations. The Christian looks to the shed blood of Jesus Christ for the remission of his sins.

Medicinally, blood is the most essential modern substance. It is used in diagnosis, in medical treatment, in immunization procedures and in surgery. In terms of war or other catastrophe, the first call is for blood. Of a truth, "the life of the flesh is in the blood."

Instinctively, primitive man recognized this, though he did not know why. His beliefs were probably not true foreshadowings of the modern science of endocrinology, which partially confirms some of the ancient ideas and denies others, but the instinctive reactions of our ancestors are interesting nevertheless. They came mighty close to the truth in their estimate of the value of blood.

Ancient man believed that to eat the heart of a lion (or in the case of cannibals that of a man, preferably a strong enemy), was the secret of valor. We know better today, but we still speak of the "heart" of a race horse or of an athlete, though we no longer regard this organ as the seat of the soul. We have no need any longer to attribute magical qualities to the liver and the brain, because we know so many real values for these organs. Let's look at a few:

- The heart, so essential to life, is a muscle, automatic in action, usually pacing itself, but influenced by nervous impulses from without; it is edible like any other meat, but it tends to be tough, fortunately for us.

- The liver is the chemical factory of the living body, and its disposal plant as well; it stores needed substances like the starchy glycogen; it supplies an essential principle for the production of red blood cells; it helps in the return of hemoglobin from exhausted red cells for re-use in new ones; it metabolizes and stores fats; it breaks down drugs and other foreign matter; it supplies alkaline bile to the intestines to aid in digestion. The ancients didn't know these and many other functions performed by this marvelous organ, and they were wrong for many centuries about its shape and structure. In spite of all their ignorance, they were close to the truth in their regard for the liver as one member of "the triad of life." Incidentally, animal livers are among the best sources of iron in our diet.

- The brains of animals are still regarded highly as a food, but not for the same reasons that motivated our remote ancestors, who included this organ with the heart and the liver in the triad of life. It would be impossible here to begin to record the intricate and complex functions of the brain and nervous system, except to remark that the current tendency to *revere* the computer above the human brain is rather ridiculous, since man's brain evolved it.

The instinctive feeling that parts of the animal or human body represent special functions did not extend to some of the facts now established, with respect to other animal physiology. For example:

- The study of the skeleton goes far back into antiquity, and bones had their uses both practical and ritual, in early civilizations. Archeologists have found many skulls that had been opened, presumably by tiny saws, for the holes are circular and clean cut. The knowledge of bone as a living substance came much later. Primitive man knew that bone healed, and used splints for breaks, but he did not know the function of bone marrow in manufacturing the supply of blood cells.

- There was an ancient theory that nasal secretions came from the brain, specifically the brain appendage known as the pituitary, now called the master gland. It is a small knot of nervous tissue, said to produce an internal secretion which is not yet fully understood. It has taken a long time to ferret out some of its multiple functions, which are: It
    stimulates and regulates other glands,
    provides the hormone ACTH for medical uses,
    regulates water balance in the body,

provides a hormone useful in obstetrics,
governs growth.

These functions are carried out by a multiplicity of hormones, of which the technical details need not be elaborated
here.

* A gland working closely with the pituitary is the thyroid,
which secretes iodine-containing hormones concerned with
growth, nervous functions and intelligence. Deficiencies may
cause cretinism, nervous and emotional upsets combined with
a racing heart, high blood pressure and bulging eyes or large
overgrowths known as goiters. The thyroid is a metabolic
governor gland.

* Close to it, and sometimes actually within its substance, are
four small glands called parathyroids, which are related to
the use of calcium in the body, essential to blood, brain,
bones, muscles and teeth.

* The kidneys have use besides beef and kidney pie and the
excretion of urine; they also play a role in the regulation
of blood pressure.

* Among the glands unknown to the ancients is one situated
above and adjacent to each kidney, called the adrenal or
suprarenal gland, closely related to the pituitary; its most
important hormones are the cortisone from the outer layer
(cortex) of the gland and epinephrine (adrenalin) from the
interior. Cortisone is widely used in rheumatic, allergic and
other systemic conditions, and in skin diseases. Epinephrine
governs the blood-pressure level, acting as an emergency mobilizer of energy in the presence of danger, to facilitate
fighting or running away. Here is the real explanation of the
fighting man who thought he got that way by eating heart
muscle.

* There is a gland under the breastbone, the thymus, which
has had what might be called a checkered career: it has
been blamed for deaths of infants in their sleep, for sudden,
unexplained deaths under anesthesia, and for deficient resistance to disease. As an organ, it shrinks after the second year
and atrophies about the time of puberty, having done its
work in blood formation in the embryo and fetus, and after
birth.

THE ACTION AND INTERACTION OF THE PRINCIPAL ENDOCRINE GLANDS AND THEIR MOST IMPORTANT HORMONES*

Hormone: from the Greek, meaning to rouse or set in motion

Pineal body: within the brain, related to normal sexual development

Pituitary gland or hypophysis: attached to the lower surface of the brain

Posterior lobe: stimulates uterine and intestinal muscles; acts as an anti-diuretic to control water balance

Anterior lobe: acts on adrenal cortex (ACTH); influences pancreatic control of sugar metabolism; stimulates red blood cell formation; influences bone growth and breast development; regulates male or female hormone production; may influence thymus and adrenal medulla

The "master" gland

Carotid bodies: attached to the carotid arteries on either side close to the angle of the jaw, help to regulate blood pressure and respiration

Parathyroid glands: two pairs near or within the thyroid regulate calcium metabolism affecting bones, teeth, blood, and nervous system

Thyroid, the "governor" gland: at the base of the neck, in front; affects general metabolism, nervous functions, heart rate, and emotional controls; develops hormone containing iodine

Thymus gland: under the breastbone, forms red blood cells in unborn, and may do so later if needed; normally disappears during childhood

Adrenal glands: one atop each kidney; outer layer (cortex) is source of cortisone; controls salt metabolism and pigmentation; influences carbohydrate metabolism and connective tissues; inner portion (medulla) produces epinephrine, controls blood pressure, and acts against allergies and on nerves controlling blood vessels; *kidneys* also have hormone affecting blood pressure

Pancreas: located behind the stomach; island cells produce hormone (insulin) that governs sugar metabolism

Liver: destroys excess hormones; in conjunction with stomach it supplies necessary factor for production of red blood cells by bone marrow

Intestinal lining cells: produce "signal" hormones to call upon liver for bile and pancreas for digestive ferments

Ovaries: in addition to producing ova, ovaries control the feminine type of body growth, and during pregnancy provide a hormone to safeguard the developing ovum; they also control the menstrual cycle

Placenta: during pregnancy supplies additional hormones controlling fetal development

Testicles: in addition to producing sperm, they provide hormones that determine masculine patterns of body growth

*NOTE: This is a greatly simplified schema, omitting all but the most important and firmly established functions; lines showing interaction of glands are omitted to avoid confusion, but attention is called to the many gland relationships that work both ways, especially between the pituitary gland and those that it stimulates; these may signal the "master" gland for more activity as it is needed. Much of the knowledge of these hormones was obtained through research involving animals. While many have been synthesized, some are still obtained from animal sources.

- Near the arch of the great blood vessel leading out of the heart (aorta) and beside the main artery in the neck (carotid) are nerve bodies which respond to changes in blood pressure. They also react to external stimuli, such as a tight collar or accidental pressures under the angle of the jaw, which may account for sudden blackouts.

- Besides producing the sperm or the egg for reproduction, the sex glands determine, by their hormone secretions, the structure, function, appearance and emotional attributes which distinguish the male from the female and are the sum total of sexuality.

The foregoing is no more than a sketchy résumé of the multiple and complicated functions of the animal endocrine system. What its relationship may be to the primeval view of their place in magic and myth is difficult to evaluate. How can we put ourselves in the places of men of ages past, whose environment would confuse us as much as ours would disorient them? How can we enter into their minds, their thoughts, their fears, their hopes, their search for the reasons behind the facts which they observed? As Garrison points out, their fund of knowledge was far from contemptible; only their interpretations were sometimes at fault. Even today, scientific viewpoints are constantly in a state of change, responding to new discoveries, new interpretations and new theories. These changes have been called fads, but this is not so. They are the necessary responses to the continuous urge for progress, which began many centuries ago and will never end—we hope!

Man has interested himself mightily in animals, but he has been even more intrigued with man. Very early in records from the past, we find his speculations about his body—its structure, its functions, its diseases, its diet, and how he might influence his environment in his favor (Chapter Four).

Chapter Eight

THE QUEST FOR BEAUTY

A major challenge among health problems today is that of emotional health. This is entirely aside from the mental diseases which tax the capacity of our mental hospitals. Rather, it is a question of the frustrations, tensions and secret unhappiness of many who have no physical illnesses of consequence and are not mentally unbalanced. They have a sense of defeatism, restlessness and vague uneasiness, a feeling of impending menace, an urge for something more and better than life offers them. In the more aggravated instances, they are figuratively looking back over their shoulders, wondering when disaster will overtake them. Even when things go smoothly, there is the haunting fear that it's too good to last.

This may be based on a real or an imaginary inadequacy to meet the requirements of daily living, or an inability to achieve the better things for which they yearn. Not infrequently this state of mind is created or aggravated by a genuine or fancied lack of personal attractiveness, which tends to create a shyness, a withdrawal and a sense of insecurity. A typical instance is the high school student who was too small for athletics, suffered from adolescent acne, and was acutely self-conscious about the thick glasses required to overcome nearsightedness. He wanted to quit school, yet he knew he would take his problems with him.

Poets and philosophers, of course, have sung and written the praises of intrinsic merit, and have been somewhat upstage about mere physical attractiveness. We find many references to vanity in literature, from the Old Testament down to modern times. The writer of Ecclesiastes referred to "vanity of vanities; all is vanity" (Ecclesiastes 1:2). The Psalms are no more tolerant: "Every man at his best state is altogether vanity" (Psalms 39:5), which is to say that the best man can accomplish is no better than vanity. The French have a proverb which says: "An ounce of vanity spoils a hundredweight of merit."

Vanity is commonly ascribed to women, but this is a false notion. True, Benjamin Franklin asked, "Why does a blind man's wife paint herself?" And Benjamin Disraeli remarked about "feminine vanity, that divine gift which makes woman charming." But Lord Byron reminds us that "even good men like to make the public stare." Arthur Wing Pinero, the playwright, considers vanity "the cause of a great deal of virtue in men; the vainest are those who like to be thought respectable." William E. Woodward, an American author noted for his "debunking" biographical books, appeared to believe that vanity "as an impulse has without doubt been of far more benefit to civilization than modesty has ever been." It may be true, as Chaucer says,

> "There swims no goose so grey, but soon or late,
> She finds some honest gander for her mate."

But she may have a long wait! There is not the slightest doubt that a woman, or for that matter a man, who makes a negative or negligible first impression may have some difficulty in displaying those sterling inner merits which are so highly esteemed by the commentators. In short, there is good use for a reasonable amount of vanity, which could be more kindly defined as self-respect.

There is, of course, nothing new about all this. The prophet Ezekiel, describes Lucifer, the fairest of the angels, as "perfect in beauty," and later asserts, "Thine heart was lifted up because of thy beauty . . . I will cast thee to the ground" (Ezekiel 28:17). We read of Helen of Troy, whose face was said to have launched a thousand ships. The comeliness of Cleopatra remains a by-word today. A lovely woman or a handsome man undoubtedly has an initial advantage over those of us who lack these attributes.

Even in earliest times, the recognition of this fact gave rise to the use of beauty aids by both sexes. Whether you buy your cosmetics in a department store or beautician's salon, or a men's shop, or from the demonstrator who rings your door chimes, you are just continuing the ancient practice of endeavoring to improve your image in the eyes of your compatriots. Whatever you use today, from bath soap to hair sprays, it has its counterpart in antiquity . . . but why not take a look in a museum and see?

BATHS AND BATHING

A clean body has always been a fundamental necessity for personal attractiveness, but it has not always been easy to achieve. The ancient Sumerians, living in what is now Mesopotamia, bathed only once a year, yet a jug of water and a drain in the floor of the entrance hall indicates that their feet were kept clean. Jugs and tall vases in the center court of each house (open to the sky) were undoubtedly set to catch any rain water that fell, for each receptacle thus filled saved another trip to the town well. So would *you* take a daily bath if every drop of water had to come in by jug on the shoulder of a hard-worked servant?

In 1790 B.C., King Hammurabi, author of one of the earliest codes of laws, all arranged in categories—personal property, real estate, trade, ownership of slaves, etc.—also entered into the more personal aspects of his subjects' lives. He ordered them to bathe every seventh day, anoint their bodies with fragrant preparations, and appear naked at the shrine of the mighty god Marduk. Perhaps the odors of unwashed bodies interfered with the king's worship.

Bathing was a vital part of the purification rites prescribed for the priests in Old Testament times. In the Christian era, baptism, originally performed only by immersion, is a symbol of cleansing from mortal sin and a resurrection to immortal life.

Public baths in Greece were connected with gymnasiums, which were schools for the mind as well as for the body, and the Romans followed this custom as they did many others of their Grecian neighbors. Wealthy citizens of both nations had their own baths, often elaborate, with water heated by underground ducts through which hot air was circulated. An excellent example of one of these is to be seen at Bath, England, connected with a steam chamber. This last was a more or less public convenience, but in the garden of the Vettii at Pompeii one can be seen in a private mansion. Does it occur to the reader that we aren't so modern as we like to believe sometimes?

Baths served more than merely the ends of cleanliness. They were centers of social life, and in many instances both sexes bathed together. The bath attendants, often slaves captured in war and sold to the rich, were frequently skilled in the cosmetic lore of the day, especially if they came from the Orient, where oils and spices originated. They gave body rubs, supplied ointments and clays, and made medicinal applications.

The original baths, of course, were in rivers, seas, lakes and pools. Where water was not available, as in the desert, sand was used as a cleansing agent, followed by oils and ointments.

Even in more primitive cultures, such as that of the American Indian, baths were esteemed. The hot springs in various areas of what is now the United States, were known to many tribes, both here, in Mexico and other Western Hemispheric locations. Therapeutic virtues are assigned to these baths, especially in Europe and the Orient, and were in earlier days in the United States. Drinking of the waters was a part of the bathing ritual, particularly if the waters were high in minerals, bubbly, hot or laxative. Modern medicine, American style, now places less faith in spa therapy than does the rest of the world. Yet it cannot be denied that restful relaxation and enjoyment may have a tension-relieving influence, even if the waters are less miraculous than reputed.

Originated in Turkey, the steam bath became popular in colder countries. The Russian version was taken by wrapping the body in a blanket and sitting over boiling water; the sauna or Finnish bath was taken with steam generated by throwing water on heated stones, and was often finished by a roll in the snow. Hot baths, both natural and artificial, were used therapeutically in ancient times for relief of joint and muscle pains, as they are today. The addition of oils and perfumes began in very early times, especially in the Orient and among the Mediterranean countries with ready access to the East.

The Sumerian edict requiring a bath every seven days seems to have skipped the Medieval era, when bathing was infrequent. In the Middle Ages, courtiers substituted heavy perfume for cleanliness; the common people just stayed dirty. Regular bathing was established in later centuries, when the Saturday night bath became a family institution and the butt of many a jest. Now bathing has become such a ritual that the daily bath is actually a hazard to the health of some skins. Doctors now have to caution against supercleanliness as often, if not oftener, than they do against neglect.

Soap has been a necessary accompaniment of bathing since its discovery. There is a rumor that soap, like glass, was an accidental result from the interaction of animal fat and the lye from the burning wood on sacrificial altars. The first real description of soap is found in Pliny's writings in A.D. 77. This Roman naturalist describes it as the product of boiling goat tallow with wood ash and water, which is consistent with the earlier legend. Soap was made by early European and American housewives in huge iron kettles in the back yard, using kitchen fats and lye from hardwood ashes. These kettles are now antiquarian curiosities, but in some regions they may still be seen in continued use.

Soap has been made from many fats—tallow, coconut oil, whale and fish oils, linseed, castor, palm, corn and other vegetable oils. The usual alkali is caustic soda. Soapmaking has not changed basically since its earliest inception, but the process has been refined and adapted to mass production. Bleaching creates white soap; injection of air makes it float; color and scent are added to appeal to special tastes, differentiate it from competition and increase sales. Soap is probably the best all-around cleansing agent, but it has no magic properties beyond cleansing the skin. The best soaps are mildly alkaline, to improve their capacity to remove dirt. The action of soap is fourfold:

- it increases the wetness of water;
- it emulsifies and dissolves grease;
- it tends to clot loosened dirt;
- it may make the dirt more slippery and easier to remove.

Soap substitutes have been found in plants which contain a cleansing agent, saponin. Among these are the soapberry, a small tropical tree; the soapwort or bouncing Bet, a perennial weed related to the carnations and pinks; and the soapbark, a Chilean evergreen of the rose family which grows also in California and the southern areas of the United States. Saponin is a detergent which foams when shaken with water, and has been widely used by rural populations as a cheaper substitute for soap. Taken internally, saponin is a poison which acts on the red blood cells.

Soap is useful in medicine primarily for its cleansing powers, but soap solutions have long been known as emergency emetics in cases of accidental poisoning. Suppositories of soap are sometimes used to stimulate bowel evacuations; soap is also used in making pills and plasters. Germicidal soaps, as a rule, are no better disinfectants than just plain soap.

Aside from the glamorizing accomplished by modern advertising methods, modern man has added little to the folklore of baths, bathing and soap—except possibly overemphasis.

HAIR, BEARDS, BALDNESS AND WIGS

The ultra-modern, bearded beatnik, the lady with a wig or with her hair piled high if not handsome, are not nearly as "in" as they think, nor as far out. Copies of ancient statues in any museum indicate that beards were the common badge of respectability, venerability and authority. The tiny figurine of painted clay, unearthed at Ur in Mesopotamia by Sir Leonard Woolley, depicts a man with a long, thin and pointed beard— probably the style for a gentleman of consequence in 3500 B.C.

About the same time Egyptian monarchs were wearing false beards, a kind of braided arrangement which was attached to the chin. In the time of King Solomon, according to Josephus, both men and women sprinkled gold dust on their hair, and the men on their beards. The Etruscans of northern Italy (600 B.C.) have left us statues of men with the modern Vandyke cut, as well as others with trimmed beards and mustaches. The Greeks and Romans of a little later period let the whiskers grow long enough to curl them into six or eight pointed corkscrews. What's this about vanity and *women?*

The Roman's chief god, Jupiter, is depicted with a beard and long, flowing locks. Among minor deities, satyrs were shown with uncut but curled hair on their chins. Neptune, god of the sea, is depicted standing in his chariot, clothed only in his beard and curly hair—but no fuzz on his body, even in the genital region!

The elders of Israel, as well as other Hebrew men, were prohibited from interfering with the orderly growth of hair on their heads and bodies, except to trim and thin to prevent too luxuriant a growth. This custom probably came about because the heathen nations around Israel sometimes offered locks of hair to their gods. But vanity of vanities, the Hebrew men not only oiled their beards, they curled them and adorned them with ribbons!

Roman legionnaires are shown both bearded and smooth-faced. "Shaving" in very early primitive days was done with sharp-edged stones, or by plucking the hairs, or by rubbing them off with abrasives. Even more rugged then than nowadays!

In the University Museum in Philadelphia bronze razor knives, four to six inches long, are to be seen, and these were used in 3000 to 2800 B.C. There are also from the same "dig" ivory and bone hairpins, a hook for removing earwax, and tweezers, all attached to a buckle, similar to the chatelaines worn by medieval ladies.

Despite modern razors, edged, bladed or electric, there is still no really easy and convenient way to shave! Maybe the beatniks have something! Yet the beard is no longer the badge of distinction which it once was; perhaps it became too much of a tiresome responsibility.

The ladies of yore were far ahead of today's women in the elaborateness of their hairdos. There is the sculpture of an aristocratic Roman lady with tightly rolled curls piled high above her forehead and over the top of her head, and the coiffure extended far backward, terminating in an oversize bun. The architectural headdress of Queen Nefertiti of Egypt, some 1300 years B.C., is well known to everyone, as is the jeweled coiffure of Queen Elizabeth I of England.

Men and women were about equally vain in early times, as they are today, though perhaps in different ways. The Greeks recognized this in their minor deity Narcissus, who became so enamored of himself that he spent practically his entire time admiring his image in a pool; his name is still synonymous with self-admiration. His efforts to reach the object of his adoration caused his death!

A bronze statuette of the Egyptian god Horus, discovered in Pakistan, shows him with a luxurious head of curly hair, topped by a pointed headdress shaped like a witch's cap. And in the 133rd Psalm we read:

"Lo, how good and lovely it is
When brethren dwell together as one!
Like the goodly oil upon the head
Which flows down upon the beard, Aaron's beard,
So is the dew of Hermon that flows down upon the mountains
  of Zion;
For there has the Lord commanded the blessing;
Life forevermore."

Care of the hair required about the same variety of materials as it does today. They had, of course, no sprays under pressure, but they used oils, unguents, perfumes and powders. Many ancient tombs in Sumeria and Egypt have yielded boxes for various ointments. The people practiced shaving the head, a procedure compulsory for priests as part of their rituals of purification.

Wigs were found in Egyptian tombs, commonly made of human hair, but sometimes of palm fibers; the curls were kept in place by beeswax. The cone-shaped headdress of Horus, mentioned above, may have been a ceremonial-ointment cone containing perfumed unguent in fat. When this melted and ran down over the head and the garments, one must conclude that suffering for the sake of beauty is not exclusively a modern phenomenon. The wigs, of course, created problems of comfort and cleanliness, not to mention vermin.

Samuel Pepys, the famous diarist of the seventeenth century, recalls a hilarious episode when his wife removed his wig, and they were "very merry" together over the discovery of head lice under it, "above twenty, both great and small." Wigs were, and are hot, too. And the Egyptians had a device not found, so far as I know, in modern wigs—a small trap door operated by a string which allowed air to enter beneath the wig. One of the more amusing sidelights on Roman wigs is a statue in the Louvre,

Paris, which has a set of interchangeable wigs so that the hairdress will never be out of style.

The early Christians discountenanced wigs as worldly vanities, but in the Middle Ages false locks returned to favor. They have been worn by the judges in British courts since the reign of Queen Anne in the early eighteenth century. The Speaker of the House of Commons, the parliamentary clerks and the Lord Chancellor, all wear wigs on ceremonial occasions, as do certain lawyers.

Now, women wear wigs for adornment; men for the same reason, but also because a good appearance and the semblance of youth counts heavily in the business world.

Since the days when Egyptians battled baldness, there have been many attempts to grow hair on bald heads. They all come to the same end; when the hair follicle is dead, that's it, and nothing has been found, or at this writing seems likely to be found, that will "restore" lost hair. Following are some of the more bizarre of the "falling hair" remedies, which seem to persist as long as hope springs eternal in the baldest heads:

- the Egyptians had faith in the fat of a lion, a hippopotamus, a crocodile, a cat, a serpent and an ibex—mixed together and used to anoint the head of the bald person; in South Africa the fat of the python is esteemed;

- paw of a hound, date seeds and hoof of an ass, boiled "thoroughly in oil";

- a mixture of salad oil, origanum, rosemary, lavender, cloves, mixed and shaken together, to strengthen hair and clean the head;

- salts of tartar, tincture of cantharides (a powerful irritant), with camphor and lemon juice was offered as a "sure remedy" for scalp disease;

- in very bad cases a mixture of alcohol, acetone, oil of cade, sulphur, pyrogallic acid, chrysophanic acid, and bichloride of mercury was recommended; and

- in thousands of cases, the evil of baldness was said to have been overcome by boxwood shavings, with spirits of rosemary and spirits of nutmeg;

- three onions steeped in a quart of rum for twenty-four hours yielded a liquid which was to be applied to the scalp every second day; the "slight" onion odor was said to disappear shortly after application;

- camomile tea was recommended both as a blond dye and for stimulating hair growth; for the latter purpose it was to be boiled until it was black as strong coffee, then diluted and the resulting liquid applied to the scalp after the shampoo;

- a shampoo nightly with a mixture of salt and quinine in brandy.

Such instances could be multiplied indefinitely, but these are sufficient to establish the point. And lest we think the old-timers were just too credulous, it might not hurt to remember that there still remains current today, a considerable body of faith in the following mistaken beliefs:

The Fallacy	The Fact
Hair is living tissue:	Not so; only the follicle from which it grows is alive;
Singeing hair seals in the life:	There isn't any life to seal in!
Falling hair is abnormal:	Only failure to grow new hair is abnormal;
Tight hats make men bald:	Male baldness is usually hereditary;
Hair tonics will grow hair:	Not even ultraviolet will do this;
Hormones will grow hair:	Experimentation has been unsatisfactory;
Massage or vibration will grow hair:	Another vain hope!
Commercial systems will grow hair:	A waste of money!

The *apparent* success of some of the useless methods cited above is explained by a common abnormality of hair growth, a disease called alopecia areata (patchy baldness). This may affect the hair on the scalp, the beard and brows and hair on the body. In most instances it is temporary, though it may recur. It is easy to understand how a remedy applied during an attack of this condition might be credited with marvelous restorative powers.

Treatment with hormones, especially pituitary, has been tried for growing hair; when it appeared to succeed, the growth was fuzzy, unpredictable and not necessarily of the same color as the individual's remaining hair. For these reasons and because of reluctance to administer continuous doses of potent hormones which might adversely affect the general metabolism, physicians soon gave up this approach. Some success has been achieved with transplanting patches of skin containing hair follicles; this is a tedious process suitable under appropriate circumstances, especially for entertainers or other public figures. Success is not assured in all instances.

A modern relic of old-time medical folklore is the recommendation by food faddists for the use of household common foods as hairdressings:

- vodka and red pepper to make the hair grow (or stand on end?);

- put mayonnaise on the hair between two shampoos, spaced an hour apart;

- for oily hair, skim milk and salt;

- skim milk to set the wave and restore protein to the hair;

- wheat-germ oil to tame frizzy hair.

It seems too bad to use good food in such a manner!

Since all folklore goes back to Sumer-Akkad, Egypt, Greece, Rome or ancient China, we may as well begin by mentioning a few of the fundamental tricks of the trade.

In the first century A.D., the Roman, Juvenal, tells how, with a bent stick, the curve of the brow is elongated and daubed with moistened soot, while the "twitching eye" (lashes?) is painted upward. Egyptian and Oriental women used kohl (kohol), a powdered antimony compound, to create the dark shadows.

In China the same effect was attained by ink; in Russia by charred hazel nuts; in Turkestan by the bluish extract of an indigo-rich plant. The Tartars dripped camphor in their eyes to achieve a naïve childish expression, while in Spain this was accomplished by dilating the pupils with belladonna, the deadly nightshade. The Mediterranean peoples admired the blond Germanic types who, as it happens, did not make up their eyes.

Beauty is indeed a matter of taste.

Painting the face and the lips is as old as the Old Testament, where Jezebel did so, as probably did her great-great-great-grandmother! The prophet Isaiah says the daughters of Zion are "haughty, and walk with stretched forth necks and wanton eyes, walking and mincing as they go, and making a tinkling with their feet." And Jeremiah says, "though thou rentest thy face with painting, in vain shalt thou make thyself fair." The use of cosmetics was a privilege of the aristocratic women and a defiant gesture on the part of the women of easy virtue. It was commonly frowned upon by the serious-minded, and strongly condemned by the religious. It was also regarded by the nobility as presumptuous if practiced by the common people, and there are even instances of women being thrashed for imitating their "betters"!

Pigments used for retouching the skin you love to touch are varied and ancient. From the royal tombs at Ur in Mesopotamia come cockleshells, one silver imitation shell and a gold one, all containing evidence of paint, presumably used as a cosmetic. Green seems to have been the most popular color, but there are also receptacles with white, red and black in them. Rouge and paint were used by both men and women, fingernails and toenails were tinted with henna-plant juice, and heavy black lines were traced around the eyes—all this about 5500 years ago!

The tomb of Tutankhamen disclosed some of the beauty secrets of his time, 1350 B.C. Red pigment used for coloring cheeks and lips was analyzed and found to be red oxide of iron—just ordinary rust! The right shade was assured by mixing on an alabaster palette.

About four hundred years before Cleopatra came on the scene of history, the women of Greece and other Near East countries painted their lips and cheeks with a rouge made from the polderis root—a plant I am unable to identify from any modern source. They were derided for the practice by the squares of their day.

Columbus found the native women of the New World using the red pigment from the leaves of bignonia chica, a climbing South American vine. In the days of the American settlers, cosmetics included carmine and cerise rouges and Spanish papers. The latter were papers impregnated with a carmine dye, applied by rubbing the papers on the skin. Some of them were supplied in book form, with one perfumed leaf. Carmine is a preparation of cochineal with alum or gelatin. Cochineal is the dried body of a female insect enclosing the young larvae. It is still used as a dye for various purposes, and in chemical analysis.

Cosmetic advertising in the good old days almost out-does the current extravaganza which lures women along the path to beauty; behold!

> *"BLOOM OF CIRCASSIA"*: "It is allowed the Circassians are the most beautiful women in the world. However, they derive not all their charms from nature. A gentleman, long resident there in the suite of persons of distinction, well known for his travels throughout Greece, became acquainted with the secrets of Liquid Bloom, extracted from a vegetable, the product of that country, in general use there with the most esteemed beauties. It differs from all others in two very essential points. First, that it instantly gives a rosy hue to the cheeks, not to be distinguished from the lively and ornamental bloom of real beauty, nor will it come off by perspiration, or the use of a handkerchief. A moment's trial will prove that it is not to be paralleled."

It's all there—instantaneous beauty, naturalness, permanence. Could today's copy writer do better? And much more refined than the episode attributed to King Louis XIII of France, who is said to have spewed a mouthful of red wine over a feminine guest at a banquet, giving her an instant rosy blush which was greatly admired. In France, though, the red rouge was applied with heavy hand over a chalky-white face. You can see some of the same today. And the most *mod* eye make-up of the moment goes way back to the Egyptians and the Greeks; the Koran gives its adherents the promise: "And theirs shall be the *Houris* with *large dark eyes* like pearls hidden in their shells."

Face powders were mainly of two varieties, flour of wheat or rice or orrisroot, or compounds of lead. The former were unsatisfactory in appearance, and some persons were allergic to orrisroot. Lead-based powders used over a long period, gave rise to lead poisoning through accidental swallowing of the powder, not through skin absorption, since intact skin absorbs practically nothing. Both were replaced by chalk, or better, by talc. Tints and perfumes were added, as they are today.

The American Indian used cosmetics exuberantly, painting not only his face, but his entire body, to express his emotions all the way from war to sex appeal. The men used paint far more lavishly than the women, perhaps as a symbol of male supremacy, so marked in their culture.

Red was their best-loved hue, obtained from hematite, an iron oxide, or the mineral clays (ochres) which gave shades from pink through yellow to brown or even black, or cinnabar, a mercury compound which yielded the favorite vermilion. Yellow came from limonite, another iron-oxide clay, or corn pollen, and possibly saffron. White came from kaolin, an aluminum clay, limestone or gypsum. Greens were procured from various copper ores or phosphate of iron. Black was usually obtained from charcoal or soot, occasionally from corn smut (a fungus) or from manganese ore, pyrolusite.

The Indians obviously knew their natural resources. They were even cognizant of uranium, the source of modern radioactive weaponry. A major use of paint was in festivals, contests, games and war, and to designate rank and achievements and other symbolic uses. Women, for the most part, were not expected to be beautiful so long as they were industrious and obedient. Some did, however, paint the parting in their hair, redden their eyebrows and circle round spots of color on their cheeks and in the middle of their foreheads.

The painting of the face was important in religious rites and in making medicine, either for healing or for warfare, romance, good crops, rain and plenty of game. We still use cosmetics for some of these same purposes.

Painting the skin was not enough. It had to be softened, too. Here is where the oils came in, especially olive oil and sheep fat. Today every woman who watches TV or keeps up with the cosmetic ads, knows that the magic ingredient for skin softening is lanolin. What she may not realize is that lanolin comes from the fleece of the sheep, and that the principal contribution of modern chemistry has been the removal of the strong odor of the animal. Despite efforts to cover it with strong perfumes, ancient ladies found the smell annoying, even frustrating.

A modern development, difficult to understand, is the commercial popularity—at substantial prices—of the oil from the ugly rough-shelled turtle as a source of velvety feminine beauty. Rose water with glycerine, a stand-by of Victorian ladies, was also known to the ancients. Modern uses of these substances have not advanced far beyond the past in the matter of changing the skin—smoothing and tinting the surface is about as far as we can go with safety. Anything beyond that ceases to be cosmetic and becomes medical.

PERFUMES

Frankincense, a resin from a tree of the balsam family, is perhaps the best known of the ancient perfumes. It has been used in the religious rituals of all peoples, primitive, medieval and modern. To obtain the resin, an incision is made in the bark of the tree in much the same manner as turpentine is harvested. The whitish juice that exudes from the cut is allowed to harden for several months in the summer sun, and then marketed in lumps called "tears."

Isaiah and Jeremiah mention it as of Arabic origin; the Song of Solomon suggests a Palestinian source. Actually, it is found in the mountains of central India, in Ethiopia and on the Coromandel coast of India as well. It was used in the past medicinally as a balm as well as ritually.

As an ingredient in perfume, it was mingled with the flour in the meal offering and its bright flame lit the holy place in the Hebrew Temple in Jerusalem. Considered a most expensive item, it was one of the three gifts offered to the infant Jesus by the Magi. The suggestion has been made that it, with the other two costly gifts, gold and myrrh, may have financed the sojourn of the Child and His elders in Egypt (Matthew 2:13–15). Perhaps it was part of the "very precious ointment" that was poured on the head of Jesus while in the house at Bethany shortly before His crucifixion (Matthew 26:6–13).

The scents used for perfume have not changed greatly through the centuries. Aromatic spices such as cinnamon have been used since ancient times, as have myrrh, musk and ambergris. Musk from the musk deer and ambergris from the sperm whale, are still in use as fixatives, which give the perfume its lasting power. Other fixatives come from the beaver or the civet cat. These substances are oily fats or other secretions with strong odors related to the sex organs of the male animal.

Naturally, many of the more fragrant flowers have been used for perfumes and toilet waters, especially the rose, as have aromatic herbs. Except for refinements in processing and the development of synthetic chemicals, the modern art of perfumery does not differ too widely from what was known centuries ago.

BEAUTY AND HEALTH

Good looks depend as much upon personality and fitness as they do on perfection of face and form. The languid, insipid enchantress was once the vogue, but now it is no longer fashionable to be beautiful but "dumb." We have returned in part to the Grecian ideal of beauty, which was based on fitness, character and intelligence. True, we still use make-up, and many times misuse it, especially those old enough to know better. And we still put faith in modern beauty "miracles" hardly less fantastic than some of the horrible examples cited above.

A sensible quest for good appearance is more than vanity. The frustrations experienced, or imagined, by persons of unattractive looks can have a serious effect upon personality, and thus upon emotional health and successful adjustment to living. Modern medicine recognizes the relationship of personality and of unfavorable psychic impacts upon the physical economy of the body. Peptic ulcers, some forms of colitis, vague states of low vitality, and digestive disturbances without apparent physical cause can develop; all resulting from emotional disturbances reflected in malfunctioning of the glands of internal secretion. Many other conditions have emotional content as well as physical, among them high blood pressure, asthma and other allergies, and skin diseases. Any serious or disabling disease inevitably influences the sensitivities of the individual: a vicious circle!

Such modern measures as plastic surgery, scar and tattoo removal, hair transplants, skillful use of cosmetics and other measures to improve the image created by first impressions, can be real factors in well-being and success.

We have a great advantage over the ancients, at least in the more privileged areas of the world. We have better control over disfiguring diseases. We have a more dependable food supply. We have medical and surgical measures for the correction of defects or the repair of damages due to accidents. We know a lot more than did our remote ancestors, but we still have the same human frailties; we do not do as well as we know.

So who are we to feel superior?

Chapter Nine

"GRANDMA IS NOT ALWAYS WRONG"

When Dr. Bruno Gebhard, founder of the Cleveland Health Museum, made the statement which is the title of this chapter, he was saying that the "grannies" who practiced folk medicine deserved more appreciation than they customarily receive. We tend to turn up our noses at many of their practices, because we have so many better ways today. We forget, too often, that they lived under difficulties and had to do the best they could with what they had.

Frontier life may be romantic to look back on, but it was a dreary round of poverty, hard and grinding toil, great danger, and frequent illness. There were often no doctors to be had, or if there were, these practitioners were lacking in the qualifications we of today take for granted. Some of them had had virtually no medical education.

Sickness was so common that many diseases were not even regarded as such. Many a frontiersman suffering from malaria was so used to it that he did not consider himself sick. It was only the universal complaint—the "ague." An 1837 cookbook, which contained many remedy recipes, actually advised *against* calling a doctor except for smallpox, "inflammation of the bowels," nosebleed, and "gravel" (kidney stone). Even for the last-named, the book had a remedy:

"Juice of horse-radish made into thin syrup, mixed with sugar; a spoonful every four hours."

This book did not even stop at cancer, for which it was suggested that the affected area be "annointed" several times a day with the juice of the friar's-crown (woolly-headed thistle).

Dentists were as scarce as doctors, or more so. Naturally then, there would be many home remedies for toothache and for the prevention of tooth decay. One of the latter sounds quite modern: keep the teeth clean! Grandma, indeed, was *not* always wrong. Following are some of the suggestions found in traditional medicine for keeping the teeth at their best*:

- *To make teething easier:*
  have a baby wear a chain of amber beads about the neck;
  or the seeds of Job's-tears (an ornamental grass with seeds used in the Orient as beads);

- *To prevent decay:*
  wash your teeth daily with your own urine,
  rub baby teeth with: a rattlesnake's rattle,
                  the brain of a rabbit,
                  the tooth of a wolf,
  hang a rabbit's tooth around the neck on a string,
  encircle the neck with a string used to hang three mice;

- *To cure a toothache:*
  pick the tooth with: a coffin nail,
                  the middle toe of an owl,
                  a needle used to make a shroud,
                  a splinter from a tree struck
                    by lightning,
  apply the juice of the "toothache plant" (prickly ash)
  pack it with cotton soaked in oil of cloves
  rub it with sumac (poison oak) gum
  chew the root of a thistle;

- *To pull a tooth:*
  attach the tooth by a string to a bent sapling and let the sapling spring back (this is the granddaddy of the method still in use, tying the tooth to a doorknob and then slamming the door).

These practices may seem outlandish today, but they made sense in the framework of the times, since they appeared to work,

* "Granny Had a Cure for Everything"; Richard Dunlop, *Today's Health*, American Medical Association, May, 1963 (page 30).

at least sometimes, and there was nothing better available any-way. At least they satisfied the human impulse to "do something" to help those in distress. The fact that sometimes the folk remedies not only failed to help, but actually did harm, could not really be blamed on anyone, since all were doing the best they could.

So now let's take a look at an assortment of all kinds of "grannie" medicine, and try to see why it seemed logical at the time. Here we go. . . .

TEETHING

Teething was a universal problem, and Granny had an answer; give the youngster a rattlesnake rattle or a six-shooter to chew on. Both were always handy! Popular opinion favored the rattle. We have had an era, since then, when pacifiers or teething rings were taboo. Now, they are back in favor, especially for babies who do not nurse at the breast. And babies still worry their parents at teething time (See also CONTAGIOUS MAGIC, later in this chapter).

BIRTHMARKS

There was a universal belief in *"marking"* the unborn by so-called maternal impressions—seeing spiders or snakes or having other unpleasant experiences. Birthmarks, webfeet and other physical deformities were blamed on "maternal impressions." We know now that this is impossible, and that most birthmarks were formed prior to the alleged experience. Yet the belief still per-sists. Perhaps there are still those who would resort to certain ancient remedies, though this is doubtful.

We should know better than to believe that birthmarks can be removed by rubbing them with the hand of a corpse or the head of a live eel three mornings in succession. We should be skeptical, too, of the method said to have been practiced in Texas, of rising early on nine successive days and licking the birthmarks three times each morning, meanwhile being careful not to speak a word to anyone during the ritual. Since birth-marks often fade, the reason for continued belief in such methods is apparent.

WARTS

The kids in the old days had *warts*, too, just as they do today. Where did warts come from? Well, toads have warts, so naturally if you touch a toad, you get warts. And what do you do for them? Take your choice among just a few of many wart remedies commonly practiced then, and I suspect, even now, here and there:

- rub with a killed cat and bury the cat in a black stocking;
- rub with a rooster's comb; bury it;
- rub with a stolen steak and bury it where three roads cross;
- rub with a peeled apple and give the apple to a pig;
- rub with a stone and hide the stone;
- tie a knot in a string for each wart; hide the string; (if you find a knotted string, let it alone or you'll get somebody's warts!)
- rub with a penny; throw the penny away (not for thrifty souls);
- stick a pin in the wart to kill;
- put a stone in a bag for each wart, tie it up and throw it away.

There are about two hundred such "remedies," and they seem unbelievable to us today, because we know now that warts are virus infections, and must be treated medically, usually by electric cautery. But we know something else about warts, which goes far to explain why these strange remedies got such a reputation. We know now that warts may disappear without any treatment. And I hope that some day we will learn that home treatment with caustic chemicals is dangerous, often complicated by infection, and leaving needlessly disfiguring scars.

"RHEUMATIZ"

One of our worst health problems, and one as old as history, is *arthritis*, more popularly—or unpopularly—known as rheumatism, rheumatics or "rheumatiz." There were numerous remedies for this condition, too. Here are just a few of them:

- carry buckshot or a "buckeye" (which is not a real chestnut) in your pocket;

- take the powdered ashes of a turtle shell, internally;

- chew a thistle root;

- carry a peeled potato in your pocket until it turns black;

- wear shoes with copper nails to "ground the pain";

- wear copper bracelets;

- rub the joints with snake oil;

- apply heat—either from hot springs, poultices from various seeds or from manure, or by applying the hot bodies of split fowls.

- take a "tea" made from willow bark or leaves;

The last two items make sense.

Heat does help arthritic pain, but we have found better and less objectionable ways of applying it. Also, the use of teas made from the bark or the leaves of various species of willow trees, while based on experiences rather than on research, has proved out. Today's most effective antirheumatic drug is aspirin, a derivative of the salicin contained in the willow bark and leaves.

FEVER AND CHILLS

Fever, a symptom of many diseases, and the accompanying chills, were common problems for many centuries, and naturally called forth innumerable remedies, some of these were merely bizarre, others repulsive. Among them are the following:

- chew turnip roots;

- take a tea of the ground bark of the wild snowball (red root);

- take a tea of the bark of the wafer (stinking) ash;

- eat watermelon;

- make a cooling drink of scarlet sumac bark (poison oak!);

- take a decoction of the leaves of the sheep sorrel (sour dock);

- eat grapes;

- make a tea of the leaves of the sourwood (lily-of-the-valley tree);

- brew up and drink a tea of the common chickweed;

- make a red-pepper tea and put black pepper in your stockings;

- apply cool water externally.

The last-named procedure is still as good today as it ever was. The cool pack, and in some emergencies such as sunstroke where fever is dangerously high, an ice pack, is good therapy, often better and safer than drugs. The reputation for success attained by many fever remedies was due mainly to the fact that spontaneous recovery due to natural resistance often overcame the disease and abated the fever.

In Peru, and elsewhere in South America, the natives learned the value of Peruvian bark for treating their periodic recurrent fever and chills, which we recognize now as malaria, still a major world-wide health problem. This bark, derived from the cinchona tree, gave the world quinine. Until synthetic drugs were devised, this was the only specific remedy against the world's number one disease, malaria. It was for many years one of the few truly specific curative drugs. We are indebted to the shrewd observations of these relatively primitive peoples for one of our most important medicinal agents. Malaria is gradually being brought under control today, but there are still many areas where the Anopheles mosquito continues to spread the disease, and where quinine or one of its alternates remains important.

BOWEL "INFLAMMATION"

In frontier conditions or on remote farms, with hard work, rough or spoiled food, and often polluted water or infected milk (when they had milk), it was inevitable that there would be many a "bellyache." This was called inflammation of the bowels or dysentery, and was not differentiated into appendicitis, gallstones, food poisoning, typhoid fever, cholera or true amoebic dysentery, or cancer or intestinal obstruction—the causes of these conditions had to await the discovery of bacteria, the X ray and other more modern developments. The four main symptoms of abdominal illness—gas, pain, constipation and diarrhea, were treated as such. It was the only way they could be.

For constipation, a long list of common herbs was advised, usually to be taken as a tea, such as the familiar camomile. Other *cathartic* herbs included:

sarsaparilla (sweetroot)	swamp milkweed
wild senna	flowering dogwood
burning ash	boneset (Indian sage)
American white ash	marsh iris (blue flag)
buck bean (water shamrock)	May apple
queen's-delight (yawroot)	field bindweed
devil's-walking-stick	Indian lettuce (meadow pride)

Where stronger action was desired, additional sources were called upon:

common milkweed (poisonous)	common celandine (wartweed)
white pine buds	Mexican poppy (thorn apple)
wild indigo	field bindweed

For abdominal pain, often referred to as colic or *"stomach trouble,"* one finds the following recommendations for medicine to take internally:

- boil sumac (poison oak) leaves in beer;

- steep water-lily roots in wine;

- tie a cormorant skin across the abdomen (cormorants have large stomachs);

- mix wolf dung and white wine (for colic!).

In addition, at least fifteen "carminatives" and twenty-two "stomachics" are listed in just one book on herbal medicine (Coon), for the treatment of one or another kind of stomach distress. Carminatives, or reddeners, bring more blood to the stomach and so may aid digestion; stomachics are credited with much the same function. Both are now largely outmoded.

For the diarrheas which occurred as the result of irritating or toxic diets, or infections, specific plant drugs were valued:

pigweed	black snakeroot	wild strawberry
wild geranium	life everlasting	partridgeberry
bayberry	prickly pear	common plantain
wild tansy	apples	white oak
blackberry	slippery elm	tea
persimmon	butternut	black walnut
dogwood bark	hollybark	lilac bark
larch bark	alder bark	

Tea from any herb that was "tall, pink, red or purple and waved in the wind," including:

sweet rocket	fireweed
wild phlox	loosestrife
knotweed	dianthus

goldenrod

One wonders whether the last group bears any relationship to the common practice of referring to intestinal gases accompanying digestive upsets as "wind"—a possible expression of the doctrine of signatures previously mentioned?

Today, we recognize constipation, abdominal pain or distress, or diarrhea, as symptoms, not diseases. We suspect such conditions as ulcers, gall-bladder stones, inflammations, appendicitis, intestinal inflammations, obstructions, or cancers. None of these could possibly be influenced by herbal medicine. Often they require surgery. We can readily understand why many ways were tried in the effort to be helpful, often when there was no help. Even the most modern treatment may come too late, and that is one of the main reasons why we no longer rely on the remedies of the past.

INJURIES

Injuries seem to be part of man's struggle for existence; they are as frequent today as they have ever been, if not more so.

Though the causes are different, the emergencies remain the same:

Bleeding was controlled by applying cobwebs or powdered sumac seeds in honey, or trillium petals or nettle pulp, or puffball spores to the wound, or the nose, as the case might require. Also by tourniquet. Today we use simple direct pressure by a large clean pad over the wound, reserving the tourniquet for professional use or for bleeding not otherwise controllable.

Aches and pains were treated with poultices of cow manure; hot mashed potatoes; or a plaster of onions, rum and neat's-foot oil; skunk grease or wildcat grease. Pain of a stroke was said to be eased by powdered root of the jack-in-the-pulpit, with lard.

Snake, bee and spider bites called for poultices of plantain leaves or of mud, or were charmed away with the "snake ball" (see BEZOAR, below) or bone.

Bees were believed to prefer stinging redheads and to avoid idiots and those with good dispositions; also they would not sting if ignored, and that they sting only once. This is interesting because it comes very close to the facts. Some persons *are* ignored by stinging insects (and they need not be red-haired); because of body emanations, others are sought. It is true also that insects do not sting except when alarmed, and they do lose their stingers in the process in many instances, if not always.

Burns were treated with a decoction of the inner bark of a pine tree; with lard or other grease; or with oak bark infusion (tannin).

Frostbites, unfortunately, were rubbed with snow or massaged to bring back the blood, when they should have been warmed gradually without friction; the pine bark decoction used for burns was also applied to frostbites, with poor results, as was a poultice made of cow manure and milk.

What happened when a bone was broken, a joint dislocated, or a gunshot, an arrow wound or a cut from an ax, saw or knife was sustained was likely to be tragic. At best it was very painful, and often permanently disabling, at least partially. Bones were "set" and crudely splinted according to the best skills of whoever was available. In compound fractures, where bone fragments pierced the skin, infection was almost certain, often with loss of the limb. The same was true of wounds; amputations were often necessary. They were crude procedures, accomplished with little anesthesia other than massive doses of whiskey. Poorly set bones left limbs deformed and function impaired. Crude efforts were made to keep the wounds from festering, but the science of bacteriology was as yet unborn. Recovery depended on luck and a rugged constitution. Yet some of the efforts at bandaging, poulticing and cleansing with whiskey, hot iron or oil, after the method of the French pioneer Paré, showed a groping progress toward the safeguards we now practice routinely.

KIDNEY DISEASES

Kidney diseases, and especially stones, were the subject of much herbal and related lore. Kidney beans, because of their shape, were regarded as "good" for the kidneys. So were asparagus and parsnips. Kidney stones were said to be helped by powdered bone taken from the middle of the backbone of a codfish, or the head of a dogfish. They were also believed to be dissolved by saxifrage tea, because this plant grows among stones and its roots break up the stones, as do those of many plants. Kidney stones, if they are not too large, can be passed sometimes, and recurrences prevented by controlling the chemical reaction of the urine, so this is a folk remedy that may be useful. When stones were passed spontaneously, it wasn't any fun! It still isn't.

MISCELLANEOUS REMEDIES

Browsing in the records of old-time medical methods, one finds such miscellaneous information as:

Ulcers of the skin were helped by a decoction of the outer bark of the pine tree; scabs were softened by lamb's fat, marshmallow, linseed or gelatin containing some of the carminatives mentioned above (see abdominal pain); healing wounds were treated with warm compresses of slippery elm, flaxseed, licorice, chickweed or starch paste.

Boils and carbuncles were treated by "drawing" the inflamma-

tion to a "head" with hot poultices, which might be of anything which would hold heat, from the split carcass of a
chicken to bread and milk or a variety of plant seeds; whatever
good effect was achieved was due to the heat rather than
any specific virtue in the substance employed, other than its
ability to retain heat.

Mouth infections and related problems were attacked by eating hazel nuts; lobelia and tulip preparations to cause saliva
to flow more freely, or if it was already too copious, a weak
tea of one of the nightshades soon set it right, or so Granny
believed. The nightshade, which contains belladonna, may indeed have been effective in the latter case.

Headaches required applications of counterirritants to the forehead to make the patient forget the headache, or he could hang
the head of a buzzard around his neck.

Measles, which get well in seven days—or don't—was "cured"
by pennyroyal or plantain leaf tea.

Lung conditions of various kinds were treated by sweating,
accomplished by heat and by hot teas of Jacob's-ladder, joe-
pye weed, boneset, magnolia and even weak versions of the
hazardous aconite. For whooping cough the wood anemone
was chosen. For pleurisy or pneumonia the milkweed, appropriately named pneumonia herb or pleurisy plant, was the
favorite.

Asthma, not then recognized as an allergy, was treated with
fumes from pennyroyal, mullein, or tobacco, and with the
Jimson weed, the poisonous *Datura stramonium*, which acted
like atropine. The fumes of the Datura, the nightshade, had
a limited usefulness due to their atropine content, but the
aftereffects were not good. Asthma, hay fever and other allergies are now treated in more specific ways, with a high
percentage of success. One of the ancient folk remedies of
China, mahuang, is the basis of a highly useful modern drug,
ephedrine.

Croup was treated without discrimination as to its origin by
steam inhalations, laced with spruce pitch, mint oils, eucalyptus, benzoin (spicebush), pine-needle oils, camphor and the
Biblical frankincense derived from the torchwood plant. Some
of these aromatics are still useful and pleasing today. But

now we recognize the dangerous diphtheric croup, which yields to no local remedies, and rid ourselves of it by immunizing against diphtheria in advance. In the old days, even within my childhood memories, diphtheria killed many a child by strangulation, or by paralysis from absorbed toxins.

Baldness and falling hair, or dandruff, were naturally remedied (or were they?) by grease from a hairy animal, the bear; or in South Africa to this day, by the fat of the hairless python; also by applications of boiled hemlock.

Coughs and colds naturally called for a multitude of "cures":

A strip of raw pork or one of red flannel, or a dirty scarf around the neck;

Skin of a dead fish tied to the feet, or split onion, or just greasing the soles;

Whiskey, internally—naturally!

Kerosene, internally, with or without sugar (a dangerous remedy);

Tea of cherry bark, tansy, spikeroot, smartweed or the old reliable camomile;

Syrup of fir balsam or brakeroot pith;

Pass the child three times under a horse's belly;

Give pine needles and molasses—it doesn't say how!

Quilted jacket around the chest—this makes sense;

Hot bath, hot drink and put to bed—this is good too.

We haven't yet learned enough about colds, except that they are virus infections, and that they hang on or get well at about the same rate, no matter how they are treated. We do know that pneumonia, bronchitis and other lung complications may follow repeated colds, and that what acts like "just a cold" may be tuberculosis. And some persons can be immunized against common influenza which bothers us every cold season, but immunization attempts against actual colds have thus far been disappointing. Some of the old drugs like hoarhound, wild-cherry bark and the mint, *heal-all,* as well as sassafras, slippery elm and catnip, may still be found useful as flavorings and for their mild, soothing functions. We may as well admit that progress against the common cold, in spite of volumes of research, has been extremely discouraging.

GOITERS

Swollen necks due to *goiters* were common, especially in young girls, before the relationship of iodine to the thyroid gland became known. They occurred in areas where the water and the soil were devoid of sufficient iodine, and so the vegetables and fruits were lacking in this important nutrient. These localities included the high mountains of Switzerland, the American Sierras and the entire basin of the Great Lakes. Dwellers near the sea were exempt because of the iodine content of the sea food they ate and of the iodine-rich crops raised on land close to the ocean. This was not understood until the early 1920s.

One of the old-time remedies for goiter was the wearing of amber beads around the neck. An experienced doctor who remembered the medical traditions of times past, and who understood people, was asked by a mother whether this would really work.

"Yes," he replied, "as long as you use iodized salt and eat plenty of sea food."

The reply illustrates the value of remembering that Grandma is not always wrong, and that her ideas should be discouraged only when necessary, and then gently, not with ridicule.

Grandma's ideas about health included many relating to foods. Some of the more interesting ones have to do with the common advice given to children about eating bread crusts. My mother always used to tell us that doing so would give us bright eyes and curly hair; a variation on this was blue eyes or rosy cheeks. An old couplet reads:

> "If you eat crumbs 'twill make you wise,
>   If you leave the crust,
>   You're sure to bust."

Actually, aside from taste, the crust is the least important part of the bread.

Grandma was also convinced that bananas were fattening—an impression still prevailing.

FOLK MEDICINE IS STILL WITH US

A fine example of the persistence of folk medicine and its practice is found in the heart-warming, autobiographical story of his youth by Sam Levenson, well-known and loved TV personality and lecturer.* His mother "practiced medicine without a license," but with a religious philosophy which regarded the human body as the dwelling place of the spirit, and that this created the obligation to keep it in good order so that the spirit should not suffer. This reflected the attitude of the good homemaker toward her house or apartment. He sensed in her care for him a feeling of security, of being ministered to; a feeling which the later psychologists attributed to Tender Loving Care, a concept implicit in the love and concern of a mother for her children. He called it *Mothercare*, and remarked that it preceded Medicare by half a century.

Doctors played a small part in the Mothercare plan. They were called only when home remedies had failed. Respect for good doctors was mingled with the hope that their services might never be needed, and such wry comments as that the doctor arrived too late; the patient had already recovered. Or the mother's remark to a neighbor that her child had been so ill that she had almost called a doctor.

Levenson grew up in a tenement, but his book reflects happy memories rather than grim ones. His mother and others like her relied on folk medicine, collective experiences, exchange of ideas, improvising and that invaluable quality, common sense.

The most commonly used drug was castor oil; the sight or even the mention of the horrid stuff was sufficient to trigger a miraculous "recovery" even in a really sick child. A popular chocolate-flavored laxative was preferred, and the kids even ate it on the sly for the chocolate, in spite of the disagreeable aftereffects.

Mothercare included many of the practices already mentioned here; mustard plasters strong enough to take off the hide, substituting a new pain for the original; garlic and onions, necklaces of camphor crystals to ward off disease. Sometimes a good idea

* *Everything But Money*; Sam Levenson, Simon & Schuster, New York, 1966.

went wrong, as when mother provided a sanitary cup to protect the family against germs, and they all drank out of it. Faith in medicinal foods was manifest in the use of small red radishes, a "hot" vegetable believed to keep one warm in winter.

A sovereign remedy was perspiring, which was induced in many ways, including kerosene and sugar internally; a salt herring wrapped around the neck; steaming tea kettles filling the air with moisture until even the walls "perspired," vinegar and salt-water gargles and rubdowns with goose fat. Cupping was sometimes performed by a barber; from this remedy, recovery took longer than the illness! (Cupping is a process of draining blood from the body by scarification and the application of a cupping glass for receiving internal congestion.) There was firm adherence to the belief that the stronger the remedy, the better. Great confidence was reposed in the "experience" of neighbors—whatever seemed to have succeeded for them was promptly imitated, often with poor results.

Faith in neighborly ministrations extended to conferences at the bedside, described as "socialized medicine." Here many a "cure" was proposed:

make the patient vomit;
give him a lemon to suck;
have him breathe into a paper bag;
put his head between his knees;
hold the patient upside down;
shave the patient's head;
pull on his tongue;
pull the shades down;
pull on his ear.

When everything else failed, consideration was given to changing the patient's name in order to confuse and deceive the Angel of Death.

All this happened in the early years of this century. It is undoubtedly happening today, if my correspondence during a third of a century answering laymen's inquiries for the American Medical Association is any indication. Readers' questions from my newspaper columns, broadcasts, magazine articles and books indicate that folklore is very much alive today, despite the availability of physicians and of more advanced medical knowledge. It is quite certain that incidents like the following cited by Levenson are still occurring:

A youngster suffered from severe abdominal pain. An old woman who "cured" people by incantations was called in. She allowed the hot wax from a burning candle to drip into cold water, studied the resulting mass intently, and announced that two intestines had become glued together. At this point, the frightened child vomited and felt better. The old woman was credited with a miraculous cure.

If there had really been an intestinal obstruction, the child would have died, unless prompt surgery had been invoked. When this event happened, such surgery was being performed. This illustrates the dangers in relying too long on home remedies, although these may be useful for minor illnesses. But who is to know what is really trifling, and what may become serious?

The reliance upon chicken soup, already mentioned above, has been cited by Levenson, who reports what he calls a classic story of his childhood days:

A mother brought home two chickens, live and unplucked. When she got home, she found that one of them was sick. So she killed the healthy chicken, made chicken soup, and fed it to—the sick chicken!

FOLKLORE AND CHILDBIRTH

The spectacular and mysterious function of bringing new life into the world would be expected to produce many beliefs, and customs based upon them, in many parts of the world. And so it has proved.

Many of these beliefs were concerned with the placenta, commonly called the afterbirth:

- In Queensland, part of the child's spirit is believed to stay in the afterbirth, so it is buried in the sand, marked by a circle of sticks with their tops tied together to form a cone. The spirit is then expected to reappear in another baby.
  Putting mud "babies" into the vagina was considered a good way to favor conception.

- In Molucca, clove trees in bloom are treated like pregnant women, protected against noise, light or fire, and saluted by removing the hat, as to a woman, *because* if the fruit is dropped too soon, women may lose their babies.

- *In Greenland,* pregnant women and those who have recently given birth are believed to be able to lay a storm by going outdoors, filling the mouth with air, then going indoors and blowing it out.

- *In Sumatra* women in labor were bound tightly around the body to keep the soul from departing; other members of the family were required to keep their mouths shut, and the mouths of all domestic animals were tied shut to keep them from swallowing the soul.

- At *Innisfallen in Killarney* is an "eye-of-the-needle tree"; a woman who can squeeze through this opening is believed to be assured of long life and safety in childbirth.

There are many taboos connected with the menstrual function, which was long regarded as "unclean," as was the uterine discharge which follows childbirth. This belief laid restrictions upon menstruating women, or those who had recently given birth, with regard to:

- anything they touched,

- paths they walked in,

- all association with the male, even by sight,

- separation of their dishes, pots and pans, and subsequent destruction of such utensils.

A miscarriage, especially if concealed, was believed to cause weather upheavals, and possibly to destroy an entire family or tribe. The purification rituals of the Mosaic law illustrate the importance attached to these beliefs. While we tend to smile at them a bit incredulously today, they were far from stupid. Many of the precautions now taken by physicians in caring for women in childbirth, are grounded in the same protective principles underlying what now seem strange and fantastic customs.

Taboos relating to childbirth applied to men as well as to women. In Celebes, for example, a husband whose wife is more than four months advanced in pregnancy may not tie any knots or sit with legs crossed, for fear of causing a knot in the umbilical cord or an obstruction which would interfere with delivery. In silk-worm-culture areas, men are required to maintain strict chastity while hunting, fishing or waiting for the silkworms to hatch. This, by the way, still remains the only certain contraceptive, despite the "pill" and other modern "improvements." And "morning sickness" is still not uncommon in husbands whose wives are pregnant.

In Western Australia a man's swimming ability is believed to be governed by whether his mother remembered to throw his umbilical cord into the water, or not. Many of the ancients regarded the cord or the placenta as a brother or sister of the child, and so guarded and protected it in various ways, in order to assure the child's welfare.

In the United States today, we still harbor some of the oldest ideas, such as:

- The expectant mother must eat for two, which is quite correct if it is not regarded as an invitation to gorge and grow fat. She must indeed assure her child of good nutrition by eating wisely, though not too well.

- The expectant mother can assure a smaller baby and easier delivery if she eats very lightly. This is not so.

- Handling a rope, or stretching and reaching, may cause the child's cord to become knotted or be caught around his neck. There is no foundation for this.

- The pregnant woman should avoid baths, especially tub baths. Bathing is permissible, but care must be taken not to fall getting in and out of tub.

- During pregnancy, physical exertion must be kept to a minimum. Exercise is beneficial in normal pregnancies.

- The pregnant woman must do no painting. (See explanation on following page.)

- For every child, a tooth must be sacrificed, possibly several. No!

- Pregnancies beyond the age of forty are dangerous. Not necessarily.

- Sexual intercourse during pregnancy is detrimental to mother and baby. This is possible only during the last few weeks, and at times when the menstrual period would normally be due.

- The sex of the child can be determined. Not yet! The diagnosis as to which sex it is has only recently been approaching accuracy. The experienced physician still predicts the sex opposite to that desired by the parents, which either proves him right or pleases them because they got what they wanted.

We have largely abandoned the confinement of women to bed for ten days or more after childbirth, because activity favors more prompt return of the genital organs to normal, helps restore the natural feminine figure and, above all, prevents blood clots with resultant milk leg or even more serious embolism. We now know that the pregnant, or menstruating woman, can and should bathe, either in the tub or shower as she prefers. Unless there are special problems, she need not baby herself. She can paint, too, even walls and ceilings, provided she uses paints which do not contain lead. Pregnancy is now recognized as one of the healthiest periods in a normal woman's life. One finds it difficult to believe today that the ancients regarded it as a nine-month *disease*.

VARIOUS OTHER MEDICAL CONCEPTS

In different parts of the world, "witch doctors" have played an important part in medical folklore. Wise foreign doctors, like Dr. Schweitzer, have learned to co-operate with these native healers instead of trying to discredit them—on the principle that there is no real harm in incantations, driving out devils by rattling animal bones or teeth, and making "good medicine" for the patient, or "bad medicine" for his enemies—so long as the trained physician gets a chance to use his scientific skills in the patient's behalf.

The psychology of the witch doctor is often of the most intelligent and effective variety, since he understands the patient's thinking and desires better than any foreigner can. One woman missionary doctor invited the witch doctor to learn how to sterilize needles, fill syringes, use cotton swabs soaked in alcohol, and aim the point at the recipient's buttocks. In this way she multiplied her own effectiveness, received co-operation, avoided offending the witch doctors, and enhanced the willingness of patients to receive her ministrations. They were reassured by the participation of their own doctors in her methods.

The old-time country doctor in the United States, who often had little enough to work with in terms of scientific knowledge and medical education, did have something that many patients miss in the modern, scientific physician and his highly efficient but sometimes impersonal system of practice, which they mistakenly interpret as indifference.

The traditional medical concern for the patient remains unchanged, but it often fails to come through the routine and the machinery and, above all, the delegation of services, the fractionation of the patient among specialists, and the disappearance of the home call. There is good reason for these changes, but they have not yet been sufficiently sold to the patient. Indeed, at a recent American Medical Association Conference on Medical Quackery, it was stated that one of the reasons why patients go to quacks is that they feel more at home with them than with scientific doctors.

FOLKLORE AND THE MODERN QUACK

The quack of today does not, of course, have the virtue of sincerity and belief in his own "line" that characterized the primitive medicine man. The quack knows what a phoney he is, and cynically classifies the patient as a sucker.

So let's have a look at some types of medicine men, here and there around the world.

In the Southwest, such a witch doctor practiced many of the healing arts, leaning heavily on psychological practices, such as the religious dances, for which he prepared the necessary drug stimuli, the cactus narcotic *peyote*, which is still used by the Hopi and other American Indians in their rituals. The alkaloid mescaline, derived from cactus, is one of the drugs currently in controversy in psychologic observations involving the perceptual faculties (psychedelic).

Under the heading of witch doctoring comes what Frazer describes as sympathetic magic, or the law of sympathy. This he divides into two varieties, *homeopathic* and *contagious*.

HOMEOPATHIC MAGIC

Homeopathic magic as practiced by the witch doctors in many areas, includes harming, killing (or helping) a person by making a likeness of him and dealing with it according to whether the purpose is to help or to injure. If harm is intended, the image is needled or burned, or buried if the intent is to kill. It is treated with respect if good medicine is the purpose. This was often repeated seven times on seven days, reciting a verse such as:

It is not an image that I am needling,
It is the liver (or other organ) of my enemy (name).

This sometimes appeared to work. Individuals against whom bad medicine was made were known to have sickened and died; whether this was due to coincidence, to psychologically induced fear reinforced by superstitious belief, or even to secretly administered poison, it all worked to enhance the reputation and the power of the witch doctor. Many modern groups including Orientals and some American Indians, still object to being photographed for fear of putting their image into the power of a potential enemy.

Witch doctoring to cure, employed the "like cures like" philosophy of the now almost defunct medical theory of homeopathy. In order to cure jaundice, for example, the witch doctor might mimic the condition by "transferring" the yellow color to another yellow object such as a bird or the sun. The patient would be covered with yellow porridge or pigment, which was then washed off, and he was given water to drink which had been poured over the back of a red bull. This was supposed to restore his normal color. The whole procedure was accompanied by incantations descriptive of its purpose. Since most cases of mild jaundice recover, the chances were in favor of success. In serious cases such as gall-duct obstruction or cancers, the explanation for failure was "bad" medicine more powerful than good. Even so, the odds on the side of the doctor would look good to any gambling man.

Another way of exercising sympathetic magic was for the witch doctor to imitate the symptoms of his patient, and then simulate the desired recovery. In most instances this took place, since so many diseases are self-limited.

Sympathetic magic may extend to influencing nature in providing an adequate food supply. British Columbian Indians put images of fish into the waters, meanwhile uttering prayers that real, edible fish may be caught. The modern fisherman uses lures, too, but his incantations are not generally classified as prayers. In some East Indian islands the natives make fish traps out of wood from trees which attract birds, in the hope and belief that the same attraction may be exercised toward fish.

CONTAGIOUS MAGIC

The other manifestation of sympathetic magic is called contagious, due to contact, which is based on the belief that things that have once been together will always remain so. Severed portions of the body, such as nails, hair, skin or teeth, if possessed by an enemy, are believed capable of being used to do harm to the individual. This is a close parallel to the attitude toward images, photographs, etc., except that any one can make an image, but such body parts are particularly intimate. They must be carefully guarded against harm or improper disposal. The burial of the placenta following childbirth, and the burial of amputated limbs, often with ceremony, is still practiced in some quarters.

In Germany, children practice sympathetic magic when they lose a tooth. They put it in a mouse's hole, or go behind the stove, throw the tooth backward over the head, and call upon the mouse to give an iron tooth, so there will be no more toothache. The mouse, a rodent, is a significant choice for folklore since gnawing animals depend heavily on good teeth. The modern child puts his tooth under a pillow or a flatiron, and expects to find a quarter in its place. In my youth, before inflation, a dime was satisfactory.

In Raratongo, when a child's tooth had to be extracted, the following prayer accompanied the operation:

> Big rat, little rat, here's my old tooth; pray
> give me a new one (there's the rodent again).

Parenthetically, they didn't know what we know now, that rodents' teeth continue to grow as they are worn down, but maybe they had a hunch!

A singular example of contagious magic is the old-time belief that when a man has wounded an enemy with an arrow, the wound can be made to inflame if he—not the wounded enemy—drinks hot and burning liquids or chews irritating leaves. The reverse of this belief is that if one has been wounded by an arrow or a spear, inflammation in the wound will subside if the weapon can be procured and kept in a cool, damp place. Or if he can manage to spit on the hand that wielded the weapon, the same result will ensue.

As late as the seventeenth century, supposedly scientific observers gave credence to the weapon-salve treatment for wounds. The salve, concocted of the patient's blood and human fat, was applied, not to the wound, but to the weapon which had inflicted it. The wound was merely wrapped in wet lint. This reminds one of the recipe for rabbit stew—"first catch your rabbit." Some attributed the cures supposedly effected by this curiously inverted measure to "animal magnetism." The clergy attributed them to black magic by the devil.

THE HEALING TOUCH

Animal magnetism was strongly in vogue during the sixteen hundreds—and many cures were attributed to stroking or laying on of hands. Touching for "scrofula," a form of gland and skin tuberculosis, was a prerogative of royalty, practiced in France as early as the tenth century, and by monks even earlier. Later it was adopted by English kings.

Another example of touch medicine was the *bezoar stone.* This is a mass of varying composition, sometimes soft and sometimes stony hard, which forms in the intestines of domestic animals. Some bezoars are the familiar hairballs known to every pet owner, which occur in the stomach of cats. Other bezoars may contain fruit and vegetable fibers along with hair. These stones were in common use for the cure of various diseases by touch, especially rabies. This latter gave them the common name of "madstone." The bezoar was a vulgar version of the elaborate touchpieces of gold coin used by British monarchs.

This old theory was put to profitable use in 1740 by one Dr. Elisha Perkins, who went about stroking patients with what he called magnetic tractors. They were rods of metal, one part iron, the other brass; they came in pairs, one white and one yellow. Perkins had been President of the Connecticut State Medical Society, which later expelled him for his tractor hoax. However, he traveled widely, promoting his idea. It was accepted by many physicians, both in America and abroad, and many cures were reported. Perkins was honored in London and Copenhagen; a Perkinsian Institute and a society named after him were established in London. He got out of England with over 10,000 pounds sterling, then worth $50,000. His theory was finally discredited by the use of ordinary wooden sticks painted to resemble the metallic tractors, with equally good results. The magnetism was composed entirely of Perkins' persuasive promotion, plus the hope which springs eternal.

While you smile at such gullibility, reflect on some much more recent and far more revealing use of the touch-magnetism cure technique: spikes of "gold" were sold for three hundred dollars to highly successful modern businessmen with golden claims for glowing health. The "Magic Spikes," as they were called, were not even of gold, but there was gold in them for the promoter. He sold them to an astonishing number of people in public life, including the politically astute mayor of a major American city. This is an instance where medicine and magic got well mixed together, and deteriorated into quackery, with a modern touch!

SO WHAT ABOUT GRANDMA?

We may seem to have wandered a long way from Grandma, but actually not. Grandma is closely related to these ancient beliefs, many of which dominated her ministrations. Grandma appeared in many guises in many environments. There was the Scandinavian "Leech," who used leeches to suck away bad blood from rheumatic joints. There was the pioneer woman in the covered wagon, who did everything medicinal except set broken bones. We have already met the Mexican "curandera" in Chapter Two. And there was your grandmother and mine, always ready with a remedy for your troubles and mine. Many of her treatments consisted mainly of tender loving care and good nursing, needed today as much as it ever was. Some of her practices have developed into important medical progress. In the days when doctors knew little more than the rest of the people, Grandma was a pretty important factor in the family's health.

Perhaps this chapter should have had a different title, like *Grandma Was Often RIGHT!*

Chapter Ten

NEW THERAPY FROM OLD REMEDIES

We have seen, in the preceding chapters, how many procedures have been valued in medical folklore for numerous purposes. Many of these have fallen into disuse, but a large number have produced modern therapy of value, discovered and refined with the growth of chemical, physical, electronic and other scientific knowledge.

Herb remedies formerly used as teas or powders made from the roots, leaves, stems, bark or seeds of plants were known as simples. When these were chemically analyzed, they were found in some instances to contain important and valuable active principles which explained the real usefulness of certain ancient remedies. We shall now have a look at a selected few of many, which will serve as examples of how, by instinct or by chance, or more likely by trial and error, our ancestors discovered help for their pains in the lilies of the field and the weeds by the wayside, in the forest or the swamp.

ALCOHOL

If there is any drug better known to the ancients than alcohol, it would be difficult to identify it. Alcohol is a natural product of fermentation of sugars occurring in fruits, and secondarily of starches found in roots and vegetables. Yeasts growing in nature cause this action. In the absence of refrigeration or other preventive procedures, such fermentation happened frequently, and could scarcely escape notice. The alcohol here referred to is *ethyl* or grain alcohol, which is only one of a large series of compounds of similar composition, known as alcohols.

The natural effect of consuming fermented beverages was either exhilaration or depression, depending on the amount taken and the nature of the imbiber. Carried to great excess it ended in unconsciousness or death. Its original uses were sacrificial or convivial; the ancients poured libations to their gods and wine flowed at banquets. Wine still remains a symbol in many religious sacraments and at celebrations.

In time, the stupefying effect of alcohol was utilized to deaden the pain of surgical procedures or the treatment of accidental injuries such as fractures, and in dealing with wounds sustained in combat. Drunkenness was recognized and disapproved by some, condoned and enjoyed by others, just as it is today. Alcoholism was unquestionably a problem then as now. For a time alcohol was regarded as the elixir of life by the alchemists; a belief apparently honored today by the devotees of the cocktail party.

In folk medicine, alcohol became a useful solvent for some of the herbs, barks, and roots which constituted the home remedies for many centuries. This vehicle was usually wine. In the older pharmacopeias, alcoholic solutions now known as tinctures and made with grain alcohol, existed as solutions in wine, and were known as "wine of" whatever simple was concerned. Medically, alcohol is still an important solvent for drug tinctures, and for elixirs, which are water-alcohol, sweetened medicinal vehicles. It is useful also as a solvent or preservative for many other medical preparations.

As a medicine, alcoholic beverages had a vogue in a simpler therapeutic age, but have declined in importance to some extent. Before the discovery of insulin, unsweetened alcoholic drinks, especially whiskey, were relied upon as a last resort in the treatment of severe diabetes, because alcohol supplies calories which are not converted into carbohydrates, as are starches, sugars and proteins. Alcohol is not, however, a good food, since it supplies only calories and is not economically metabolized.

More recently, the use of light wines has been reinstated in favor, especially for older persons, as a gentle relaxant and a pleasant addition to meals. This brings us right back to one of the principal early uses of fermented beverages, which were the main variety before the Arabs introduced distillation into the Western world.

ANESTHESIA

The first recorded "anesthetic" as well as the first reported "surgery" are described in the 21st verse of the second chapter of Genesis:

"And the Lord God caused a deep sleep to fall upon Adam, and he slept; and he took one of his ribs, and closed up the flesh instead thereof."

Other ancient references include the Egyptian *nepenthe* put into the wine of Telemachus, as related in Homer's Odyssey; the *bhang* or Indian hemp (see marijuana) mentioned in *The Arabian Nights*; and the hemlock which poisoned Socrates. Henbane, dewtry (thorn apple), and even lettuce, were known to the Orientals and the Greeks for their sleep-inducing action. Shakespeare knew of "drowsy syrups," and there was a formula made from some of these ingredients called *oleum de lateribus*, used in the form of a "somniferous sponge or soporific confection." These were all taken internally. In some circumstances, a blow on the head with a wooden bowl, practiced by the Babylonians, or to the point of the jaw, was found potent if crude and unpredictable. And there was, of course, always alcohol.

Alcoholic intoxication was probably the first intentional use of a plant-based derivative for producing unconsciousness to permit the performance of such ancient operations as plastic surgery, trephining the skull, amputations and cutting for the stone. Many such operations were performed without anesthesia, a fact which put a premium on surgical speed as well as skill. Even today there is virtue in making an operation as brief as possible, in order to minimize shock. Speed, however, is now secondary to safety and success.

In addition to alcohol, other drugs soon became known for their sedative properties. In the Orient the poppy yielded its opium; in the Near East and Europe the mandrake became a common agent for causing unconsciousness. The story of the mandrake has already been told (Chapter Five).

The henbane, also known as hog's-bean, insane root, poison tobacco and stinking nightshade, contains two powerful alkaloids, hyoscyamine and hyoscine (scopolamine). Hyoscyamine is now seldom used, but scopolamine remains important. It was once, in conjunction with morphine, used in the so-called twilight sleep narcosis during labor. This had to be greatly modified because too many babies died. Scopolamine is now employed as the popularly misnamed "truth serum," which is not a serum at all. It causes a sense of well-being, accompanied by drowsiness, amnesia, fatigue and sleep without dreaming, but may also cause delirium, restlessness, talkativeness, excitement, or hallucinations.

Closely related to scopolamine is atropine from the so-called deadly nightshade, *Atropa belladonna*. Atropine is not strictly an anesthetic, but is valuable in surgery for its effects on respiration, and the drying of excessive secretions in the breathing passages during surgery (see Belladonna).

The alkaloids of the nightshade family are found also in the *Datura* genus, which includes the thorn apple, Jimson (Jamestown) weed, stinkweed, apple of Peru and devil's-apple.

Hemlock is a poisonous perennial herb, not to be confused with hemlock trees. It grows in Europe, Asia and the Americas. It is also known as spotted parsley and spotted cowbane. The dried unripened fruit was formerly used for sedation, relief of pain and to ease muscle spasm.

The anesthetizing properties attributed to lettuce have been discussed in Chapter Six (Medicinal Foods).

Two of the principal inhaled anesthetics came into use in relatively modern times, beginning in the 1840s, as a result of fun and games. There were earlier gropings, such as the experience of the chemist, Priestley, who discovered nitrous oxide in 1776, and found that by inhaling it he derived a sense of greater muscular power and an impulse to action, gradually decreasing as he inhaled more, until he dropped the mouthpiece. In 1799, Sir Humphrey Davy announced that nitrous oxide relieved pain and suggested its use in surgery. In 1844, an itinerant lecturer and entertainer came to Hartford, Connecticut, and distributed a circular offering to administer "only to gentlemen of the first respectability" a gas which would make them sing, dance, speak, laugh, or fight—no reference was made to switching.

A dentist named Horace Wells attended the show, and later tried the gas in his practice, with initial success, but when he attempted to demonstrate it at Massachusetts General Hospital, it failed. Wells became discouraged and embittered. He abandoned his practice and died insane. The discovery of ether in 1846 put nitrous oxide in the background, but it remains today a useful anesthetic in appropriate circumstances.

A modern misuse of nitrous oxide is as a substitute for psychedelic drugs such as LSD-25; it gives an exhilarating effect and is obtainable without violating any laws. It is less convenient, however, since inhaling apparatus must be improvised.

Ether was used for "jags" by medical students and others who knew of its stupefying effects, long before prohibition produced "needled" beer. Dr. Crawford W. Long of Georgia, observing the effects of ether, used it as an anesthetic to remove a small tumor from the neck of one of his patients, but failed to report the case in the medical journals. He has, therefore, been denied the priority of discovery, and a bitter, useless controversy ensued when Dr. William Thomas Green Morton successfully demonstrated the use of ether in Boston. Some other individuals with whom we are not here concerned were involved in the dispute, and Morton made the mistake of patenting his discovery, an unethical procedure for a physician. Our main interest is the fact that both ether and laughing gas originated in nonmedical sources, if not in actual folk medicine.

The anesthetic effects of *chloroform* upon animals had been noted for some years when Dr. James Young Simpson of Edinburgh accidentally succumbed to the fumes of chloroform while experimenting with rabbits. His wife found him unconscious under the dining room table. He used chloroform to relieve pain in childbirth, but was opposed by the clergy, who cited Scripture to show that woman was destined to bring forth children "in pain and sorrow." Simpson quoted the Bible right back at them with the passage cited above about Adam's deep sleep. What really won the battle was Queen Victoria's acceptance of chloroform for the birth of her eighth child, thus conferring royal approval upon the procedure.

A modern relative of ether, *ethyl chloride*, was used briefly for introducing ether anesthesia to prevent the "going under" distress, but has been superseded by more effective and safer methods. It continues useful as a freezing, local anesthetic for minor operations. Another related anesthetic is *ethylene*, first discovered in trying to explain why flowers in a greenhouse failed to open. The cause was the illuminating gas which contained a small percentage of ethylene. The anesthetic properties of ethylene were discovered by Dr. Arnold Luckhardt of the University of Chicago in operations performed in 1923.

Cocaine, the "granddaddy" of the local anesthetic, was first known, and used for centuries by the South American Indians as an endurance drug, due to its stimulation of the central nervous system. Cocaine is derived from the leaves of the coca trees found in Bolivia and Peru. Locally, cocaine blocks pain transmission along the nerves, and so is useful in operations not requiring unconsciousness. It has been extensively used in eye surgery, both for its anesthetizing action and for pupillary dilation. It has also been useful in dentistry for nerve blocking. Cocaine is, however, a powerful drug, and may be poisonous even in small doses in certain individuals. This fact has led to the development of many synthetic derivatives with similar local anesthetic properties and lower toxicity—these can usually be identified by their terminal syllable "-caine." Among them are procaine (novocaine), monocaine and a number of others of interest mainly to physicians. All have their roots in the distant past, in a drug not even recognized in folklore as an anesthetic.

Cocaine, like other potent drugs, is subject to misuse. Known as "snow," it is sniffed for its stimulating effect. Popularly regarded as a narcotic, it is actually quite the opposite. The confusion comes about because it is grouped with the true narcotics in legislation governing the use of *habituating* drugs, to which classification it does not belong.

ARROW POISON

When the Amazonian Indians shot their blowgun darts at their enemies, they meant business; they poisoned them with a gummy black or dark brown material called curare. This came from various species of plants, especially a vine known as the moonseed liana. Curare is known also as *woorari* or *urari*, which are variations of the Indian phrase, "He, to whom it comes, falls." This describes the action of curare, which is a muscle-paralyzing agent, or in controlled dosage, a muscle relaxant.

Curare is such a powerful poison that minute doses can kill animals or birds in a few minutes. In its crude form it has many ingredients, and varies in strength; the Indians classified it as "one-tree," "two-tree" or other similar terms, based on how far a monkey could go from tree to tree after being hit.

The weaker varieties were used to paralyze animals which the Indians wished to capture, just as modern hunters paralyze animals for zoos or for research. Curare-relaxed game was said to have a better flavor than that killed while in a state of rage or fear. This belief may well be sustained by modern knowledge of the chemistry of emotional turmoil. The exact secret of preparing curare was restricted to witch doctors and medicine men, and seems to have been lost by the modern Indians. However, fortunately, the active ingredients are known, and in use today.

Many scientists interested themselves in curare, but its real modern development began in the 1940s, when it was first used to promote muscular relaxation in surgical operations. This still remains its most common use. But curare derivatives are useful in treating many other varieties of muscle spasm or convulsions, such as occur in tetanus, in certain drug poisonings, and in dislocations or fractures. It aids in relaxing muscles during the performance of diagnostic explorations of the lungs, larynx and esophagus. It relaxes muscles during electric-shock treatment used in some forms of mental disease.

A most interesting account of the source of curare and its uses and folklore is found in the book *Green Medicine*, listed in the bibliography of sources.

BELLADONNA

Belladonna, the deadly nightshade, *Atropa belladonna*, has already been mentioned in connection with anesthesia, but it has a much wider significance. It was used by fashionable women to dilate their pupils and give their eyes that naïve look of wide-eyed innocence, from which the name *belladonna* (beautiful woman) is said to have been derived. The other part of the name comes from the Grecian mythology; after the oldest of the three Fates, Atropos, who was said to cut the thread of life. Belladonna was a common drug used for poisoning in medieval times, since its action was difficult to identify when skillfully used.

Atropine, the active alkaloid of belladonna, and its related compounds, are useful in eye refractions in children and young persons, and in anesthesia, as already mentioned. It also acts on any other smooth muscle, which is not under voluntary control. Because it helps to check excessive nasal secretion, it has become part of the formula of cold and hay-fever remedies. The usefulness of atropine is limited by some of its undesirable side effects, but it has a definite place in modern therapeutics (see Anesthesia).

CACTUS, MUSHROOM AND MORNING GLORY

A tribe of American Indians, the Mescalero Apaches of the western plains region, discovered some interesting effects from the juice of the peyote cactus, and utilized the influence of the substance in religious ceremonies. The taking of the peyote juice (mescaline) by mouth caused the user to see bright-colored lights, animals and sometimes people, as well as geometric designs; orientation was sometimes disturbed. These effects lasted about twelve hours. The use of peyote spread northward from the Mexican border. Churches employing peyote have combined to organize the Native American Church, and have resisted attempts to discourage the use of the drug, claiming the constitutional guarantee of religious freedom.

Mescaline has been used in medicine as a research tool for studying visual hallucinations and investigating some psychotic conditions. There is a resemblance between the effects of the alkaloid mescaline and epinephrine, a hormone of the adrenal glands, and also a similarity to the effects of amphetamines which are the ingredients of the widely misused "pep" pills or "bennies." Mescaline and other alkaloids derived from the peyote cactus have now been synthesized, but modern therapeutic practice does not include their use for the purposes for which the

Indians continue to use them: aching teeth, rheumatic pains and tuberculosis.

Similar to peyote is the action of *psilocibin*, a constituent of a hallucinogenic mushroom found in southern Mexico, and there used by the natives to induce trancelike states. Still another is *ololuiqui*, from a vine resembling the familiar morning glory that produces a small fruit which when dried has lentil-like seeds. These have been used by native *curanderas* as sacred narcotics for divining purposes. In addition, the ololuiqui has been valued for pain-killing properties. Tests with frogs have shown narcotic action, but this has not been explored further.

Another Aztec sacred hallucinogenic mushroom has been found in the vicinity of Oaxaca, Mexico, called *teonanacatl* in the Aztec language which means "God's flesh." This had been described by the clerics of the Spanish conquest as harmful, and intoxicating like wine. It was believed to have been used in the coronation of Montezuma.

From the remote past in the Orient comes hashish (*cannabis indica*) and its American cousin, marijuana. This too is a psychedelic drug used for a number of years; the weed grows wild in many parts of the United States. It is not habituating, a fact which has been misconstrued to mean that it is not dangerous. The fact is that the marijuana-high individual, the smoker of "pot," is a menace to himself and others while he is disorientated and irresponsible under its influence. More will be said of this drug later (Chapter Twelve).

These plants, with the exception of marijuana, received relatively little attention until the discovery of the most important, the most exciting and the most dangerous of all the hallucinating drugs—lysergic acid diethylamide or LSD-25. This drug is related to ergot, the fungus of the rye which has been known for centuries, and is useful in obstetrics. LSD is a relatively new discovery, dating back to 1938. Its effects are similar to those of mescaline and psilocibin, but perhaps more spectacular. In addition, its action is less predictable, and the aftereffects are likely to be serious, including permanent psychological and mental damage. The drug is highly controversial. Its active proponents are engaging in a determined effort to discredit the Federal authorities who have banned the use of these drugs except in established religious ceremonies. Even research with LSD has been curtailed, and the manufacturer, as this is written, has withdrawn the product from distribution. Nevertheless, illegitimate sources of supply are being exploited.

Until the effects of "taking a trip," "turning it on" or smoking "pot," as the vernacular describes the use of these substances, has been scientifically clarified, and safe practices established, the course of wisdom is to let them alone. A "bad trip" may take you beyond the point of no return. The advocates of hallucinating-drug use to expand the mind claim that such a practice does not lead to heroin or other drug addiction. Nevertheless, association with illicit-drug distribution certainly exposes the individual, needlessly, to the temptation to try something new and alluring just once "for kicks." The kick *back* may be disastrous.

CATHARTICS AND LAXATIVES

When I was a child and not feeling well, my aunts and the childless friends of our family always looked wise and ominously remarked, "All he needs is a good physic."

Since I didn't know what a physic was, I was properly impressed, not to say scared. Later I found out that "physic" in those days was practically synonymous with "medicine," and had been for centuries. If you will look back at Chapter Five, you will see a formidable list of laxatives and purgatives—differing only in degrees of ruggedness. The idea that man must empty the bowel daily or oftener has had a hold on human thinking since the days of the Pharaohs, if not earlier; they had specially appointed courtiers who concerned themselves with the eliminative functions of their royal masters.

The preoccupation with fecal matter extended to the inclusion of animal and bird droppings, and even human excrement, in medicinal prescriptions—the so-called pharmacy of filth mentioned earlier. Even today the number and variety of laxatives offered to a credulous public is almost without number—always with the coy reference to the dangers of "irregularity."

Not only drugs, but foods are touted for their laxative qualities.

Even the professionals are caught out once in a while; one famous doctor solemnly demanded of those who would be healthy that their bowels act three times a day. The idea is by no means dead yet; countless unfortunates are desperately straining to achieve the impossible, the emptying of a harassed bowel already swept clean by needless and often powerful purgation, repeated day after day. True constipation is much less common than the laxative-induced state which is mistaken for the genuine.

The ancients knew enemas; the Greeks called them *clysters*, a term which remained in use until comparatively recent times. The invention of the enema is credited by Pliny to the Egyptian god Toth, who is said to have observed the ibis using its curved beak to wash its lower-digestive tract. Egyptian instruments resembling hollow horns may have been used for giving enemas. The Apache Chirichuas poured the enema fluid into a hollow wooden tube, and injected it by blowing into the tube. Syringes did not come in until the middle ages.

Many moderns become addicted to enemas as well as to laxatives. One of the modern nonmedical healing cults thrives on the colonic irrigation, a dangerously forceful flushing of the lower bowel. The enema is a useful medical procedure, but it is not always popular with the patient. The story is told of a soldier who had suffered more than he wanted of this experience; he awakened from a nightmare screaming, "Halt, who goes there, friend or enema!" The story may be apocryphal, but it has the ring of sincerity.

There are four main types of cathartics:

- *stimulants* include cascara, senna, phenolphthalein and castor oil: of these all but phenolphthalein are of folklore origin, along with numerous others;

- *saline* (salt) cathartics include such well-known substances as Epsom and Glauber's salts, magnesium citrate and milk of magnesia; these are modern chemical compounds;

- *bulk-forming* cathartics are those which absorb moisture and swell up, giving a mechanical stimulant to the bowel; among these are plantago (psyllium) seed, agar, tragacanth and bran, well known in folk medicine, and more modern synthetic forms of cellulose;

- *lubricant* cathartics are typified by mineral oil, not as harmless as is generally believed, for it robs the body of fat-soluble vitamins A and B.

Mention should be made of obsolete cathartics. This would include most of the herb medicines listed in Chapter Five, for the simple reason that they are outmoded by their ineffectiveness and the inaccuracy of compounding, inevitable in the average home. Modern drugs are better when needed. But this group also includes some that are dangerous:

- *calomel*, the reliance of many persons for many years, is unreliable, and dangerous because it disturbs the mineral metabolism of the body and may result in chronic mercury poisoning;

- *aloe* causes severe griping and possible kidney damage and the sugar-coated pills have poisoned many children; it should be abandoned;

- *rhubarb* has both a constipating and a cathartic action, and the former is likely to overshadow the latter;

- *cathartic resins*, many of which are found in the traditional laxative plants, produce too much colic and should not be used; among them are jalap resin, podophyllum (May-apple root), gamboge (an Asian dye-stuff), colocynth (bitter apple) and its alkaloid, elaterin, and ipomoea (scammony) or Mexican jalap;

- most dangerous of all is *croton oil*, which blisters the skin and death has been caused from as little as twenty drops.

Some of these substances have been used in irrational mixtures which, if taken continuously as so many cathartics are, may cause potassium and sodium depletion and severe dehydration.

No discussion of laxatives is complete without the warning that laxatives should never be used when there is abdominal pain.

Physicians have long since abandoned purgation as a routine, and have tried to persuade patients that the secret of healthy elimination lies in the diet and the formation of proper habits and, above all, the cessation of laxative dosing. Even so, too many persons still persist in maintaining the laxative habit.

The best disposal of the laxative, as a general rule, is the direct route down the toilet, instead of the indirect one through the patient's long-suffering digestive tract.

THE CALABAR BEAN

The *Calabar bean*, an ornamental garden plant, is one of many poisons found commonly in herbaceous borders. This bean comes from a perennial climbing woody plant which grows on stream banks in tropical West Africa. It is also known as chop nut or Esere nut, and was used by natives as an ordeal poison, administered to a person accused of witchcraft. If he or she survived, this was considered proof of innocence. The plant was brought to England in 1840, and studied by many investigators. A pure alkaloid was isolated in 1864 and again by another investigator a year later. The first named it *physostigmine*; the second called it *eserine*, after the bean. The earliest therapeutic use was in 1877, for glaucoma, for which it remains useful even now. It keeps the pupil contracted and so improves eye-fluid circulation and prevents build-up of ocular pressure. Starting with physostigmine, chemists developed related compounds. Neo-stigmine was found useful in stimulating intestinal action, and in treating *mysathenia gravis*, a disease in which there is severe muscular weakness. Physostigmine has also pointed the way to an important group of chemicals which influence the metabolism of choline, a vitamin.

THE COCA TREE

For centuries, the leaves of the *coca tree* have been chewed by Peruvian and Bolivian natives to increase their endurance. Their experience is validated by modern medicine through the discovery and use of the drug *cocaine*. This drug is commonly classed as a narcotic, but this is a mistaken concept, due probably to the fact that many other addicting drugs are narcotics.

Cocaine has two main actions. It blocks pain locally; it is a powerful brain stimulant, which accounts for the traditional use of coca leaves to increase endurance. It may also increase mental power; as the devotees of Sherlock Holmes may remember, the famous sleuth made use of it, despite the disapproval of Dr. Watson. Cocaine is a potent drug, and acute poisoning is not uncommon. Addiction is a serious problem; the sniffing of "coke" or "snow" results in actions attributed to narcotic users, but which are more characteristic of cocaine—that is, the use of force and weapons for procuring the drug or avenging alleged persecutions. This is totally unlike the morphine addict, whose drives are lessened rather than stimulated, and who resorts to theft or prostitution rather than violence.

Cocaine is a valuable local anesthetic; its toxicity has been important in stimulating research for other local anesthetics, of which the best known is procaine (novocaine), and a number of others all ending in the suffix -caine (see anesthesia, page 204).

The similarity between the names of the coca tree and the African kola tree has created some confusion; the kola tree is not the source of cocaine (see coffee).

COFFEE, COCOA AND TEA

Who knows where the use of coffee originated?

The prior of an Arabian convent who observed exceptional liveliness in goats which had eaten coffee berries? And his experimental use of coffee beans to keep him awake during the long nights of prayer? And the violent opposition of his priestly colleagues who regarded this practice as unorthodox? It makes a good story, and who can prove that it isn't so. Indeed, it bears a strong resemblance to the opinions which divide modern coffee lovers from those who classify the use of the bean as a vice along with alcohol, tobacco and other unholy indulgences dear to the average person. After all, the prior merely created the precedent for one of the most-valued industrial fringe benefits, the coffee break.

But, seriously, coffee, tea and cocoa are the sources of three important alkaloids sometimes called xanthines—caffein, theophylline and theobromine, chemically related to uric acid, the villain in gout. These alkaloids are found also in *maté* or Paraguay tea, widely used in South America, and in the kola or guru nuts chewed by natives in the Sudan. "Teas" brewed from these plants have been in use for more centuries than can be accurately identified. The modern consumption of such beverages is astronomical, including soft drinks made from the kola-tree nuts (guru nuts).

Coffee contains *caffeine*; tea, *caffeine* and *theophylline*; cocoa, *caffeine* and *theobromine*; maté, *caffeine*. These alkaloids have the same general effects upon the body, but in differing degrees:

Comparison of Xanthine Alkaloids*

1 maximum   2 intermediate   3 minimal

Alkaloidal Action	Caffeine	Theophylline	Theobromine
Central nervous stimulation	1	2	3
Stimulus to breathing	1	2	3
Relaxing involuntary muscle	3	1	2
Stimulating kidneys	3	1	2
Dilating coronary arteries	3	1	2
Stimulating the heart	3	1	2
Stimulating voluntary muscle	1	2	3

This comparison indicates differences between the three alkaloids of interest and importance principally to physicians. Fortunately, the use of the popular beverages in reasonable moderation does not entail the taking of sufficient quantities of these drugs to disturb the normal individual; in some instances, physicians may advise limitation or abstention for established, clinical reasons.

Parents who may not have realized the close resemblance between cocoa and the other beverages, need not be concerned that cocoa or chocolate will harm their children, unless the physician so advises them. After all, what is life without chocolate to a child?

* Adapted from *Pharmacological Basis of Therapeutics*, Goodman and Gilman, Third Edition, Macmillan, New York, 1965.

THE ERGOT FUNGUS

The ancient Greeks objected to the grain from Thrace and Macedonia. They called it the "black malodorous product." This was probably the same as that referred to in an Assyrian clay tablet of 600 B.C. as a "noxious pustule in the ear of grain," and by the Zoroastrian Parsees in one of their sacred books about the fourth century B.C., which describes "noxious grasses that cause pregnant women to drop the womb and die in childbed."

The references are to a fungus which may affect any grain but to which rye is the most susceptible. Even today, rye is subject to government inspection because of the possibility of this infestation. The fungus is called *ergot*. The Romans used little or no rye flour, but in the Middle Ages its widespread use caused epidemics in which the hands and feet grew gangrenous. The burning pain and the bloodless amputation of the limbs by the disease were attributed to holy fire. The disease was called St. Anthony's Fire, because a pilgrimage to the shrine of the saint was the best source of relief. Quite likely because he was spared his ordinary diet of infested grain. The cause of the outbreaks was identified as the ergot fungus as early as 1670. Prevention is now quite simple, but even so, Russia had an outbreak in 1926, Ireland in 1929 and France in 1953.

Our interest in ergot stems from its useful alkaloids rather than from its poisonous character, although it does illustrate the fact that almost any potent drug has dangerous possibilities if not accurately and intelligently employed. The use of ergot in obstetrics began even before it was identified as the cause of St. Anthony's Fire, and midwives preceded the medical profession in employing it to produce labor pains and uterine contractions.

It soon became evident that while ergot would speed delivery, it also was responsible for too many stillborn babies. So the original name given it, "powder of parturition" was changed about 1824 to "powder of fetal death," following a study of this effect. Its routine obstetrical use is now restricted to the control of bleeding following the delivery of the afterbirth. The action of ergot is due to a number of natural alkaloids, and some synthetic derivatives. Certain of the ergot alkaloids can be combined with lysergic acid; one such compound is lysergic acid diethylamide or LSD-25.

Ergotamine is useful for the treatment of migraine. To illustrate how folk medicine continues to contribute to medical knowledge, patients with migraine taking ergotamine noticed that strong coffee helped them; this observation has been clinically verified, and preparations of ergotamine and caffeine are now available.

IPECAC

From the Indians of Brazil comes our knowledge of the value of Brazil root or *ipecacuanha*; they used the dried root for the treatment of diarrheas. The French Government bought it as a secret remedy in 1658, and it was soon in wide use in Europe and India. The explanation for its effectiveness, at least in some cases, was not apparent until 1912, when its alkaloids were recognized as specifics in the amoebic type of dysentery; *emetine* is the most effective of these.

Ipecac syrup has a somewhat limited use in modern medicine because it causes severe intestinal irritation and vomiting, some of which is avoided by the use of the alkaloid emetine. However, poison-control experts are now advising homemakers to keep on hand a small quantity of syrup of ipecac, and to get instructions from their physicians in how and when to use it, in the event of emergencies in the home when poison has been swallowed and there is not time to wait for medical help.

Ipecac will cause vomiting, but vomiting should not be induced if there are signs of caustic acid or alkali burns about the mouth.

FOXGLOVE

The foxglove (folk's glove) blooming wild in England's rural lanes, and known also in Scotland as bloody fingers or deadmen's bells, and in Ireland as fairy thimble has already been mentioned as a source of the heart stimulant *digitalis*, but this is only one of a number of drugs of similar type, known in ancient times, though not in modern days.

Squill, or scilla, a Mediterranean-area member of the lily family, includes the English bluebell or white hyacinth, which is mentioned in the Ebers papyrus, a 1500 B.C. Egyptian medical document. The Romans used squill to promote vomiting, presumably after a banquet at which they had stuffed themselves. They used it also to stimulate kidney activity, as a heart tonic, and to poison rats! Strophanthin, derived from a number of tropical plants and used as an African arrow poison, was discovered in 1890 by an English investigator. Going even farther back into antiquity, we find the ancient Chinese using dried toadskins as styptics. These contain epinephrine, the "adrenalin" secreted by human adrenal glands. Toadskins were employed also against dropsy, as was the digitalis "tea of the Shropshire granny" who gave Dr. William Withington the idea of using it in heart cases with dropsy.

Digitalis was at first used with little discrimination for such unrelated conditions as skin ulcers and epilepsy, neither connected with the heart. It took a great deal of experience and some tragedies to assign to digitalis its role as a specific drug for congestive heart failure due to weakening muscle action. It is definitely contraindicated in the heart "attack" due to coronary artery disease, where heart muscle must be rested, not stimulated.

Digitalis and related drugs stand as a striking example of how folklore foreshadowed modern scientific medicine. Dr. Withington hailed the future of the foxglove in these words:

> "The foxglove's leaves, with caution given,
>   Another proof of favoring Heaven
> Will happily display:
>   The rapid pulse it can abate;
> The hectic flush can moderate
>   And, blest by Him Whose will is fate,
> May give a lengthened day."

THE "ITCH"

Itching can be more exhausting than pain. Perhaps that is why certain types of itching have been called "seven-year itch," not because they lasted that long, but because they seemed to.

Itching is only a symptom, but symptomatic treatment was the usual method of folk medicine, so it is not surprising that many herbs were used to relieve itching:

- poultices of borage (star-flower) leaves;

- juice of celandine (tetter-wort), (tetter is a common name for skin eruptions);

- ointment from the whole plant of *balm*ony (snakemouth);

- salve made from witch-hazel bark;

- decoction of white oak bark (tannic acid);

- sphagnum (peat) moss poultice;

- comfrey (healing herb) poultice.

A particularly interesting idea, cited by Coon, is the use of a powerful irritant, the stinging nettle, to overcome pains of itching and of rheumatism, by beating the sufferer on the affected areas with whips made of bundles of nettles. This seemingly cruel idea of disguising one pain by creating another is not uncommon in the medical lore of the past. Perhaps a pain *is* better than an itch! This principle of counterirritation still has a limited usefulness.

Itching due to the common parasites of scabies (a mite) and head lice were often treated with kerosene or benzine (dangerously flammable), balsam of Peru, infusions of delphinium or larkspur, or by pyrethrum (feverfew or Spanish camomile). They are now treated more effectively and safely by modern drugs, supplemented by cleanliness, proper care of the skin and hair, and simultaneous elimination of the parasite from all members of the household to avoid repeated reinfection.

MA HUANG

The Chinese employed an active drug derived from various plants for over five thousand years before it was introduced into Western medicine in 1924. It was first prepared synthetically in 1927. Known in China as *ma huang*, its medical name is ephedrine, from the genus name *ephedra* of the plants in which it occurs. This name is similar to epinephrine, an active principal of the adrenal glands; the two substances have similar actions and comparable uses; they raise the blood pressure by contracting the smaller arteries through action on the sympathetic nervous system. Both also relieve bronchial spasm, and are useful, therefore, in asthma, hay fever and related allergies, and in relieving nasal congestion. This is one of the most striking examples of how folk medicine became a forerunner of modern scientific therapy, through both plant and animal contributions.

MARIJUANA

Cannabis (Indian hemp) is a drug of Chinese origin, mentioned about 2700 B.C. in the herbal of the Emperor Shen Nung. It has various familiar names; *charas* in the Far East; *hashish* in the Middle East and North Africa and *marijuana* in the United States. The dried leaves are called *bhang* and the resinous substance obtained from the flowers is called *ganja*, and these terms are also applied to the drug in any form.

Cannabis belongs to the group of drugs which have stimulating effects upon the individual's nervous and emotional state, especially when smoked, but it does not produce actions totally alien to the personality of the user. Nevertheless, its immediate effects indicate that its use is highly inadvisable. Marijuana has been restricted by law, as has possession of the drug, growing of the hemp plant from which it is derived, its sale or other distribution. Even so, it is widely used and abused. There are no presently recognized medical values for marijuana.

MESCALINE

see CACTUS

MORNING GLORY

see CACTUS

MUSHROOMS

see CACTUS

OPIUM

Opium, which comes from the Greek word meaning *juice*, is so named because it originates from the milky juice of the unripe seeds of the Oriental poppy. It was probably opium which was known to the ancient Sumerians in Mesopotamia about 4000 B.C. They called it *hul gil* or joy plant. The Greeks recognized the propensity of the substance for producing physical dependence, now called addiction. At first it was used principally for the control of diarrheas, then commonly called dysenteries. The medieval physician Paracelsus is credited with the first preparation of an alcoholic solution or tincture of opium, called laudanum, a term from the same Latin root as the verb to praise or laud. It is still in use today, often in its camphorated form, paregoric. Opium smoking did not come into use until the eighteenth century, and was not originally in such disrepute as it is today. Opium "eating," which was really drinking of laudanum, never grew so common nor so objectionable in earlier times as the abuse of alcohol.

Chemically, a number of pure active ingredients have been isolated from opium gum, some used medically, some rejected:

- *morphine,* named after the Greek god of sleep, Morpheus, is one of the most valuable medicinal agents known, in both medicine and surgery. It acts on the nervous system to dull pain, reduce apprehensions and permit sleep or relaxation. It causes the pupils to contract. It slows breathing. In these respects it simulates sleep, but it may cause nausea and vomiting. Unless its use is carefully controlled, there is danger of addiction. Morphine is one of the narcotic drugs commonly employed by addicts who get their supplies illegally through secret, underworld channels. Addiction to morphine requires a continuous supply of the drug, in order to avoid serious physical and psychological withdrawal symptoms. Cure of morphine addiction is difficult and uncertain; relapses are common;

- *codeine* is less potent than morphine, but has many of the same characteristics. It is an ingredient in a number of commonly used cough syrups, in such small doses, however, that prescriptions are not required for their purchase. Buyers are required to register, in order to prevent accumulation of quantities of codeine by addicts. Codeine addiction is much less important than morphine addiction;

- *Apomorphine* is a derivative of morphine once valuable to induce vomiting, but is now used much less frequently;

- *heroin* is another morphine-related drug; it has no useful medical function which is not performed by other drugs, and since it constitutes the most serious threat of addiction, its use, possession, manufacture, importation or sale in the United States is illegal;

- *other opium alkaloids* are used for varying medical purposes, especially in proprietary preparations sold commercially and available in some instances without prescription.

Many synthetic drugs with pain-relieving properties have been made by chemists in the effort to improve upon the opium derivatives, especially with regard to their nauseating and addictive side effects. In medical hands, many of these are useful, but none has replaced the opium derivatives, springing out of the distant past.

PENICILLIN AND OTHER ANTIBIOTICS

In the days of Imhotep, Egyptian physician of 3000 years B.C., inventor of the pyramids, political counsellor and perhaps attending physician to a Pharaoh, it was common practice to treat wounds with molds that grew on bread or on wood which had been immersed in water for a long time. The practice has continued among nonmedical people in various parts of the world to this very day.

Now, as Professor Paul Ghalioungui of Ain Shams University, Cairo, remarks, this practice, like others "long considered ridiculous, has just received its warrant of nobility." He refers to the observation made in 1928 by Sir Alexander Fleming, a Scottish physician, who discovered that the accidental introduction of a mold into a bacterial culture in the laboratory, had prevented growth of bacteria in its immediate vicinity. This might have gone unnoticed, but Fleming followed through on his observation, and discovered that this bread mold contained a powerful inhibitor of bacterial growth, and that it could be given to animals without causing untoward effects. He called it penicillin, after the bread-mold penicillium. His discovery was ignored; twelve years elapsed before Sir Howard W. Florey and Ernst Boris Chain used this substance successfully in the treatment of individuals suffering from serious diseases such as erysipelas, blood poisoning (sepsis), staphylococcus infection and pneumonia. The three scientists shared the 1945 Nobel prize in medicine and physiology.

During World War II, penicillin saved countless lives. Its manufacture in quantities sufficient to serve the needs of the armed forces is one of the most fascinating stories of the American pharmaceutical industry. Not only did the drug companies save lives then, but they have since made numerous other scientific advances.

Penicillin is not only the first of the antibiotics—meaning life inhibitors of bacteria!—it is also the forerunner of numerous other antibiotics, developed from various sources such as funguslike organisms found in the soil. Many are now manufactured in the laboratory.

Antibiotics are of two kinds, bactericidal, which kill bacteria, and bacteriostatic, which keep them from growing and multiplying. In either case, they assist the body in overcoming infections. They have been called wonder drugs or miracle drugs, but this is unfortunate, because they have their limitations. This should not detract from their usefulness, which has given physicians a large measure of control over many diseases formerly much less amenable to treatment.

The antibiotics have names which often end in "-mycin," a term derived from mycellium, the threadlike fibers which characterize the structure of many molds.

Did Imhotep and his contemporaries know anything about bacteria and molds? Only what they could observe without microscopes or refined laboratory procedures. But they saw what they looked at, and they drew some pretty sharp conclusions. That, of course, does not justify the continued use of moldy bread, when more refined measures are available.

QUININE

see Chapter Nine

SPICES

Eucalyptus

A large variety of trees native to Australia and Tasmania, but grown also in California, are the members of the *eucalyptus* genus, which range from shrubs and bushes to large ornamental trees. The bark is valuable for tanning, and the wood for its fire and worm-resisting qualities. The oil distilled from the leaves has been a popular ingredient in nose drops and sprays for its pleasant odor and mildly soothing qualities, despite the fact that it has no important medicinal effect. Eucalyptol, prepared from the oil, has been used as an intestinal antiseptic and to treat diarrheas. The resin which oozes from the bark is an astringent. Similar oils are obtainable also from the *cajuput*, a California laurel, wormseed (related to *sage* and others of the *artimesias*) and *lavender*.

Menthol

Menthol is another folk-medicine standby. It is an aromatic derived from oil of peppermint or prepared synthetically, which has the property of seeming to cool, while it is actually warming. Its main use is counterirritation. It is common in commercial nose- and throat-remedy formulas. Medicinally its value is slight. The psychic effect of rubbing it on the chest of someone with a cold may be out of proportion to its real value, but it remains far below the claims with which it is commonly promoted.

Camphor

Related to menthol is *camphor*, known to the Chinese for many centuries. Natural camphor comes from the wood and bark of a tree *cinnamomum camphora* found mainly in Japan and Formosa. Its principal use is on the skin to help itching and pain.

Note the relationship of these drugs to common spices—sage, peppermint and cinnamon.

Wintergreen

Another flavoring agent, *oil of wintergreen*, comes from a long history of folk medicine. Chemically this oil is composed mainly of methyl salicylate, a derivative of salicylic acid, which in turn comes from salicin. Salicylic acid is the source of the principal compounds now so widely used for the relief of pain—sodium salicylate and aspirin. The acid has also been used to keep food preparations from spoiling, but this practice is not permitted in the United States.

Salicin occurs naturally in the bark of willow trees, of which there are numerous species, and in some varieties of spiraea. Teas from the willow bark were esteemed by the ancients for the treatment of rheumatic and other painful conditions, and in fevers. The oil of wintergreen too was regarded as an excellent antirheumatic; it has become the basis for widely exploited commercial preparations, "penetrating" applications which do not penetrate because the skin does not absorb them. Their value is limited to mild counterirritation, possibly combined with the pseudo-warming effect of menthol. For some time, a long and bitter controversy raged over the relative merits of natural versus synthetic oil of wintergreen, but this died down with recognition that no liniment is absorbed, and that the value of these old-time favorites is hardly sufficient to affect even the "minor" pains for which so many remedies are offered.

For a time, the principal medicinal derivative of salicylic acid was sodium salicylate, which had the disadvantage of being highly irritating to the stomach. This has been remedied in part by the development of acetylsalicylic acid (aspirin), and still further by the chemical process of buffering. Aspirin, alone, buffered or combined with other agents, forms a principal ingredient in many commercial pain-relieving preparations. It is at once the safest widely useful drug and, paradoxically, the most common source of serious or fatal poisoning in children.

Most salicylic acid derivatives are now manufactured rather than obtained from natural sources.

Other Spices

Still other spices and flavoring ingredients have had medical uses attributed to them in the past; prominent among them vinegar and honey which, like many an honest folklore misconception, has been corrupted into modern quackery.

Here are a few brief notes on other agents:

- *capsicum*, the red pepper best known as Tabasco sauce, is an internal irritant, formerly used as a carminative;

- *cinnamon*, an agreeable spice, had similar uses;

- *cumin*, a principal ingredient in chili powder, is a pungent and aromatic flavoring agent derived from a small plant of the carrot family;

- *tomatoes*, once considered poisonous and also regarded as "love apples," have become the main ingredients of catsup and other meat sauces; and make important contributions of vitamin C to the diet;

- *mustard*, popular with the hot-dog set, comes from plants classed by many farmers as noxious weeds, which yield volatile oils from their crushed seeds; it is a pungent condiment which can be strongly irritating to anyone if used to excess, or to sensitive persons even in small quantities; its ancient use as a carminative has been replaced by better approaches to digestive problems. Important modern derivatives such as the nitrogen mustards have been useful in some forms of cancer. The old-time mustard plaster still has its adherents among home-remedy enthusiasts, but the recipient of the ministration is not usually among those who admire it;

- *cardamom*, derived from a tropical Asian plant, was formerly valued as a carminative;

- *nutmeg* and *mace* originate from the fruit of a tree native to the East Indies; the nutmeg was introduced into the Levant by Arab traders from the Molucca or Spice Islands. Nutmeg comes from the fruit; mace from its hull. The expressed and volatile oils were valued in folk medicine for rheumatism;

  Nutmeg is more than the ordinary useful spice with a history of more or less obsolete medicinal value; it contains a number of medically active ingredients, of which the principal one is the oil of *myristicin*. This gives symptoms resembling atropine poisoning—red skin, racing heart and dry throat. Psychologically, grated nutmeg may, if enough is taken, produce feelings of unreality, depersonalization, agitation, stomach cramps, dizziness and dry mouth. Some users never feel the psychedelic effects but experience only a hangover.

The nutmeg is only one of scores of common plants, including the sacred mushrooms of Mexico, Brazilian *ayahuasca*, the Polynesian pepper plant *kava*, and other plants containing alkaloids derived from the harmala or harmel herbs found in Asia and Africa. Nutmeg users are common among prison inmates, and recent reports indicate that many students who use nutmeg responded to a newspaper advertisement by a research pharmacologist in a major university. So it seems that we are swinging in a wide circle from folklore to the newest in drug research, the study of substances which affect the mind;

- *vanilla* has been known to the Mexicans and their ancestors since long before the Spanish conquest. The vanilla bean comes from a climbing orchid native to hot climates. It yields an aromatic crystalline principle, vanillin, which has been used as a digestive "stimulant" and is now the basis for perhaps the most popular flavoring agent. A derivative of vanillin has also been used as a styptic, an antirheumatic and a hypnotic, but it is not prominent in modern medicine. Vanillin is found also in the leaves of the deer tongue, commonly called button snakeroot or blazing star. Cheaper forms of vanilla flavoring are made from cloves, ethyl acetate or a by-product of wood-pulp manufacture, *lignin;*

- *turmeric,* a principal ingredient of curry powder, is named from a combination of two French words, *terre* (earth) and *merite* (excellent). It comes from the *curcuma longa* (saffron), a plant indigenous to India, where curried foods are very popular. The perennial roots of the plant are powdered. It is useful also as a dye (saffron), a chemical test substance and a medicinal stimulant;

- another source of *saffron* is the purple crocus, whose orange-colored stigmas furnish the dye, the seasoning and the medicinal agent, a rubifacient or reddening medicine. The safflower (bastard or false saffron), is a plant cultivated in the Orient and in southern Europe. This is the source of a yellow dye, a little-used medicinal principle, and the safflower oil which is presently enjoying a tremendous vogue among the proponents of eliminating all animal fats from the diet to prevent heart diseases, a proposal by no means unanimously accepted by the medical profession;

- *garlic*, a member of the onion family, has been prominent in medical folklore for centuries, being recommended variously as an antiseptic for wounds and for treating ivy poisoning and internally for asthma, bronchitis, rheumatism, coughs, colds, hoarseness and worms; never, apparently, for halitosis. There is, however, a recipe for disguising garlic odor in medicinal mixtures; it calls for caraway and sweet fennel seeds bruised and boiled for a short time in vinegar before adding to a garlic-and-honey syrup. In recent times, commercial efforts have been made to repopularize garlic for treating high blood pressure, but more effective modern medicines are available;

- *cloves*, source of an aromatic oil and useful in dried or powdered form as condiments, have long been a stand-by in treating toothache, before the days of fluoridation, brushing after every meal with industriously publicized toothpastes and regular dental care, made this emergency less familiar than formerly; a similar attribute has been assigned to a garlic "clove"; like other aromatic oils, the oil of cloves has been recommended as a carminative, a class of remedies now outdated;

- *caraway*, *sesame*, *allspice*, *ginger*, the *mint* family, and other spices have been recommended from time to time for home-remedy purposes, but are now regarded mainly as pleasant flavoring agents, if not too enthusiastically employed, when they may become irritating.

TRANQUILIZERS

The love philters and hate potions of ancient times indicate man's belief in the ability of plant or animal substances to influence psychological states for better or worse. Hippocrates classified people according to their humors as sanguine, choleric, phlegmatic or melancholy; he also proclaimed the brain as the organ of the mind.

One of the significant advances of the twentieth century is the improved treatment of psychic disorders, which for the first time in many years has caused a decline in the occupancy of mental hospital beds. This has been achieved largely through the tranquilizer drugs. These do not cure mental illness, but they greatly facilitate its treatment.

One of the most widely used has its origin in ancient India, where it is described in the Vedas, the religious writings of the Hindus. It was used for snakebite, high blood pressure, insomnia and "insanity" and, mistakenly as we now know, for epilepsy and dysentery. The drug came from the snakelike root of a plant, now known as *rauwolfia serpentina*, but commonly called snakeroot, which differs from the American garden variety. Its use for snakebite is an example of sympathetic magic, already mentioned. The modern name for the plant comes from that of a sixteenth-century botanist who never even saw or heard of it—Dr. Leonard Rauwolf of Augsburg, Germany. The whole root was used until the discovery of the active alkaloids, of which reserpine is a typical example.

Reserpine and the other tranquilizers, many of which are synthetic, are not limited to the treatment of mental illness. They are useful also in relieving stresses, anxieties and other emotional disturbances which are increasingly common in the fast tempo of modern living.

The rauwolfia alkaloids have become the basis of numerous drug formulas of great efficacy. They represent a major step in treating mental and emotional disturbances, and typify one of the many modern drugs derived from ancient remedies.

WORM MEDICINES

In situations where sanitation was primitive, intestinal worms were a natural consequence, and so was belief in plants to which curative properties for infestation were attributed. In one modern herbal one finds the following herbs mentioned for the treatment of worms, often without specifying what kind of worms:

garlic—the old reliable "cure" for whatever you've got(!)
  wormseed (chenopodium),
    white walnut, especially for tapeworms,
      hoarhound,
        buck bean,
          red mulberry-bark tea,
            oil from arbor-vitae foliage.

BUT, one does not find the only ancient drug which has survived the scrutiny of scientific medicine, male fern, now listed in the literature of pharmacognosy (recognition of drugs) and recommended for the treatment of tapeworm infestation. Male fern was known to the Greeks and the Romans as a worm medicine, and then appeared to have been forgotten for centuries until it was reintroduced by a French physician, Jabert, in 1869.

A group of aromatic plants, including such familiar ones as lavender, pennyroyal, marjoram, sage, hyssop, peppermint and spearmint, includes some which were valued for a time as vermifuges—thyme and monarda (horsemint). These are the source of a volatile oil which yields the phenol-related thymol. While this has been superseded as a worm remedy by more effective agents, it is valuable in treating skin diseases due to fungus infections.

Modern drugs for treatment of worm infestation include the synthetic hexylresorcinol, effective against beef, pork, fish, and dwarf tapeworms, round worms, whipworms, and pinworms. Quinacrine, a synthetic anti-malaria drug, is useful also against tapeworms. Gentian violet, the dye, is used for treating threadworms which infest horses, cattle, sheep and dogs, and sometimes man. The annoying pinworm, which often seems to haunt families like the seven-year itch, is successfully treated with a synthetic drug *piperazine*. Male fern is second choice in some forms of worm infestation, particularly tapeworms.

Another casualty of folklore beliefs is the idea that grinding the teeth during sleep is a sign of worms. This is now recognized as an indication of emotional tension, and is totally unrelated to worms. These are diagnosed by examination of the excretions for segments in the case of tapeworms, or the worms or their eggs in the search for other varieties.

ADDITIONAL EXAMPLES

The list of specifics in this chapter could be extended to a much greater length, but enough has been cited to establish the point that our ancestors, some more and some less remote, gave us a pretty good start on the first steps toward the fund of knowledge we have accumulated today. True, they made some mistakes, but we are not immune to that possibility, nor will we ever be.

Without bacteriology, virology or chemistry, the early efforts at surgery were surprisingly successful. Despite the "laudable pus" in infected wounds, which was regarded as a sign of healing, many wounded recovered. There were numerous survivals after such operations as cutting for the stone, Caesarean section (performed first by sow-gelders, and *not* on Julius Caesar's mother), trephining of the skull, and replacing the prolapsed uterus. The ancients were not too bad at setting broken bones, so long as the skin was not pierced, and they knew how to replace dislocated joints. They were skillfull at bandaging.

Early attempts at antisepsis, such as bathing the wound with wine or treating it with hot oil were intelligent if primitive approaches. Surgeons learned to control bleeding by pressure, tying or twisting the bleeding vessel or sealing it with a hot iron; the first-aider today is taught to apply firm pressure over the point of hemorrhage, and the surgeon ties or twists the bleeding vessel, or performs bloodless surgery by cautery or freezing. When we smile tolerantly at the ridiculous concept of the weapon salve, applied to the spear or sword instead of the wound, we might remember the many sensible efforts on which we build our more sophisticated modern methods.

Indeed, it might be a wholesome thought to ponder, that many of the literary classics, much of our scientific knowledge, all continuing religious and spiritual faiths, most valid philosophical thought, and no small share of mechanical advances, originated in antiquity or were influenced by historical events in the distant past. Medicine is no exception. Like all the other disciplines, it originated in the minds of independent thinkers and observers, many of whom had little or no education as we know it. One is forced to conclude that there is little evidence to indicate that modern man is more intelligent than were his early ancestors. He is somewhat like the Greek youth, Narcissus, so enamored of his own image that he could not tear himself away.

We are simply blessed with an accumulation of knowledge which others pioneered. And a good part of the time, we do not appear able to use this great fund of information to our own best advantage.

Chapter Eleven

OUR DEBT TO MEDICAL FOLKLORE

You have probably heard the old, old story about the man who approached a friend for a loan, and was refused, whereupon he launched upon a long recital of the favors he had done for the unresponsive ingrate. After a while the latter interrupted:

"Okay," he said, "okay, but what have you done for me lately?"

To get a rough idea of what folklore has done for us in this scientific age, let us assume that you are, for example, a man or woman in the middle thirties, who has seen military service or for other reasons has spent some time in the tropical areas of the world. You have not been feeling well, and you finally decide not to postpone your visit to the doctor any longer. Here is what might happen to you.

First, the doctor will ask you a lot of questions, some of which may make you wonder what they could possibly have to do with your complaints of vague fever, poor hearing and attacks of severe cramping pain in your left side. Having finished the history, the doctor proceeds with the examination. He looks into your nose and your ears with a lighted instrument. He thumps your chest with his hands, listens to it with a stethoscope, kneads your belly while you take deep breaths, taps your knees and your elbows to make your muscles twitch, and takes your blood pressure. He draws your blood—or has it done—for further examination. He then hands you a little bottle and departs to permit you to produce a specimen of urine. Later, he gives you his diagnosis, recommends treatment, and probably touches on your diet, weight and other sensitive topics.

This is only a superficial sketch suggesting the highlights of an average medical examination. Many go much farther, depending on what the basic findings disclose. Commonly there is a need for at least some X rays; it is now routine to ask for films of the chest, plus such others as symptoms and signs may suggest.

What has all this to do with folklore?

In this particular case, with a patient who has been in the tropics, and who is having fever, the doctor at once suspects malaria or other tropical disease. The blood examination in this instance discloses the presence of a parasite called *leishmania donovani*, after Leishman and Donovan, doctors who helped identify it. The disease is called kala-azar or dumdum fever in one form, Oriental sore in another which mainly involves the skin. The treatment is based on compounds of antimony. And here is where folklore comes in.

Fever was once regarded as a disease, not just as a symptom of many diseases, as we know it now. One of the most common causes of fever was malaria, which still remains the world's number-one disease, despite considerable progress in its control. In the example here presented, the distinction between kala-azar and malaria was made by examining the blood, so the modern doctor was able to decide upon antimony rather than quinine or other antimalarial drugs. In the past, fevers were treated simply as fevers, without further diagnosis.

Antimony was introduced into medicine by one Johann Thölde, described as a "chemiatrist" or alchemist, one of the prescientific chemical dabblers who claimed among other things to transmute baser metals into gold. He wrote under the pseudonym of a probably mythical fifteenth-century monk named Basil Valentine. Antimony was used indiscriminately for centuries as treatment of any fever. It was also employed for treating syphilis and, in the case of Louis XIV of France, typhoid fever. The antimony vogue died out, but in 1913 the successful use of tartar emetic (antimony tartrate) for leishmaniasis gave it a specific place in scientific therapy.

If the tropical disease had been malaria, the story of its treatment from folklore days to the present would have read like a romance.

The earliest attitude toward malaria was simply that it was "the ague," a succession of annoying and, sometimes, serious episodes of chills with fever alternating with relative well-being. There was a decided tendency to deterioration of health as time went on. It was sometimes treated by wearing a spider hung about the neck in a nutshell, and by other equally ineffective measures. Malaria was recognizably described in Homer's tenth *Iliad* and attributed to the damp marshes and the destruction of forests, a view precisely confirmed by modern science, but with one difference. The ancients attributed it to the night air arising from such areas as the Pontine marshes near Rome. It remained for the moderns to identify the anopheles mosquito and the *plasmodium malariae* as the cause and means of spread.

About 1630, or earlier, the Countess of Chinchon, Spanish vice-reine of Peru, was reported to have been cured of malaria by Peruvian bark, long known to the Indians. This remedy was brought to Europe in 1632 by Jesuits. Its introduction as a specific cure for lingering fevers marked a turning point in medical practice. At last there was a sure way, evolved from folklore, for the treatment of a large percentage of vague fevers. But not all. Folklore has often given medical progress a real stimulus, but the refining process remained for the scientist to achieve. Doubt has been cast upon the relationship of the Countess to the discovery of Peruvian bark's virtue, but the story persists.

The great eighteenth-century naturalist Carl von Linné had an inkling of the role played by parasites and of the relationship of malaria to water sources. An Italian, Bernardino Ramazzini, described malarial outbreaks in the Po valley near Modena. Giovanni Maria Lancisi, at about the same time, foreshadowed the later discoveries by attributing "swamp fever" to "miasmas" (night air), but mentioned the possibility that the mosquitoes might play a part in the disease. British and Indian doctors in the sixteenth century advanced the knowledge of climate-related diseases. In 1849, a Virginia physician, John Kearsley Mitchell, presented the first definite theory of the parasitic origin of malaria, without knowing about any actual parasite. It should be noted, however, that the transmission of malaria by mosquitoes was suggested in the Sanskrit *Susruta*, the medical annals of the leading surgeon of ancient India, more than two thousand years ago.

The big break against malaria came through the Scottish physician, Sir Patrick Manson, who did much of his work in Formosa.

He proved the part played by mosquitoes in transmitting malaria, previously foreshadowed in conjecture, by infecting his own son. His work was an important factor in furthering the discovery by Sir Ronald Ross of the Indian Medical Service, who identified the female anopheles mosquito as the spreader of the malarial parasite. He found the organism in the stomach of a mosquito which had fed upon the blood of a malarial patient. The parasite had previously been found in patients' blood by Alphonse Laveran of Paris, in 1880.

For many years quinine was the only drug available for the cure of malarial fevers. World War II brought about a crisis when many sources of quinine fell into the hands of the Axis powers at the same time that Allied forces were compelled to fight in malarious areas. Chemical ingenuity provided synthetic substitutes, and these are now widely used both for treatment of malaria and for preventive purposes when residence or travel in malarious areas becomes necessary.

This is a brief panorama of what lies behind your doctor's examination and subsequent treatment of that puzzling fever. There are, of course, many other causes of fever which he must eliminate from the picture before he decides what is wrong with you. And it all grew out of observations, theorizing and experience beginning in a primitive way and gradually developing into increasingly scientific progression.

So much for fever. Now about that pain in the side?

Your doctor's investigation, with the aid of urine examination and X ray, discloses a diagnosis of kidney stone, and the pain has been due to the passage of small stones commonly called "gravel." Surgery is advised.

So we go back again to history and folklore.

In Egypt between 2900 and 3000 B.C., the designer of one of the earliest pyramids was also a physician and surgeon. Then there was that Sumerian mentioned some while back in our story, who listed the herbs and other materials he used in treating his patients. But in the Code of Hammurabi, we learn about the charges a surgeon was allowed for surgery—and what happened to him if the operation proved unsuccessful!

The following is quoted from the Johns translation:

"If a doctor has treated a gentleman for a severe wound with a bronze lancet and has cured the man, or has opened an abscess of the eye for a gentleman with the bronze lancet and has cured the eye of the gentleman, he shall take ten shekels of silver.

"If the doctor has treated a gentleman for a severe wound with a lancet of bronze and has caused the gentleman to die, or has opened an abscess of the eye for a gentleman with the bronze lancet and has caused the loss of the gentleman's eye, his hands shall be cut off."

On the other hand, if the son of a poor man was operated on, the charge was five shekels, and a gentleman's servant would cost the gentleman two shekels. If the slave died, the doctor had to buy another slave for the owner.

Like the Egyptians, the East Indians had attained much skill in surgery by 2000 B.C., and Bible students find strange the fact that nothing in the Old Testament gives information of such interest. The Romans absorbed the skills of all the peoples they conquered, and the military hospitals that have been excavated are not unlike our modern ones. Soldiers of the Empire received the best treatment known to their day when wounds or illness put them to bed. Incidentally, medieval hospitals were less clean, although those for the disabled and the poor had been established by religious communities, and quite separate from the work of the physicians and surgeons.

And so we come to the time of Samuel Pepys of the seventeenth century. Can any one who has read his famous diary forget the amusing account of his annual celebration of his operation for "cutting for the stone"? By his time, removal of kidney and bladder stones was a well-known procedure. A quick rundown of the highlights of progress will provide a good illustration of the way medical science had evolved from the fumbling efforts of pioneers to its present status—and still there is virgin territory to explore!

The first mention of cutting for the stone, properly called lithotomy, starts a lengthy chain of events:

Eleventh Century: an Andalusian physician called Albucasis living near Cordova, published a three-volume treatise on medicine, containing a full description of this operation, and many others;

Twelfth Century: Mundinus of Bologna published a description of this operation;

Sixteenth Century: a Neapolitan surgeon in 1535 gave the first account of a new and improved technique for removing stones from the bladder by an approach from below, between the legs. At about the same time, itinerant operators called *Norsini* performed surgery for hernias and kidney stones, and others known as *Colots* cut for the stone only;

Pierre Franco, a contemporary of the famous French military surgeon, Paré, helped to put the operation on a dignified, professional basis; he was the first to enter the bladder through the belly.

In 1697, a "wandering lithotomist" (Garrison) called Frère Jacques, who began as a "bungling experimenter," became expert by his extensive knowledge of anatomy;

Eighteenth Century: an English surgeon, William Cheselden, introduced the lateral operation (an approach to the kidney from the side), which has scarcely been improved upon even in modern times. He customarily performed lithotomy without anesthesia for the patient;

Nineteenth Century: in 1811, another English doctor, John Bell, published a beautifully illustrated book, with his own engravings, in which he devoted 248 pages to the history of this operation;

In 1820, Nathan Smith of Harvard and Dartmouth, who was the second to perform the removal of an ovarian tumor, pioneered by Ephraim McDowell in Kentucky, became famous also for his success in lithotomies;

In 1824, Charles Aston Key, a pupil of the famous English surgeon, Sir Astley Cooper, introduced further improvements in technique;

A physician named Benjamin Winslow Dudley performed 225 or more of these operations with a very low mortality;

Philip Syng Physick of Philadelphia, often called the Father of American Surgery, is said to have done more lithotomies than any other of his day, including the famous case of United States Chief Justice John Marshall, who suffered with over a thousand kidney stones.

Of course these names and dates may mean little in themselves, except to students of medical history, but they do provide an interesting example of how today's medicine grew from the itinerant "barber-surgeons" of medieval days and the bungling experimentations of a strolling monk to the more sophisticated improvements which came so much later. Today, lithotomy is not usually a serious operation. The more pressing problem now is to keep the stones from forming in the first place, and to prevent their recurrence, once removed.

Your hearing problem turns out to be quite simple; just too much wax in the canal, which is easily removed by softening with oil. But just to be sure, the doctor makes a thorough examination of your nose and throat, where ear troubles frequently start.

Much of the knowledge of the ear and its functions goes back to a sixteenth-century Roman physician, Eustachius, who discovered the tube which now bears his name. This tube connects the throat with the middle ear and equalizes the pressure inside the eardrum with that of the outside atmosphere. It also permits access of infection to the ear, with subsequent complications.

Among many contributors to knowledge about the ear is the French postmaster, Guyet, who first probed the eustachian tube in 1760, and Sir Astley Cooper who first punctured the eardrum for deafness resulting from closure of the tube. Cooper got a baronetcy from performing a slight operation on King George IV. A Hungarian physician, Politzer, was the first to get pictures of the eardrum, and his name is attached to a device and method by which obstructions to the eustachian tube are sometimes cleared, when your doctor pumps air into your nose while you say "hick!"

All this would have been available to you if you had needed it. But there is even more.

The lighted instrument used to examine your eyes and ears depends upon discoveries and developments in a purely physical science, electronics, from which medicine has benefited greatly. But the idea of looking into the interior of the body, in this case the eye, was preceded by development of eye surgery in the sixteenth century, described by the court oculist in Dresden in 1583. This man was originally an ignorant barber-surgeon. But if we really want to go back to beginnings, we must remember Paul of Aegina, seventh-century Greek doctor, who gave a full account of the eye surgery of antiquity—which goes back who knows how far!

The opthalmoscope, for examining the eye, was invented by one of medicine's most outstanding scientists, Herman von Helmholtz. It is but one of many "scopes" by which the doctor explores the internal organs, including the otoscope for the ears. All of them have the common ancestor, the lenses developed by the Dutch draper (tailor) and janitor of the city hall in Delft, who played with lenses and built microscopes and found what he called "little animals" in drops of supposedly pure water. You remember Anton van Leeuwenhoek, mentioned in Chapter Four. His little animals forecast the extensive work on germs which was to crown the medical progress of the nineteenth century.

I have gone into these matters at some length to establish a pattern which is more or less the same in basic structure, varying in detail with the subject. These instances illustrate the often-repeated statement that medical research is like an iceberg—only the summit shows above the surface. Under and behind every breakthrough there lies a story of step-by-step laborious, often disappointing, and sometimes dangerous search and research (note the hyphen indicating repetition and endless patience). Not infrequently, sacrifice of health and even of life was the lot of the medical researcher. Note also the international origin of the various parts of each pattern, from ancient origins to modern achievements. Observe especially the numerous contributions from nonmedical sources, summarized by Oliver Wendell Holmes in these words:

> "It (medicine) learned from a monk how to use antimony, from a Jesuit how to cure agues, from a friar how to cut for stone, from a sailor how to keep off scurvy, from a postmaster how to sound the eustachian tube, from a dairymaid how to prevent smallpox, and from an old market woman how to catch the itch insect. It borrowed acupuncture and the moxa from the Japanese heathen, and was taught the use of lobelia by the American savage."

We have already enlarged on some of these. Let's look at the rest, and then add a number that even the great Holmes did not mention, even though some of them predated his summary just quoted. We do not even need to depart from consideration of the more or less commonplace medical problem presented by our patient, because he benefited from all of them and more.

Gout was first described by Rufus of Ephesus in the first century A.D. Benjamin Franklin contributed to the understanding of this disease. Relationships between gout and the uric-acid content of the urine were first established by discovering the chemical in gouty nodules during the eighteenth century. In the nineteenth century, Emil Fischer, a Prussian doctor, established the connection between gout and the purine compounds (caffeine from tea and coffee, theobromine from chocolate and related compounds from meat, especially the organ meats as distinguished from muscle meats).

Treatment for gout goes back far beyond the understanding of the disease, and was based on accumulated experience of the herbalists, beginning as early as the Greek, Dioscorides. The first recommendation for colchicum was made by Alexander of Tralles, a Byzantine physician of the sixth century. In early times, the common autumn crocus, meadow saffron or colchicum was used sparingly because of its poisonous qualities. The corm first, then later, seeds were used as early as the seventeenth century in Britain. The active ingredient, an alkaloid called colchicine, was isolated in 1820. It remains today the best and, indeed, the only effective remedy for gout; it is useful also for the prevention of attacks. Diet, long regarded as important, is now considered less so, though overindulgences, especially in alcohol, are discouraged.

Undoubtedly your doctor asked you when you had last been vaccinated against smallpox, and quite likely you wondered why; when there is so little smallpox in the United States, it hardly seems worthwhile to be vaccinated. Of course that's why there is so little, but the principal explanation is that the Public Health Service exercises constant vigilance to prevent introduction of smallpox from areas of the world where it is still rampant. This is done by requiring all returning travelers and all others who enter our country to have evidence of a successful vaccination within three years.

Vaccination goes straight back to folklore, plus the sharp eye of an observant country doctor, Dr. William Jenner. Milkmaids, who got skin eruptions on their hands from the udders of infected cows, could nurse smallpox patients without becoming infected themselves, so Jenner tried it out experimentally, and it worked. Neither the dairymaids nor the doctor knew anything about viruses, but they recognized the world's first preventive vaccination.

Before vaccination, efforts at smallpox prevention were made by the process of inoculation. This word has since been used to define all varieties of immunizing procedure, but its original application was to smallpox. A summary of this procedure, published in the Journal of the American Medical Association*, attributes inoculation knowledge to peoples before the "beginning of our chronology." It was used in China and the Indus civilization, in what is now called Pakistan, and Turkey, whence it was introduced into England by Lady Mary Wortley Montague in 1721. Inoculation consisted of introducing dried crusts from smallpox eruptions into the nose, or clothing the subjects in shirts from patients, or by scarifying the arm or forearm and applying the crusts to the scratches.

Cowpox, or vaccinia, the discovery attributed to Jenner, was known "since the earliest recollections of man" to Indians in the Mexican Cordilleras, and was similarly known and practiced by the Eluhat clan in Beluchistan. It was widely known in the dairying regions of Europe. Probably the first person in Europe to vaccinate with vaccinia was a Dorset farmer named Benjamin Jesty. He observed that two of his dairymaids who had previously had the cowpox, were able to attend smallpox patients without becoming infected, so he vaccinated his entire family.

This priority takes nothing away from the fact that Dr. Edward Jenner was the first to place the folk-medicine belief on a sound experimental basis, which established the methodology for immunization principles governing infection. So grows the tree of medical knowledge, often with its roots in the experience of the common people.

The doctor's chest thumping tells him the difference between the resonant sounds which indicate air-filled lungs and the dull ones which indicate solid matter underneath. It helps him to map out your heart and to detect fluid or other abnormality in the chest or abdomen. Before the days of X ray this was the only way he had,

* "Medical Discoveries by The Non-Medical," George M. Gould, M.D. J.A.M.A. XL, No. 22, May 30, 1903-1477/1487.

except for the stethoscope, and we'll come to that. The doctors learned percussion from a physician named Leopold Auenbrugger, who remembered his childhood days in his father's tavern about 1750. He recalled how the level of wine in the great casks in the cellar was estimated by sounding the wooden vessels to discover just how much fluid each contained. Applied to the human chest, it worked out well, and became a standard medical practice.

The stethoscope too has an interesting origin. Physicians formerly listened to the chest by placing the ear directly against the skin. This raised some problems of close personal contact, both in physician and patient, and was unsatisfactory in fat patients whose chest walls did not readily transmit sound. Though one does not find it in formal histories, the accepted story is that young Dr. Laennec, a French military surgeon, observed some boys playing in a lumberyard. They were signaling to each other by tapping on one end of a log and listening at the other. Laennec tried the method first by making a cylinder of rolled-up paper, which greatly improved the sound transmission. Later stethoscopes were made of wood, and still later the earphones and the familiar rubber tubes were added, and diaphragms replaced the older bell applied to the chest. Multiple stethoscopes enabled groups of students to listen to heart and lung sounds while the instructor explained them. Electric stethoscopes refined the listening quality, and today tape recordings can be sent to distant specialists for interpretation. This is but one of the innumerable medical progress sequences rooted in folklore observations.

Another contribution from nonmedical sources came through the inventive genius of an English clergyman, Stephen Hales, who published in 1733 the first measurement of blood pressure by inserting a long glass tube in the artery of a horse and observing how high the column of water it contained was raised with the heartbeat, and how it receded when the heart rested. Now the doctor uses a compact instrument which measures a column of mercury that is much heavier, and requires only a few inches of height compared with the greater height of the column of water. The same measurement can also be made by a mechanical pressure meter registering on a dial.

Examination of the blood as carried out today is the result of many investigations, of which only a few can be cited here as examples.

It would be natural for even the most primitive observers to become interested in blood. They soon found out that loss of blood led to weakness, pallor, breathlessness and thirst, and if not staunched, to death. In their efforts to explain the workings of the living body, they postulated four *elements* and four *humors*. These are more fully discussed in Chapter Four; here it is sufficient to mention that one of the four humors was blood.

The earliest concepts of how blood functioned were confused and erroneous. Arteries were known, but were regarded as tubes filled with air, from which their name was derived. This was because arterial walls do not collapse when the vessel is empty. Since air was one of the four elements, the belief that it came to the body from the lungs through the arteries was logical but wrong. How logical it was is demonstrated by the fact that arterial blood does carry the essential element, oxygen, derived from the air by the lungs, and carried to the tissues in the red blood cells. All this was to be demonstrated many centuries later, but the glimmering of an idea was there.

Even before the circulation of the blood was understood, bloodletting or bleeding was in vogue as a treatment in most primitive eras, when only sharpened flints or fishes' teeth were available as instruments. An English monk, the Venerable Bede, wrote a treatise on bloodletting in the eighth century. In the fourteenth century, an Italian (Lanfranchi of Milan) differentiated arterial from venous bleeding and controlled hemorrhage by styptics, finger pressure, twisting the vessel or even tying it off. It is interesting in this connection to note that the preferred modern method of first aid for bleeding is to apply pressure directly over the bleeding point. Lanfranchi was unhappy that bloodletting was largely in the hands of the barbers! Sucking a wound was common in Europe during the Middle Ages, performed either by the injured person himself, by relatives, or by professional bloodsuckers and by leeches; the latter gave their name to medieval doctors. In the fifth to seventh centuries, the medical code of the Visigoths penalized a doctor in a sum equal to about $225 if he injured a nobleman as a result of bloodletting, and if the patient died he got no fee. As in Sumer, centuries before, if a slave died, the doctor had to replace him with one of equal value.

A somewhat gruesome light is cast on bleeding by the medieval practice of judging the guilt or innocence of a suspect by the spontaneous bleeding of a corpse, supposedly in the presence of the true murderer.

Fifteenth century (1475) bloodletting was systemized according to signs of the zodiac, diagrammed in a figure with exposed viscera and directional lines showing where to bleed the patient during each of the astrological periods (Chapter Two). A somewhat later version is the wound-man (1517), a figure stuck full of knives, darts and swords indicating the proper places for bleeding. Still later illustrations convey the same recommendations by means of tattooing. Many additional "developments" and theories appeared as time rolled on. Bloodletting is now performed only rarely and on a highly selective basis, after careful diagnosis has established its genuine necessity.

Despite the prevalence of bleeding, little was really known about the blood and its circulation. Among the earliest contributions were those of the great artist and scientist of the Renaissance, Leonardo da Vinci. Among his many anatomic drawings, which were ignored from 1512 for more than two hundred years, were those of the major blood vessels, and the anatomy of the heart. Muscles, valves and vessels of this important organ were carefully drawn and included the band of special tissue in its right side which was identified more than three centuries later as the impulse-conducting tissue that regulates the automatic heart action. The anatomist, Andreas Vesalius, also a sixteenth-century figure, ridiculed the idea propounded by Galen that blood "sweats" from one side of the heart to the other through the dividing septum; he also was first to describe aneurysms of the aorta (1555).

The first theoretical concept of the two circulatory systems, that of the lungs and that of the remainder of the body, is credited to an Italian, Andrea Cesalpino in the late sixteenth century, but he offered no convincing experimental evidence. The first and almost final demonstration was provided by William Harvey of England about 1615 that the heart was a muscular pump and that blood had to be pumped out and returned again and again. This he did by estimating the quantity of blood and the speed of its motion. He made observations on himself, on other subjects and on animals. Harvey did not learn how the blood got from the arteries to the veins. That was demonstrated in 1660 by Marcello Malpighi of Pisa, who first described the capillary vessels which make this transmission possible. This was one of the many discoveries facilitated by van Leeuwenhoek's lenses.

One might cite numerous other advances since then, but our theme here is the examination of folk medicine and what our modern knowledge owes to it, so we can merely emphasize again that the complicated instrumentation of modern cardiac diagnosis, the medical treatment of heart disease, the surgical correction of heart and blood-vessel defects, and the knowledge of prevention of heart disease, all hinge upon an understanding of the fundamentals of blood circulation.

So obvious a function as the excretion of urine, with its periodic demands for attention, could hardly escape observation. Urine was regarded by the Roman Galen as a product filtered from the blood by the veins, which might be regarded as a rough forecast of what was later to be recognized as a kidney. The earliest urine examinations consisted of observing the fluid in specially graduated glasses in which the various scums and sediments were observed; the significance of the observations was based purely on theory. A Persian manuscript of the eleventh century sets forth an elaborate procedure for such examinations.

A detailed treatise on urine was published in the thirteenth century by a Byzantine writer, Johannes Actuarius, who perpetuated the Galen theory. Uroscopy, or "water-casting," is represented in medieval art, often showing elaborate urinals borne by pages, with capped and gowned physicians solemnly inspecting the specimens, which they disdained to touch. The urine was sometimes sent to the doctor, who then made a diagnosis by remote control. There were, of course, quacks who made the most of this situation, just as there are today those who fasten themselves upon legitimate science (and not only medicine) like barnacles on a ship.

The first observation of the sweetish taste of diabetic urine was made by Thomas Willis, an English farmer's son. A black-urine disease now recognized as due to abnormal metabolism of certain amino acids was first recognized in 1609. Albumen in the urine, indicative of certain forms of kidney disease, was detected in 1694 by boiling the urine with acetic acid. Urea, an important chemical with clinical implications, was first observed in the urine in 1773, and a year later came observations of sediments in the urine of patients with fever. In 1824 the discovery was made that substances taken into the body with food or as food may appear in changed form in the urine, an observation which led to many more accurate ways for studying nutrition. In the middle of the nineteenth century there were successive discoveries of chemical tests of the urine for sugar, blood, and specific gravity, plus a classic study of urinary stones in bladder and kidney. Today the urine is one of the main indicators of the body's condition and functioning.

No consideration of kidneys and urine would be complete without mention of Dr. Richard Bright, who in 1827 published a description of the principal type of kidney disease, still known by his name. He distinguished between dropsy due to kidney failure and that due to heart disease.

Scabies, the "seven-year itch," which doesn't last seven years, is now known to be due to an itch mite, a member of the arachnid family to which spiders belong. Holmes attributes its discovery to an old market woman, and incidentally he calls it an insect, which it is not. Historically, the first description of the itch mite is credited to Avenzoar, a Moslem physician in Spain. Anyone who has ever attended an Oriental market will have no difficulty in believing that an "old market woman" may well have been intimately acquainted with the itch. Avenzoar lived during the twelfth century, a time when physicians learned much from nonmedical people, since they were not too far advanced in medical knowledge themselves.

Food deficiencies in this day are limited to the underprivileged areas of the world or to underprivileged groups anywhere, and to those who follow bizarre notions about diet. It was not always so. That is what gives significance to the discovery by a sailor of how to prevent scurvy, a condition which need never trouble anyone who can and will eat properly. Scurvy is due to the lack of sufficient fresh fruits and vegetables in the diet. Specifically it is caused by deficiency of vitamin C (ascorbic acid). It was prevalent in milder form in underfed populations, and in prisons or camps where food was poor. It was manifested by bleeding gums, sore bones and joints, hemorrhages under the skin, and in extreme and prolonged deficiency it was fatal.

Scurvy was first described in 1250, though it appeared as early as 1218. It plagued the exploratory voyage of Vasco da Gama, and was prevalent along the coasts of Germany, Holland, and the Scandinavian countries. It occurred also at the siege of Breda (1625) and at Nuremberg (1631) and Augsburg (1632). Yet in 1535, the Iroquois Indians cured scurvy for Jacques Cartier at Quebec with infusions (tea) of the bark and leaves of the hemlock spruce.

In 1740, England's expeditionary fleet against the Spanish in South America under Lord Anson suffered scurvy in 75 per cent of its personnel. In 1779, the channel fleet had twenty-four hundred cases after a ten-weeks' cruise. Doctor James Lind, generally credited with the discovery of scurvy prevention, suffered three hundred and fifty cases in his ship in ten weeks at sea. He refers to orange and lemon juice used by the Dutch in 1564 and by the British mariners Sir Richard Hawkins (1593) and Commodore James Lancaster (1600). Lind recommended these measures and included preserved orange and lemon juice among his suggestions. A British Admiralty order requiring its use banished scurvy once and for all.

Holmes, who wrote his summary of medicine's debt to folk medicine in 1883, naturally could not be aware of medical progress in the future, or he might have omitted mention of lobelia, used for bronchitis and asthmatic conditions by the American Indians. This plant, commonly called Indian tobacco, was later found to contain an alkaloid, lobelin, which was employed for some time in the treatment of the conditions mentioned. The availability of sulfonamide drugs and antibiotics, the recognition of allergies as underlying causes of asthma and the development of antiallergy drugs, have relegated lobelia and lobeline to virtual obsolescence. But I can remember in my childhood the reeking fumes of vaporized drugs for my chest colds, the use of cubeb cigarettes and the inhaling of tobacco smoke for bronchitis.

That leaves only two of Holmes' references, acupuncture or needling and moxa, a primitive form of cautery.

Acupuncture is an ancient Oriental practice employed in China, Japan and other Asiatic countries. It is a form of counterirritation, consisting of puncturing the skin with needles, some sharp and some dull, and sometimes twisting the needle in the puncture. The principle is the same as that of the more modern mustard plaster. The body was charted into minutely defined areas supposedly corresponding to the internal organs, and the needling was performed in accordance with these concepts. The areas were determined by the existing knowledge of the circulation, which was far from accurate until Harvey's discovery centuries later. The first treatise on acupuncture was published in China during the Tsin dynasty about A.D. 200 to 400.

The moxa consisted of small cones of flammable material prepared from the downy leaves of the Chinese mugwort, possibly resembling the cones of Chinese incense now purchasable. They were placed on the skin at points similar to those which governed acupuncture.

Both of these methods were employed against such maladies as rheumatism and gout, and for the treatment of the internal organs related to the skin-surface areas to which their relationship was attributed. Both are now outmoded, but it is interesting to note that the underlying principle was sound, though the details were erroneous. In 1893, an English doctor, Henry Head, demonstrated a relationship between pain and tenderness in specific skin areas and disease of internal organs.

However, Head did not attribute this fact to the circulation; he recognized that it existed by reason of nerve distribution. Skin areas whose sensory nerves came from the same spinal ganglion (nerve center) as do the nerves to the internal organs, manifest pain or tenderness when these internal organs are distressed. This explains the common experience of gall-bladder patients, who may feel the pain in their backs or shoulders rather than directly over the gall bladder. Head's zones, as these skin areas are called, have great diagnostic usefulness today.

Needling was used as lately as 1890 for the treatment of aortic aneurysm, but has now been superseded by replacement surgery. Needling is still practiced by Chinese folk healers.

Counterirritation by plasters, heat and massage remain in use, but on a more scientific basis, to bring the healing power of the patient's blood to affected areas. Cupping and blistering are more rarely employed, if at all, by modern physicians. But we must concede credit for the basic idea to folk medicine.

One more item remains for consideration with regard to the fictitious patient, who might easily have been you or someone close to you. That is the X ray, one of the most modern medical developments, which appeared in 1895 as the result of keen observation by a German-Dutch physician, Wilhelm Konrad Roentgen, who called them X rays—X for unknown—until others named them after him, roentgen rays. These were the results of an accidental observation, as were many other medical discoveries which have revolutionized medicine. Of course their discovery was not a pure accident, though the observation happened unintentionally. The interpretation is what Pasteur referred to as the functioning of a prepared mind.

These are but a few of the innumerable factors which lie behind your doctor when you consult him for what seems to be just a pain, a vague sense of discomfort, or other unpleasant or perhaps handicapping circumstances. His approach is different from that of the folk-medicine pioneers, who dealt largely with symptoms, because they did not understand causes. And still, they showed keen and often intuitive appreciation of unknown factors which later discoveries proved to be sound. This tremendous storehouse of knowledge is available to the physician, who now seeks for causes before he attempts to apply remedies. He can do this because original observers, often without medical training, were alert and intelligent. If they had not been, we would still be living in the dark ages of medicine.

There are many other situations besides the one which has here been explored at some length. In Chapter Ten you will find a selection of the most important of these. Some of them may never touch you, your family or your friends. But some may, and it will be both interesting and profitable to know about them.

Chapter Twelve

POISONS IN YOUR PLANTINGS?

Wherever you live, town or country, cabin or high-rise, it's a good bet that there is someone in your family who prides himself on having a green thumb. Everybody loves a garden; some love to look at them, some to sit and smell them, and some to work in them. Nothing adds so much to a well-designed house as skillful use of flowers, trees and shrubs. Flowers and growing plants grace the interior as well.

Perhaps you want to screen off some of the yard for a children's play area or hide the garbage and waste cans; what could be better than a hedge of box? At the front, you may like some tall flowering bushes next to the foundations—rhododendron perhaps, or azalea. Japanese yews can be grouped at the junction of the sidewalk with the walk to the front door to discourage short cuts. Along the lot-line, mountain laurels help to give privacy without confinement. The gable and side of the house is a natural site for climbing English ivy. You will, of course, have spring flowers—daffodils and wild blue iris—and lilies of the valley for ground cover in that difficult corner where nothing much grows.

In your herbaceous border you will want the gorgeous vari-colored plumes of delphinium and the bell-like foxglove, as well as the deep-blue-flowered monkshood. In front of these you may desire bleeding hearts, larkspur, snow-on-the-mountain, star-of-Bethlehem, daphne and Christmas rose. Add anemones and autumn crocuses in appropriate places. If you need some more big plants, the elephant ear or dumb cane, or the castor bean will fill the bill.

Charming, isn't it? It would look fine on your half-acre, or even in the postage-stamp plot behind your house. There's only one catch. *Every plant named is poisonous!*

Suppose, though, that you live in a high-rise apartment, where all the gardening must be done indoors or on a balcony during the warmer months. Even here you need to be alert to possibilities of poisoning, in order not to experience the ordeal of the woman who was working with her house plants. To avoid the trouble of going for a knife, she bit off a stalk of dumb cane (Dieffenbachia or elephant ear) and suffered severe burning and swelling of the tissues in her mouth and throat. So distended did the membranes become that she was threatened with suffocation, and only prompt help saved her. If she had swallowed much of the plant or its juice, she would surely have died.

Probably few gardeners realize the number of poisonous plants with which they deal from day to day. It is estimated that more than seven hundred poisonous varieties grow in the Western Hemisphere alone. Many of them are not planted intentionally by gardeners, but they appear as weeds, or they may be encountered in woods and fields by careless or curious people who want to touch and taste without realizing their danger. A few of the poisonous plants and herbs are valued garden flowers, as is readily apparent from the description above, based on a charming fictitious garden by Hubert Creekmore.*

The prevalence of poisonous plants is further illustrated in the following listing, based upon a publication of the National Agricultural Chemicals Association† and other sources:

FLOWER GARDEN PLANTS

HYACINTHS, NARCISSUS and DAFFODILS have poisonous bulbs, which cause nausea, diarrhea and vomiting; a a large dose may be fatal. Others of the daffodil family include the amaryllis, basket flower, spider lily, snowdrop, snowflake, zephyr lily, yucca and century plant. The danger from such poisonous bulbs is that they may be mistaken for onions if they

* *Daffodils Are Dangerous*; by Hubert Creekmore, Walker and Company, New York, 1966.

† *News and Pesticide Review*, Vol. 23, No. 5, June 1965, Washington, D.C.

are stored between seasons in such a manner that this error may happen.

Children may also be tempted to sample them if they are left about on benches or elsewhere while undergoing transplanting.

POINSETTIA, symbol of Christmas, pride of Florida and California, has leaves so toxic that just one can kill a child.

CASTOR BEAN: Although it is the source of the laxative castor oil which is merely unpleasant, the castor bean itself and other parts of the plant are powerfully poisonous. A single seed has caused death in children. One or two castor-bean seeds may be enough to kill an adult. The nonpoisonous nature of the oil is due to destruction of the poisonous principle by cooking and processing, but even the most adroit flavoring or disguise will not endear the oil to children. Fortunately, its vogue has declined.

MISTLETOE loses its romantic connotation very quickly if one eats the berries; they have killed both adults and children.

LARKSPUR and DELPHINIUM represent respectively the annual and the perennial species. The young plants and the seeds are poisonous, causing depression, nervous excitement and digestive upsets. Fatalities have been observed. Cattle have been poisoned, but horses and sheep seem to be more immune. Larkspur lotion used to be employed against body lice.

MONKSHOOD (ACONITE) is probably recognized as a poison by more gardeners than are most other plants, but even so their beautiful blue flowers have kept them in many gardens. The poison resides in the root, which should not be mistaken for edible root vegetables like horse-radish or celeriac (turnip-rooted celery). Monkshood poison is an alkaloid, aconitine, which may act very rapidly, causing anesthesia of the tongue, nausea, and a feeling that there is ice water in the veins, together with crawling sensations on the skin, and paralysis of the heart muscle. If recovery takes place, no permanent damage is done. Monkshood has also been used as an arrow poison, and for ridding the premises of rats. A common name for monkshood is wolfsbane.

AUTUMN CROCUS, STAR-OF-BETHLEHEM: Both of these have poisonous bulbs. The autumn crocus, which is really a lily, is perhaps best known as Colchicum, a bulb also commonly grown indoors in a saucer of stones. Its other name is safflower, presently popular with devotees of unsaturated fats. Its poison is the medically useful colchicum, employed in the treatment of gout. Star-of-Bethlehem is used in some parts of the world as food, since cooking seems to destroy the poison; the bulbs are said to taste like chestnuts when eaten roasted, and they are also ground into flour. However, they contain colchicum, and may kill cattle and human beings if they are eaten raw. (Creekmore)*

LILY OF THE VALLEY: Celebrated in the Song of Solomon as the rose of Sharon (though other plants have also been so identified by later botanists), this lovely flower is as dangerous as it is beautiful. The leaves and the flowers contain a substance with an action on the heart similar to digitalis, the heart medicine, which also is poisonous if not judiciously employed. Once believed to confer good sense upon those who rubbed the forehead and the back of the neck with a "potion" prepared from it, it is no longer in medicinal use.

IRIS' underground stems are not extremely poisonous; they produce severe but seldom serious digestive upsets.

BLEEDING HEART, otherwise known as Dutchman's-breeches or golden eardrops, has roots and foliage which may be poisonous in large doses, and is of interest to farmers because it can be fatal to cattle. One of its relatives is the so-called stagger weed because of the way it affects cattle.

DAPHNE, or spurge laurel, also called mezereon is a favorite rock-garden plant with tiny trumpet flowers. The berries are poisonous; a few berries can kill a child. Adults are more resistant, but even for them the plant is a rough purgative.

JESSAMINE berries are the cause of digestive symptoms and nervous-system disturbances, which may be fatal.

FOXGLOVE: This plant is the source of the valuable heart drug, digitalis (Chapter Ten); in overdoses this drug causes dangerous heart irregularity, digestive symptoms and mental disorientation, which may be fatal.

LILIES of many kinds must be included in the list of poisonous plants. The more common kinds include:

* *Daffodils Are Dangerous* (*op. cit.*).

Solomon's seal	day lily	death camass
Easter lily	martagon lily	Madonna lily
glory lily	hyacinth	Turk's-cap lily
squill	tulip	grape hyacinth
Spanish bayonet (yucca)	Osceola plume	fritillary
		camass lily

Before considering the poisons found in lilies, it should be emphasized that some of our favorite edible vegetables are classed as lilies—asparagus, leeks, garlic, onions, shallots and chives. These, when cultivated, are standard foodstuffs; the wild varieties are not as tasty, but rural cooks who know how to use them can make them acceptable. In some parts of the world, the lily bulbs that are regarded as poisonous in this country are cooked and eaten, or may even be eaten raw. The corn lily has an edible bulb, and so does the wake-robin (Trillium) and false Solomon's-seal. Day lily shoots, when young, are edible, and so are the bulbs when fried in batter or added to soup.* But be sure they are ripe!

Various toxic drugs are found in lily roots; some of them affecting the heart. Some have been used in treating uterine conditions. Others, like squills, have had numerous medical uses. For other lilies, see also Fritillaria, yucca, hyacinth and tulip.

ANEMONES (Pasque or Easter flower), commonly called windflower, are modest little plants of great charm, but they contain a caustic juice in the leaves and flowers, so that sniffing them when crushed can cause the eyes to become inflamed, and may bring on headache and fainting. This is an oily yellow juice. A similar substance is found in buttercups.

POPPIES are, as has been known for centuries, the flowers that have supplied the juice used to make opium. This variety is not the poppy celebrated in poetry about Flanders fields, nor that which sometimes is found growing along American roadsides and ditches. The true opium poppy has the law after it! It is not permitted to grow, or to be transplanted from one spot to another in the United States. Poppy seeds used for garnishing foods are quite safe, since they come from ripened seeds. Opium comes from the unripened pod.

* Edible Wild Plants of Eastern North America, Reed C. Rollins, Harper & Brothers, 1958, New York.

SNOW-ON-THE-MOUNTAIN (caper spurge) or Euphorbia gets its name of spurge from the word *purge*, which means, of course, a cleaning out, either intestinal or political. Milkweed juice, and the many other spurges including Croton, poinsettia, castor bean, tung-oil trees, machineel and crown-of-thorns are poisonous not only internally but by blistering the skin. The substance is sufficiently caustic to be used for cattle branding in place of the heated iron, and for removing warts. The cassava root, also a spurge, is the source of cassava meal and tapioca, but must first be freed from its toxic ingredients.

FLOWERING TOBACCO or NICOTIANA is a delightful garden plant, but it is the source of one of the most active of all poisons, nicotine. The danger is increased by the use of nicotine in bug sprays. Tobacco has many poisonous relatives— henbane, black nightshade, Jimson weed and mandrake. Nicotine absorbed from the use of tobacco by smoking, chewing, or as snuff, is absorbed in small amounts, but its poisonous nature is demonstrated by the illness often suffered by adventurous youngsters showing off their grown-up status by smoking. In pure and concentrated form, nicotine is a quick and dangerous poison. The plant *is* attractive, and the flowers are so pretty that a child might be tempted to taste them, with disastrous results. The leaves are so bitter that few animals will touch them.

TOXIC INVADERS OF YOUR GARDEN

A real gardener knows that weeds are uninvited guests among his treasures. Some weeds are mere nuisances, but some are dangerously toxic. Here are the most common ones to watch out for:

DEADLY NIGHTSHADE (*Atropa belladonna*) gets its name from the Greek Fate *Atropos* whose business it was to sever the threads of life, and from the women of Venice (belladonna means beautiful lady) who used the plant juices as cosmetics. Some modern women still use the alkaloid atropine derived from belladonna to dilate their pupils and give their eyes that soulful expression. Taken internally, except in controlled medical dosage, this is a poison. The poison is found in the foliage and the berries of the plant.

INDIAN HEMP (*Cannabis indica*) has a history more than three thousand years old, having been employed in the Orient in a manner similar to tobacco and opium smoking. The common name for the drug is hashish. A drink made from the leaves is known as *bhang*, and sweets, known as *majun*; these are used as intoxicants. This is, of course, the marijuana or reefer weed which has given so much trouble to young people and their elders. The fibers are valuable for making ropes and twine, but there are many other plants with similar qualities which are often mistakenly called hemp. Commercial production of hemp is now prohibited in the United States. A relative plant, black Indian hemp, has qualities similar to those of the foxglove, source of the valuable heart drug digitalis.

HEMLOCK (water hemlock or poison hemlock) is a relative(!) of such useful vegetables as carrots, parsley and parsnips, and such innocent weeds as Queen Anne's lace (wild carrot). Hemlock is often called the most deadly American plant. Other names for it are snakeroot, false parsley, cowbane and beaver poison. The roots have been mistaken (by children) for artichokes, and two out of three who ate of them recovered after severe illness; one died. The poison is a sedative alkaloid which inhibits vomiting, thus complicating efforts at ridding the stomach of the poison. Hemlock was the drug Socrates was required to drink.

HENBANE (*Hyoscyamus niger*) is the source of hyoscine (scopolamine), commonly known as "truth serum," which is a misnomer since it is not a serum. The drug is in the seeds, the leaves and the stems. The action of the drug is to cause disorientation and irresponsible talk and actions; by removing inhibitions, it is helpful in psychiatry to facilitate diagnosis. Along with morphine, hyoscine was formerly used in so-called "Twilight Sleep" for women in labor, but was found dangerously toxic to the unborn child, and so fell into disuse.

JIMSON WEED (*Datura stramonium*) is said to be named after Jamestown, the first American colony. The original settlers were said to have cooked some of the leaves, which looked like spinach, and to have become very silly and unrestrained, not returning to normal for eleven days! Also known as thorn apple, the berries are a dangerous temptation to children. The poison is a narcotic alkaloid found in the leaves and the flowers, as well as in the seeds.

MANDRAKE and MAY APPLE are related plants. The *mandrake* ("man" plus "dragon") has been known since antiquity as an anesthetic. This is the plant that is said to drive men mad if they hear it shriek as it is uprooted, unless they put wax in their ears and make appropriate supplications to the gods. Rachel begged mandrakes from Leah in order that she might conceive (Genesis 30:14, 15). The plant was believed in the Orient to insure male babies, because one variety of it is supposedly shaped like a man; the other, like a woman. The poison in the roots is the same as that of the henbane (hyoscine). The American mandrake is more commonly known as the May apple. The ripe yellow "apple" is edible, but the rest of the plant is poisonous. The active principle is podophyllin, an active resinous purgative derived from the roots.

Comment: It is noteworthy that the potato, the eggplant and the tomato, common food plants, belong to the same family as the nightshades. Potato berries and the sprouting "eyes" contain alkaloids of the atropine (belladonna) group, and are toxic if eaten in sufficient quantity. The tomato, formerly known as "love apple," was long regarded as poisonous; it has now graduated to the more honorable position of "poor man's orange" because of its vitamin C content, and the potato is now valued for the same contribution to the diet. The eggplant, too, is a standard dietary item.

MUSHROOMS are notable both for the value of certain species as edible delicacies, and others as deadly poisons. The poisonous kind are particularly dangerous because of the great difficulty in distinguishing the "good guys" from the "bad guys" in this family. The poisonous alkaloids found in mushrooms are muscarine and sometimes an atropinelike substance. The most dangerous of the mushrooms is the Death Angel, which is deceptively like edible varieties, and the turbantop or false morel. Warnings against mushroom poisoning seem to be among the most futile gestures possible, since poisonings continue to occur in spite of them. So-o-o-o, here, in the hope that perhaps someone may be convinced, are some of the ways to avoid being poisoned:

- take the advice of the Greek Dioscorides: either mushrooms are edible or they are poisonous;

- heed the warning against amateur collecting of wild mushrooms from Creekmore: "The odds in this hobby are heavily against the collector";

- disregard common mistaken notions about mushroom poisoning, such as:

    poisonous mushrooms discolor silver; edible ones do not; (No!)

    you can counteract the poison by adding vinegar to the water in which the mushrooms were boiled, and pouring it off; (Don't try it!)

    mushrooms growing in the fields are safe; those in the forest are not or vice versa; (False either way.)

    any other sure and quick "test" recommended; (Don't trust it.)

Only experienced botanists can distinguish the safe from the poisonous mushrooms with reasonable certainty. The safest procedure is to eat only commercially cultivated mushrooms, and even then, certain precautions are advisable:

- old mushrooms spoil easily, so they should be eaten within twenty-four hours;

- left-over mushrooms should be thrown away, not saved and reheated, because poisonous substances may be formed through disintegration or by infection with bacteria.

The Mexican sacred mushroom, known to the Aztecs as "God's Flesh," is not likely to invade your garden, but it is of interest now because it is the source of a hallucinating drug related to peyote and LSD. Such drugs are legal only in the hands of designated research centers and for established religious ceremonies. Efforts to prevent their misuse are being made by Federal and other law-enforcement agencies.

NIGHTSHADES, other than the deadly *Atropa belladonna*, include in addition to those previously mentioned:

Black nightshade, wonderberry, garden huckleberry;
Woody nightshade, bittersweet;

these contain a complex poison called solanin, which produces a variety of undesirable symptoms; the best attitude
toward them is admiration for their pretty berries.

POISON IVY, OAK and SUMAC are too well known to
need description. Of course you will not *plant* them in your
garden, but you may find them there, so look out for the three
shiny leaves and, in winter, the white berries. Bear in mind the
warning doggerel:

> "Leaves, three,
>   Turn and flee;
> Berries, white,
>   Take to flight!"

Once you have found poison ivy in your garden, wear leather
gardening gloves and keep your legs and feet covered until
you are sure it is all gone. Avoid touching your skin with
gloves that have handled ivy, and take the gardening clothes
off before you get absent-minded and touch them. Do not dis-
pose of poison ivy by burning—the irritating oil is volatile
and can be inhaled.

When you have been exposed, avoid scratching or rubbing,
since this merely spreads the oil. Avoid applying alcohol or
salves, which also spread the oil. When you have been where
there is or has been, or is likely to be poison ivy, even if you
haven't seen or knowingly touched it, a good precaution is *a
warm, soapy shower without hard rubbing* as soon as practica-
ble, followed at once by a rinse and another shower and rinse.
Then *pat* the skin dry—don't rub. If, in spite of all precautions, you get the itching red rash, get medical treatment at
once—it's quicker, safer, pleasanter and cheaper than do-it-
yourself attempts. Ivy "poisoning" is really more like an allergy
than a true poisoning, but it is so universal, in the sense that
few persons escape the effects if exposed, that it is generally
regarded as a toxic manifestation (See Allergy).

POKEWEED or Phytolacca if you're a real Latin gardener, isn't
really a weed, though it isn't exactly a handsome plant either.

Properly prepared, it is a good food—poke salad is a well-known Southern dish. It contains a cathartic alkaloid which acts somewhat like belladonna; only the new leaves and young shoots are suitable for food, and even these, and possibly the berries, have poisoned children. Don't be deceived by the folk-name "cancer root"; it is not a cure or even a remedy for cancers.

And that's the story of the poisonous invaders who may enter your garden without invitation, and flourish there unless you discourage them. There are many other weeds, of course, like the dandelion, which is a pretty flower and would be appreciated if it were not so common, but these are not poisonous. And—their new leaves make quite acceptable salads.

How do the invaders get in? On the wind, by the birds, in fertilizers and mulches, even on people's clothing (burdock, for example). And even the nonpoisonous ones make just as much extra work for the gardener!

ORNAMENTAL TREES AND SHRUBS

WISTERIA, a woody climbing plant with flowers ranging from white to pink, bluish and purple, has toxic seeds and pods which cause mild to severe digestive upsets. Children seem to be attracted to them and many are poisoned.

LAURELS: Rhododendron and Azalea have poisons in all parts of the plants—leaves, flowers, seeds and roots. They cause nausea, vomiting, depression, prostration, difficulty in breathing and coma; the outcome may be fatal.

YEW, which the Roman poet Virgil called "baleful," may have been the poison to which Shakespeare referred in Hamlet, where the murder of the king was accomplished by pouring the poison into his ears. In modern times the importance of this shrub is in its common use for hedges. Untrimmed, these produce toxic berries; even the leaves are dangerous if chewed. A classic case of yew poisoning is that reported in Family Doctor*, where a baby's pram was left too close to a yew hedge, and the curious youngster got the berries all over himself externally and quite a few in his stomach. He was saved,

* "Everything in the Garden"; Peter Robson, M.D., Family Doctor, British Medical Association, London, June 1966.

but death from yew poisoning is common, and usually sudden without warning.

OLEANDERS are beautiful and spectacular, as any visitor will remember who has visited the American Gulf coast or the Scottish gardens of Lord Hume near Coldstream. Yet it is actively poisonous. A warning to picnickers lies in the experience of soldiers who used an oleander branch to stir their soup pot in the absence of a proper spoon, and were poisoned. Eating the leaves is dangerous too. They cause severe digestive upsets and act upon the heart in a manner similar to digitalis. The plant should not be burned, since poisonous particles of resin may be carried in the smoke. Oleander poisoning can be fatal.

BLACK LOCUST trees have sweet-tasting bark and roots and fragrant flowers, and they grow in poor soil and under unfavorable conditions, which has caused them to be planted in many cities. The bark is poisonous, and it is just as well not to taste any part of this tree.

LABURNUM trees, common in England, are referred to by *Family Doctor* magazine as the most dangerous tree after the yew*. The tree is very attractive, with deep-green leaves and clusters of brilliant yellow flowers. At Battle Abbey, near where the battle of Hastings was fought in 1066, a tourist, supposedly American, saw a fallen Laburnum tree and exclaimed, "Oh, what a catastrophe!" The guide immediately said, "No, madam, that's a Laburnum—a catastrophe only if you taste its flowers." The poison is so powerful that just holding flowers or twigs in the mouth causes sickness and dizziness, plus difficulty in breathing and moving. All parts of this tree are dangerous.

LANTANA or RED SAGE is a shrubby plant containing the same poison as is found in other sages such as wormwood (Chapter Five). The green berries affects heart, lungs, kidneys and nervous system, and the effects are often fatal.

JASMINE or JESSAMINE is a climbing vine or a shrub, depending on the species; the flowers are red, yellow or white. The berries are poisonous, causing digestive disturbances and nervous system damage, which may prove fatal.

CHERRY trees, wild and cultivated, may cause fatal illness if the leaves or twigs are chewed; the poison is one that releases

* "Everything in the Garden," (*op. cit.*).

cyanide when it is eaten, causing interference with breathing, excitement and prostration often appearing within a few minutes.

OAK trees carry danger in foliage and in acorns, through a slow-acting poison which damages the kidneys and may not show up for weeks. Acorns have been used for food, but only after being cooked. Children should be warned against chewing raw acorns or oak leaves.

BOX or BOXWOOD is a shrub valued for its glossy leaves and its closely woven network of branches. It makes a hedge that only snakes, insects and very small animals can penetrate. It has a pleasing cedarlike odor, but the leaves are poisonous; pigs have been killed by eating box-hedge clippings. Some types of box grow into trees, and supply hardwood for fine furniture. If allowed to flower, the shrub produces seed pods. The poison (buxine) acts in a manner similar to strychnine. Tea made from box leaves was once valued for growing hair and giving it an attractive brown color. It may actually have done the latter!

BOX ELDER is not a true elder, but a member of the maple genus. Its berries are used for wine, jellies and pies. It is not a poisonous plant and should not be confused with boxwood.

DANGER IN THE VEGETABLE PATCH?

A few edible vegetables may sometimes cause trouble by reason of toxicity, even though classed as foodstuffs. Mention has already been made of potato berries, and of green or sprouting seed potatoes.

Some otherwise toxic vegetables yield nontoxic oils like castor or safflower oil. Bulbs of the autumn crocus may be roasted or ground into flour, and cooking seems to destroy their poison. Some lily bulbs regarded in this country as poisonous are regularly cooked and eaten in other parts of the world. In some instances, young bulbs and shoots are safer than older ones, and the time of year when the plant is gathered may also make a difference. Since it takes some doing to acquire the lore needed for such judgments, it would seem safest always to approach a strange plant gingerly—even a taste of some is enough to cause severe distress or worse.

The cassava root, one of the caustic (s)purges, when detoxified, furnishes a mealy flour as well as the popular dessert base, tapioca. Reference has already been made to mushrooms, both poisonous and edible, and the hazards connected with their improper use.

Perhaps the most important vegetable playing a double role as food and/or poison is the popular rhubarb, delectable ingredient of pies and one of the most pleasant laxatives known. Every cook knows that one eats the stems, not the leaves, but perhaps not all know why. The reason is that the leaves contain a strong acid, oxalic, which can be fatal in relatively small doses. It causes intense local irritation in the mouth, throat and stomach, and this may be followed by vomiting and fatal collapse. Most of the deaths have come during wartime when rhubarb leaves were mistakenly used for spinach, or resorted to in desperation for food.

Many seeds contain the deadly prussic acid (cyanide), and some fruits contain a substance called *prunasin* from the name of the plant genus *prunus*, which includes fruits with stony seeds (apricot, cherry, plum or peach). This is converted into prussic acid when it comes in contact with an enzyme developed in the fruit when it fades or is bruised. The conversion takes place slowly, so that the danger is not so great as is usual where cyanide is concerned. The flesh of the fruit is not poisonous. Another source of cyanide is the bitter almond; as few as five or ten such meats can kill a child, and ten drops of genuine oil of bitter almonds may be fatal.

DANGER IN THE INDOOR GARDEN

When today's old-timers were young, few plants were grown indoors. Perhaps you can remember your home, where there was perhaps a fern or two, the fronds of which you were prohibited from touching. There may also have been some rubber plants, aspidistra or "forcing" bulbs. But not much of anything else. Today many homemakers enjoy puttering, or should I say pottering, with a large variety of plants. Some of these may be dangerous. Let's have a look at some of the more common ones:

The bulb plants—lily, tulip, daffodil and Colchicum—have already been mentioned, along with some others which may grow in the garden during the summer, but are brought indoors when it is cold, to be cultivated either in pots or in a dish of water with a layer of small stones. Ivy, too, may be used indoors for decorative purposes. Indeed, any room is improved with flowers, greens or ornamental plants.

Some of the more popular indoor plants, marketed through flower catalogs or florist shops, have come from distant and often tropical lands, and therefore are not familiar to the people who purchase them or receive them as gifts. This is why physicians in poison-control centers warn that any plant which is not known to be edible must be considered toxic. So must any plant whose characteristics are not thoroughly familiar to you.

Without repeating in detail the poisonous character of the various house plants, here is a list adapted from various sources:

Yellow jasmine, containing strychninelike substances which may even poison the honey made from its flowers;

Jerusalem cherry, whose red or orange berries often tempt children to taste them; they contain several potent poisons;

Crown of thorns, a (s)purge, already described;

East Indian chenille plant has toxic leaves, and so has

Copperleaf, cultivated for its ornamental leaves;

Philodendron, Caladium and Alocasia, related to jack-in-the-pulpit and skunk cabbage, and the potted

Calla lily; all members of the *Arum* family contain oxalic acid, mentioned above in connection with rhubarb;

Dieffenbachia or dumb cane has already been mentioned several times, but it is worth emphasizing here the highly toxic nature of this *Arum*.

Cyclamen, sometimes known as sowbread because pigs dig up the roots, packs a poison to human beings in those very roots;

Night-blooming cereus is believed to contain hallucinating drugs similar in action to the Mexican mushroom, the peyote, and the controversial LSD.

Trailing lantana, related to the bushy outdoor types, for floral hanging baskets, is irritating to the skin when touched and toxic if eaten—usually by children, naturally.

Amaryllis and many of the lilies, commonly found at Easter, Christmas and other special festivals, may have toxic bulbs, as may

Narcissus

Lily of the valley
Hyacinth
Azalea (small potted)
 (these have been described in connection with poisons in the outdoor garden).
Poinsettia, popular at Christmas, is another (s)purge which has caused fatal poisoning in children;
Holly berries are violently irritating to the digestive tract;
Mistletoe berries, too, may be fatal to children;
 There are probably many other plants whose beauty hides their menace, but these are the most common, and the most likely to be encountered in the United States. To venturesome souls who travel to the far ends of the earth, or even to remote areas of this country, one must emphasize the caution:

IF YOU DON'T KNOW WHAT IT IS, TAKE NO CHANCES!

POISONING OR ALLERGY

In dealing with poison ivy, oak and sumac, reference was made to allergy. This is not poisoning. The difference is that truly poisonous plants contain toxic substances which will sicken or kill any individual and most animals—there are some animals which appear to be immune to certain poisons. Allergy, on the other hand, is an abnormal sensitivity of the individual to substances which in themselves are not toxic.

Hay fever, asthma, severe reactions to insect stings, or digestive distress caused by foods which most persons can tolerate, are examples of allergy.

A given person may be allergic to any plant, whether or not it is toxic to others. Perhaps the best example of plant allergy, aside from the ivy-sumac-oak syndrome, is the common allergy to the primrose, an otherwise innocuous flowering plant, deservedly popular indoors or out.

If being near a plant, or eating a food, makes you itch, sneeze, weep or wheeze, it makes little difference whether you are allergic or whether the plant is toxic—either way, you feel ill. The best remedy is to get the plant out of your environment, or yourself out of its vicinity. If neither of these is possible, you may be in for a lot of discomfort, or a long course of medical treatment to overcome your allergy. Sorry!

HOW TO KEEP FROM BEING POISONED

1) If you garden indoors or out, or roam in woods or fields, learn as much as you can about recognizing plants, especially the dangerous ones;

2) Be suspicious of any plant you do not know and understand;

3) Learn what to do in case of accidental poisoning;

4) Keep poisonous plants away from where children play in the yard;

5) "Park" young babies for their sun baths out of reach of all berries or greens;

6) Teach children, either to let alone, or to bring to you, any interesting, strange plants they find, and under no circumstances to put them in their mouths;

7) Keep hedges with toxic berries cut back to prevent ripening of the fruit;

8) Avoid tasting strange berries, chewing leaves or twigs, or eating roots of plants that you do not know;

9) Store out-of-season bulbs far away from edible tubers;

10) Mushrooms: Buy 'em from a dealer, and be safe. Don't buy from an amateur collector.

FIRST AID FOR PLANT POISONING

When some one has apparently been poisoned, waste no time! Quick action is important.

1) Call a doctor while someone else looks after the poisoned person;

2) Follow his instructions, but if no doctor can be reached, these measures can be taken in the following order:
   a. Examine the mouth and throat. If there are signs of burning, vomiting should not be induced. Uncon-

sciousness or convulsions also prohibit the induction
of vomiting. If the patient is already vomiting, no
further measures toward this end are required.

b. When an individual vomits, his head should be lowered
and turned to one side to avoid inhaling the vomitus
into his lungs.

c. In most instances vomiting should be induced, if one
is certain a plant poison has been swallowed. Give a
dose of tincture of ipecac. It is advisable to keep
this drug in the household, and readily available. It
can be purchased in any drugstore.

d. If no ipecac is available, insert a finger in the throat,
after putting a soft object between the teeth to avoid
being bitten; or

e. Dissolve two tablespoons of table salt in a glass of
warm water and require the patient to drink it; or

f. Give him a glass of soapy water.

3) Save the vomited matter for examination;

4) Save whatever you can of the plant involved for identification, to help the doctor decide on more specific treatment.

Measures ordered by the doctor should be started as soon as
he can be reached, without waiting for his arrival, or for the
poisoned person to be delivered to the poison-control center or
a hospital.

It is advisable to keep on hand a few ounces of *activated*
charcoal for use as an antidote. Ordinary charcoal will not do;
neither will burned toast. Do not rely on so-called "universal
antidotes" so often recommended; they may not be reliable. *If you
do not have ipecac or activated charcoal, the best household
staples to use for antidotes are white-of-egg or milk.*

In anticipation of possible emergencies, every family should
have the telephone numbers of a physician, ambulance service,
hospital and poison-control center readily available, that there
may be no unnecessary delay.

If reasonable precautions are taken, there is no need to deprive
your garden of the beauty of even toxic plants. Casualties are
not frequent, but this is small consolation if just one of the
few happens in your family. Perhaps, where there are small

children, it would be best to avoid the more dangerous plants, especially those with pretty leaves, bright berries, bark or stems that intrigue youthful curiosity. Time enough to grow these when the youngsters are older.

Chapter Thirteen

IS FOLK MEDICINE COMING BACK?

History has a way of repeating itself. How many times, as you read or hear the day's news, do you stop and say, "This is where I came in"?

There are signs of a renewed interest in folk medicine, and especially in plants and herbs. Some of this interest is genuinely scientific, and may lead to exciting new sources of useful drugs, or new uses for old ones. It is being pursued by botanists, chemists, physicians, and the research staffs of pharmaceutical manufacturers. The search is worldwide, and it has already resulted in the discovery of new and interesting plants, previously unrecognized among the bewildering variety of growing things which abound in distant jungles, or maybe just around the corner from where you live.

There is, unfortunately, another aspect to the revived interest in folk medicine. That is the exploitation of old, outmoded, discredited or purely fictitious properties attributed to substances which have been found to have little or no value under the scrutiny of modern scientific evaluation. These claims are often interesting and attractive, because they promise marvelous results not attainable by tested medical procedures. They appeal to hope, and cast a ray of light into the darkness of despair that goes with illness for which there seems to be no help. But such hopes are cruel and misleading, like the false signal fires which formerly lured ships to their doom upon rocky shores so that they could be looted. Such looting of ships not infrequently involved loss of sailors' lives, and so does the raising of unrealizable expectations in persons who might be helped if they did not rely on mistaken or misrepresented values attributed to folk remedies.

In giving full credit to the benefits of folk medicine, it is only proper to point out where they have failed, and to deplore the resurrection of curative claims best allowed to rest. Bringing such claims to public attention again through the high-powered means of communication available today is infinitely more dangerous than was the former word-of-mouth transmission of ideas. One mistaken or falsified book, broadcast or news story can reach millions, and deceive a large percentage of them.

One must assume that many if not most of those who give undue weight to supposed values of common herbs do so sincerely, and with a motive to be helpful. Even in the absence of improper motives, misinformation can be dangerous. At the same time, we cannot ignore the fact that there may exist other people who can see a quick buck in promoting such fallacies. There have always been quacks in every generation—political, legal, religious, financial and medical. There is no reason to suppose that the breed is extinct, and there are many evidences that it is not.

When a sufferer seeks relief and puts reliance in any therapy that does not accomplish its purpose, it makes little or no difference to him whether the advice came from an honest person who is himself deceived or mistaken, or from a cynical character with an eye to the main chance, and let the buyer beware.

So let's look at claims now being actively advanced for an herb that is hard to ignore. It has already been mentioned among useful spices. It is a member of the onion family, and its name is garlic. Here is a list of diseases for which garlic is strongly recommended, with few or no reservations, in an herbal published in 1966:

> asthma, whooping cough and other chest diseases
> for blistering skin
> consumption (the old name for tuberculosis)
> dropsy
> fevers
> worms
> hoarseness
> intestinal disorders, diarrheas, headaches
> antibacterial actions
> high blood pressure

dysenteries, constipation, gas and bloating
"body pains," chills and nausea
preventing typhus, diphtheria, and pneumonia
pleurisy
as a nerve tonic
grippe, sore throat
jaundice
rhinitis (runny nose)
colds, lymph-gland enlargements, laryngitis, bronchitis
middle-ear disease
pimples
cancer (in animals)
nervousness
cramps, heartburn
flatulence
vomiting
getting rid of ticks
lip and mouth diseases
tumors, ulcers and wounds
hysteria
sciatica
paralysis
retention of urine

Many of these symptoms come and go, with or without treatment. This is why useless remedies get an undeserved reputation. But some items in the preceding list may be warnings of serious disease, especially if unreliable treatment causes a loss of valuable time. Let's have a look:

- *dropsy* can mean heart, kidney or liver diseases, severe anemia or serious allergies;

- *hoarseness*, if persistent, is one of the warnings of possible cancer of the larynx and vocal chords;

- *tumors* (*lumps*) are one of the seven warning signs of possible cancer, anywhere in the body;

- *diarrheas*, dysenteries, constipation, gas and bloating may be due to many serious abdominal conditions, including ulcers and several varieties of cancer, as may cramps, heartburn and vomiting;

- *ulcers* that do not heal, or heal and return, are another of the seven signs that suggest suspicion of cancer;

- *retention of urine* may indicate a number of bladder and related conditions, often requiring surgery;

- *fevers, chills and nausea* are signs of infection or, in some instances, poisoning;

- *jaundice* always indicates the possibility of serious liver or gall-tract disease demanding prompt attention.

The dangerous folly of dosing these potentially grave or lethal conditions with a particular spice recommended from nonmedical sources, with direction which merely underlines the ridiculous character of the whole matter, should be apparent. It would be funny if it were not so hazardous.

So, how does one use this panacea, garlic? One puts a poultice of the chopped vegetable on the soles of the feet for whooping cough; sticks a garlic clove in the ear for earache, and holds one in the mouth all day and night except while asleep, for colds. It is touted also for application directly to wounds, or the juice is taken internally, with or without onion juice. And believe it or not, the evidence of the efficacy of garlic is that it appears on the breath!

In three standard medical dictionaries, I found the following definitions of garlic:

Stedman, twenty-first edition, 1967; garlic: Allium,

Dorland, twenty-fourth edition, 1965; no mention,

Gould, twenty-first edition, 1951; garlic: the fresh bulb of allium sativum. It contains a volatile oil consisting of allyl compounds of sulphur.

None of these dictionaries gives any important therapeutic uses for garlic, as they do for many other substances. Stedman defines *Allium* as garlic, and credits it with a content of irritating oil with an antiseptic action; used as a seasoning and to promote sweating, kidney action and mucous-membrane secretions. Garlic is not among the drugs recommended in the literature on modern therapy, either as garlic or as Allium.

And so I turn to the herbal literature. In a 1961 textbook of pharmacognosy I find no reference to garlic or to Allium. A 1963 herbal lists garlic, and repeats some of the more conservative recommendations in a somewhat guarded manner, and with the caution that the medical profession does not agree. A physician connected with the National Cancer Institute admits "evidence of antitumor activity" in experimental animals when extracts of garlic and bloodroot are administered; this is a long way from a recommendation, expressed or implied, which should lead persons with undiagnosed tumors to treat them with garlic poultices.

In case this appears to be a big storm over a small matter, let it be emphasized again that when someone with a serious disease such as many of those listed previously, or with vague symptoms that presage the possibility of such diseases, relies on unproved claims, it makes no difference whether the claimant is honest or dishonest, credulous or predatory, naïve or calculating. The victim is like the motorist who had the right of way and turned out to be *dead* right.

Since there is no point in beating a dead horse, I will just add a few brief additional items to the list of herbal claims now being revived, for which there is little or no warrant at this time:

comfrey (see page 279 following)

myrrh, one of the Biblical balms mentioned among the three gifts of the Magi to the infant Jesus, is a gum derived from the bark of a shrub indigenous to the Red Sea region. It was used by the Egyptians for embalming. It is a pleasantly perfumed substance, formerly valued and presently being offered again as an antiseptic, tonic and stimulant, and for rheumatism, lung and chest diseases, sore mouth and gums, ulcers and tender nipples; the U. S. Dispensatory lists a few local uses in the mouth, and that is about the extent of its value;

papaya, the fruit of the tropical pawpaw tree, is the source of an enzyme or ferment, papain, which is a useful meat tenderizer; the fruit is a good source of vitamins and has a pleasant taste; but now the juice is being incorporated into tablets and promoted for stomach troubles, bleeding and intestinal worms. There are better and safer approaches to the treatment of these symptoms, which may grow serious if not properly cared for. Recommendations originating in India, for application of papaya poultices made from the leaves, to the breasts of nursing mothers, or locally for piles, enlarged liver or spleen, and to the skin for warts, freckles, pimples and corns, are not endorsed by American physicians.

LAXATIVES

Open any herbal and you will find formidable lists of laxative and purgative simples, teas and oils, dating from the days when *physick* meant medicine and medicine meant laxative. Whatever ailed the individual, he was likely to be physicked, vomited, bled, or all three. The most common, of course, was the physic, which was supposed to be good for everything from a cold in the head to appendicitis, which was not recognized as such until late in the nineteenth century. Commonly called intestinal fever or typhlitis, any such distress should be relieved by an enema, rather than "physicked." If patient is not relieved, a physician should be consulted—at once!

Even in the old days, there were distinctions between agents that stimulated bowel action. The relatively mild and gentle variety were called laxatives or aperients; the more drastic ones, purges. There was a time in medicine when powerful purges such as jalap and podophyllin were widely employed, and became known by such descriptive titles as "thunderbolt." The Egyptians and the Greeks purged themselves every month, according to Herodotus. The Druids of Britain regulated purgation and other drugging by the moon. Purgation calendars, printed in the same type as the Gutenberg Bible, were among the earliest-printed medical articles (1457); these calendars were often related to the signs of the Zodiac.

Common herbs used as laxatives included the following classifications (* denotes caution as to poisonous qualities):

Seeds which absorb water and swell	Oils which lubricate or irritate	Teas or decoctions (tisanes)	Fruits or berries
wormseed	olive oil	chicory	figs
plantago	castor oil	burning bush*	prunes
(psyllium)	linseed (flax)	white ash (U.S.) ⚑	red mulberry
flax		red mulberry ⚑	pears
		buckthorn ⚑	rhubarb
		yellow dock @	
		dandelion @	
		violet @	
	⚑ bark; x leaves; @ roots	camomile x	

More powerful than laxatives, are cathartics and purges; the following are most commonly listed (* denotes caution, poison):

Cathartics	*Purgatives*
dogbane root	buck bean leaves tea (large doses)
swamp-milkweed root	May apple (jalap)
wild-senna leaves	stillingia root (oil)
burning-bush root and stem bark	field bindweed
boneset tea, upper leaves and flowers	swamp-milkweed root
	celandine juice*
blue flag (iris) root tea	white-pine buds, tea
buck bean leaves (small dose) tea	Mexican-poppy juice
stillingia (euphorbia) root tea	wild indigo
field bindweed	
Mexican-poppy juice	
physic root	

Chemical entities introduced into medicine and adopted for popular use hardly come under the heading of folklore, but their use has become so traditional in some instances that they should be mentioned here. Perhaps the most common of these are Epsom salts, Glauber's salts, citrate of magnesia, milk of magnesia, phenolphthalein (a laboratory chemical indicator) and the mercurial calomel. The latter especially has become a favorite remedy in certain areas for almost any ailment that could be even remotely connected with digestive functions.

With the development of better understanding of digestion and elimination, physicians have realized that purgatives and, to a lesser extent, cathartics are too violent and irritating in their action to be beneficial, even while they secure results in quick time. In some forms of intestinal disease, such as ulcerative colitis and appendicitis, they can be dangerous and even fatal. The milder laxatives are safer, but they disrupt the normal rhythmic action of the bowels, and the evacuation they produce is followed by a phase of inaction which is mistaken for constipation. This triggers the taking of more laxative, until a vicious habit is established which is hard to break.

Physiologists have demonstrated that intestinal rhythms vary with the individual, and even in the same person under differing circumstances. They have also recognized that daily evacuations are not a necessity for everyone, much less the three-a-day recommendation mistakenly promoted by overenthusiastic health educators. As a rule, if fruits, vegetables and whole grains are eaten regularly, supplying sufficient indigestible-fiber residue to provide bulk, and good habits of elimination are established, no laxatives are needed by normal persons, except in unusual circumstances. Liberal use of fruit juices and other fluids is helpful, too.

No one can give an accurate guess, but it is certain that enormous percentages of the laxative preparations regularly used by the American people are beneficial mainly to the manufacturers, advertisers and sellers of the products. To the users, they are needless, and in some instances harmful. The use of laxatives should be limited to occasions when they are medically advised, or when the need is obvious. Their use should never become habitual.

SARSAPARILLA

Sarsaparilla, popularly known as sweetroot, is Spanish for thorny vine. It was a popular remedy for many years, long before most people living today can remember. It was used for treating venereal diseases, even for syphilis as late as 1928, though not by physicians. In 1928, the arsenic drugs commonly known as 606 and derivatives were available. The sweetroot was also popularly esteemed for rheumatism, scrofula (skin tuberculosis) and other skin diseases, including psoriasis. The latter is a common, scaling, itching eruption which disfigures and embarrasses the patient. It is resistant to treatment despite extensive research. It goes through periods of improvement, especially during the summer months. Any remedy in use at the time of such improvement is usually credited with a cure—until the disease returns. This is the experience of many patients with variable or self-limiting diseases. The situation is an obvious invitation to the quack, alert for a quick buck.

Sarsaparilla became a popular remedy during the nineteenth century as a so-called blood purifier and tonic, often promoted with a special slant which assured good sales. I can remember the ads which mystified me when I was a boy; they featured a bearded "physician" in a white coat, holding up an admonitory finger and announcing, "I cure men." It was some years before I realized that he was implying the restoration of sexual vigor.

The history of sarsaparilla starts in 1568 with its mention by a Spanish physician named Monardes. The Amazonian Indians used a preparation made from the cordlike roots of one of various species of this tropical plant to treat chronic fatigue or "let-down" feelings. As a folk medicine it promised much and delivered little, but now there are reports indicating the discovery of hormone sources in the root, particularly the male hormone, testosterone, and the adrenal hormone, cortisone. As a result, there is now evident a new form of promotion for sarsaparilla and the encouragement of self-medication with potent hormones, which is potentially dangerous. Testosterone tablets are reported as being on the market in Mexico and South America, with the same old claims to cure men. If these tablets are sufficiently active to be effective, they are dangerous in the hands of the inexperienced. If they are not, they are a hoax.

Commercial exploitation of medical claims, true or false, creates difficulties for scientists in their quest for new sources of useful drugs, and for the synthetic modifications which can be based on natural sources. Sarsaparilla is a good example of the new look in medical folklore. Scientists are showing a more openminded attitude toward traditional claims for folk remedies, recognizing the numerous pointers which lie hidden behind the common practices of nonmedical or even primitive peoples. Governmental agencies have joined industry in the effort to uncover new sources of drugs in the plant world. It is too bad that public understanding is in danger of being confused by misrepresentations circulated by irresponsible promoters.

Drugs from plant sources promise lower costs for important medications, and more plentiful supplies, than have been possible from animal glands and secretions, or from synthetics. Many of the more important remaining areas which lie unexplored exist in regions difficult of access. Often they are in the territories of emerging nations. In these jungles, rain forests, mountains and deserts, lies the hope of greater prosperity for these new nations through discovering, harvesting and perhaps processing the useful drugs which they may yield. Mexico has already profited to the extent of many millions through the gathering of wild yams, and their subsequent processing has yielded additional revenues. Scientists are beginning to be disturbed at the prospect of losing some resources forever through the spread of civilization into hitherto untapped country.

Many plants in addition to the wild Mexican yams have been found to be sources of steroid compounds, related to cortisone. These steroids, which resemble cholesterol, occur in onions, asparagus, agave and yucca. They are not found in the sweet potato, which is sometimes confused with the yam. Yucca and agave contain saponins, soapy, lathering agents which Indians used in a manner similar to soapbark from the soapbark tree previously mentioned (Chapter Five). Chemists can modify saponins to approximate the composition of hormones from animals. The modified products, called sapogenins, provide the base materials for sex and cortical hormones now in use. It is these preparations which help the physician govern the menstrual cycle. They are the basis for the "Pill" which makes family planning possible. In the normal individual, these hormones play a large role in determining sexuality, controlling pregnancy and maintaining normal health.

The fantastic true story of yams, of sarsaparilla and of other plants in which valuable source materials have been found, is told in Margaret Kreig's book *Green Medicine*.* So are many other important and fascinating accounts of similar sequences along the complicated path from the crude source of the finished product. Among these stories are the following:

- first steps toward the possible discovery of drugs against cancer from yeasts (first used in 1500 B.C.); garlic, bloodroot, mistletoe, American mandrake, and periwinkle (a myrtle);

- rauwolfia (Indian snakeroot), first chewed by East Indian holy men; used as a soothing syrup for babies; now a drug valuable for treating high blood pressure and some mental diseases;

* *Green Medicine* (*op. cit.*).

- the hallucinating drugs (cactus, mushrooms, morning glory, ergot and marijuana) which have potential value in research and therapy entirely aside from their current popular abuse;

- a look at the apparently inexhaustible and virtually unexplored riches of the sea, which have already given us the essential mineral, iodine, the antirachitic vitamin D, a better understanding of allergies and shock reactions, and now promise antibiotics from plankton and algae, and hormones which may be able to change one sex into the other.

But not today or tomorrow. Here the old proverb applies—there's many a slip 'twixt the cup and the lip. A promise may be a long way from fulfillment. When you read of new avenues of research opening up, do not be tempted to jump to conclusions. "Possible" antitumor activity found in a plant derivative and observed through animal experimentation, is a far cry from successful cancer treatment in man. There are many intermediate steps. Early hopes may end in disappointment. But a beginning must be made somewhere at some time. We have not arrived at our present formidable array of knowledge by sitting on our hands. Even if one hope fails, another may appear; new drugs may be useful in unexpected ways. Cortisone and its derivatives did not prove to be the long-awaited cure for arthritis suggested by their dramatic introduction, with crippled patients dancing in the wards. But a broad range of usefulness has opened up for them in a wide variety of medical situations.

When you read of a new discovery, be sure that you do not read your own hopes into it, leading you to expect too much. Always read the whole article; not merely the headlines and the opening paragraphs. The cautionary statements usually come nearer the end.

COMFREY

From sources of dubious nutritional advice comes a puff for a root called comfrey or borage, which means a "healing water plant." This has been described in sixteenth- and seventeenth-century herbals as useful for those who spit blood, for healing wounds and allaying inflammation, ulcers and gangrene—all conditions for which there was no successful treatment in those days. Case reports of questionable authenticity reported in newspapers, plus testimonials of an uncritical character from nonmedical and often poorly educated persons, now suggest the use of comfrey for asthma, removal of warts, internal tumors and other unlikely medical miracles. The borage root has been found to contain allantoin. This substance is used medically to assist in wound healing, but the suggestions now current that it will cure malignant tumors, asthma and other conditions are fantastic at best. At the worst, they are dangerous, since waste of time in procuring adequate treatment for such serious conditions is one of the principal causes for needless deaths and unnecessary suffering.

GRAINS and SEEDS

Among other claims promulgated in the byways of medical and nutritional "science" are the following:

- exaggerations of the known vitamin and mineral values of sprouted grains (malt);

- overblown virtues assigned to grain chaff, of which the true values are well understood by scientists;

- seed extracts for treating mental diseases, relieving tensions and aiding childbirth;

- pumpkin seeds, or flesh, for worms or for urinary disorders; and for "vitalizing" the prostate gland in elderly men; and for postponing old age;

- sesame seeds for piles and constipation;

- sunflower seeds for preventing malaria, for helping the eyes and treating bronchitis, as well as for keeping horses and cattle in prime condition;

- watermelon seeds for kidney and urinary problems.

No sensible person questions the value of many varieties of seed in the diet, since seeds are the source of many of our most valuable nutrients. But it is specious reasoning to extend the recommendations for the normal use of such substances, as food, to embrace medical claims for curing serious disease. This is true especially when the support for such proposals is couched in the vague and unconvincing terms which abound in pseudo-scientific literature; for example:

- we are told that . . .
- it has been recommended for . . .
- users have found that it . . .
- "case reports" from (remote and vaguely identified foreign regions)
  (unidentified physicians or "researchers")
  ("associations" of questionable reliability)
  (commercial, food-fad sources)
  (undated reports)
- rehash of ancient superstitions . . .
- we don't know just how it works . . .

There are plenty of reliable sources, and sufficient material about which we do know how it works, that we need not rely upon such unsupported "evidence." When the real scientist makes a report he identifies himself, cites his references accurately, quotes sources of established reliability, and gives dates and publication references so that his statement can be checked.

One might go on at great length discussing the vaunted qualities of licorice, passionflower, valerian, papaya, the citrus fruits, goldenseal, ginseng, rejuvenating herbs, alfalfa, and many others already mentioned. The support for exaggerated claims for such herbs comes from uncritical (usually nonscientific) observers, adherents to tradition and superstition, borderline "scientists" out of step with their colleagues, commercial promoters, and antimedical "healing" cultists who must endeavor to explain their exclusion from accredited scientific circles.

CLAY EATING

One of the more interesting survivals from traditional folklore, which has no tinge of commercialism or self-interest, is the persistence in the rural South of clay eating. According to doctors at Duke University, Durham, N.C., the practice of eating clay is widespread among Southern Negroes, and is related to the starch-eating habit, which also is fairly common. One instance is reported of a woman who ate starch—ordinary laundry starch—during pregnancy in order to control heartburn. She ate as many as four or five packages a day during several pregnancies. Starch eating has also been reported from other areas.

Now the daughter of the woman mentioned above, aged thirteen, unmarried and pregnant, eats clay; she likes it better than starch. She has been eating clay since she was a little girl. Not just any clay. There is a special brand of white clay, which is so highly prized that those who know of a good deposit of that variety try to keep it secret. Sometimes they dig so deeply into a favorable vein that they have to be held head downward in the hole to get at the clay, wiggling their toes as a signal that they are ready to be pulled out.

Some clay eaters carry pellets of clay with them, and eat them like candy. Sometimes they realize that eating clay gives them "bathroom troubles," constipation or intestinal obstruction. Doctors say it is like smoking or other habits, and that the clay eaters eat clay because they have no better substitute for oral gratification, at least none which they can afford, like candy and soft drinks. Clay eating has serious consequences in pregnancy in terms of deformed babies and miscarriages.

The clay eaters have special preferences for white, red or yellow clay, or for eating their favorite clay wet, or baking it dry before eating. Clay is sometimes kept in the oven continuously, ready for eating. Some persons will travel miles for a special clay said to increase sexual capacity. Some clay eaters consume handfuls of clay a day, others only a few pieces. A study in Alabama showed the range of clay consumption from one fifth of an ounce to over four and one half ounces a day. The habit is extremely difficult to break, according to the physicians at Duke University.

Clay eating is a form of dirt eating, medically known as *pica*, commonly practiced by children of all races and all social and economic levels. It includes the eating of excreta and the common habit of eating plaster chipped from the walls, as well as many other inedible substances. This has been popularly regarded as an instinctive effort to supply nutrients demanded by the body but not supplied by the diet. The need for calcium and the presence of lime in plaster are considered significant. This view is no longer accepted. The best explanation for the pica habit is the psychological one advanced by the Duke physicians, namely, the need for gratification of unfulfilled desires. This is an emotional problem susceptible only to indirect approach to the basic cause, which is frustration with life and its problems.*

MISCELLANEOUS BELIEFS

Other ancient folklore beliefs which persist or are reborn, include the following:

- curing venereal diseases by sexual intercourse with a virgin or immature male;

- life for the young is shortened by sleeping with an older person;

- sleeping with a well person will cure the sick and sicken the partner (this is a half-truth, since communicable disease can be transmitted to one while the other recovers);

- transferring disease to another by placing hair and nail clippings of the afflicted in a bag and placing it under a neighbor's threshold;

- to cure a boil, rub it with a flint stone, replace the stone in the ground; go away and don't look back;

- cure a corn by drawing blood from it, drip it on a cloth and throw the cloth away; the unwary finder gets the corn (this is a variation on the innumerable wart and corn cures; it also exemplifies the common use of rags and pieces of string as disease-transfer vehicles);

- cure chills, warts and other conditions which can be described numerically by counting them, tying the corresponding number of knots in a string and throwing the string away;

- to cure toothache, tie knots in a fishing line (Newfoundland);

* "The Clay Eaters": Perry Craven, *Morning Herald*, Durham, N.C., April 30–May 3, 1967.

- cure fever by mixing nail parings with tobacco and roll into a cigarette, drop the cigarette at a crossroads "without looking up" (Portugal);

- numerous instances are reported of causing pain to pass from one person to another through prayer;

- to cure jaundice, place a pot of tasty-looking food at a crossroads; whoever looks into it gets your jaundice;

- cure a goiter by rubbing a dead person's hand over it three times;

- keeping birds or other pets in the room to prevent disease is commonly practiced in many parts of the world;

- keeping animals in the sickroom to draw the disease to themselves:

  > guinea pigs (Slavic and Germanic); rheumatism;

  > goldfinches or turtledoves for "consumption" (Oldenburg);

  > cats for asthma (Nebraska); when nine cats have caught your asthma, you're cured;

- frogs will cure chills and felons; sometimes you must bury the creature head down in the ground;

- treat convulsions (West Virginia) by plucking breast feathers from a live pigeon and holding the bird to the pit of the stomach until the victim recovers;

- treat whooping cough by holding a toad in the mouth (Ireland) or a live fish (Pennsylvania);

- treat tuberculosis by swallowing a live louse, which is supposed to eat the germ (Rio Grande valley);

- treat epilepsy by rubbing the patient with a live pig; the patient sweats, the pig dies;

- placing animals, insects, spiders, et cetera, in a bag or other receptacle which can be hung about the neck is a common practice; examples are a live caterpillar for whooping cough, a spider in a thimble, or other similar combinations which vary from place to place;

- put two cockroaches in a jar to cure measles; when they die, the measles is cured (as it would be anyway in most cases) (New York).

The interesting article from which these facts have been selected, closes with this amusing example of medical lore from New York State:

"One who is afflicted with chills and fever should wrap himself tightly in a sheet, run around the house three times and jump under the bed. Thus the chill jumps into the bed, and he misses it."*

Perhaps you have never heard of many of these ideas. They may seem outlandish to the sophisticated mind, but to isolated folk with little education and limited contacts, they can be very real. They are explained by certain basic facts which are outside the experience of those who adhere to these and similar beliefs, and who do not understand that:

- coincidence differs from consequence; thus it may happen that someone who sleeps with an older person may die prematurely, but it does not follow that this was because of that circumstance;

- transferring disease by hair, nails and similar means is a modification of the ancient idea that a picture or an image of an enemy can be used to cause its original to sicken or die;

- corns, warts, chills, jaundice and other conditions not infrequently recover without treatment, so that whatever is done by way of magical transference is explained very simply by the well-known self-limitation of many illnesses;

- when an individual recovers from an epileptic seizure or other acute illness, he is likely to perspire and go to sleep, whether he is rubbed with a pig or not;

- cockroaches or other insects in a bottle are pretty sure to die by the time a measles patient recovers, which is usually

* *The Magical Transference of Disease:* in Folklore Studies in Honor of Arthur Palmer Hudson; North Carolina Folklore Society, Chapel Hill, 1965.

in about seven days; the instances when the patient dies or has serious complications are unlikely to be remembered in the light of the numerous supposed cures, which were really normal spontaneous recoveries;

• finally, there is the will to believe, coupled with the humane desire to be helpful and nurtured by the hope of success, which in the absence of more professional help, is really all that the old-timers had going for them.

In addition to the persistence and revival of unfounded folk beliefs, there is another and quite different development of great interest. This is the scientific search in far corners of the world where primitive nature is relatively undisturbed, for new and perhaps highly significant plant and herb sources of medicinal agents which may contribute to further medical advances. This is not to be confused with the slipshod promotion of unproved conjectures or the slick peddling of nutritional and medical nonsense for the profits derived from fleecing the gullible. It is a turning back to folklore in all parts of the world in a search for new plant sources of known drugs, and in the hope of finding new ones as well.

The folklore of distant areas, often isolated and difficult of access, is being explored. Perhaps some of the folk remedies not yet analyzed, will be found to contain valuable active principles. Quite possibly these may appear in unexpected sources. During a voyage on the Queen Mary, I fell into conversation with one of the ship's physicians, and happened to mention my interest in medical folklore. He introduced me to the staff captain, who has a relative in South Africa engaged in the sale of folk remedies to natives. They come from miles around, on foot, to buy the materials their native doctors have recommended. Some of the materials, of which the captain showed me samples, were:

• snakeskins, used to ward off evil spirits by burning the dried skins in the hut;

• *ciswadi*, a huge onion, of which the dried skin is used as a healing wrap for the penis after circumcision, a rite which takes place at the age of nineteen; the complete ceremony lasts three months; the youth wears the foreskin over his thumb until the wound heals;

- *Bantu snuff* is used mainly by women, to clear the nasal sinuses; it is a brownish powder carried in a small, beaded bottle suspended on a cord so that it hangs between the breasts;

- *bangalala bongo* is a brownish, rough bark used as an aphrodisiac; powdered and taken with water; this is much in demand in the United States, but its importation is forbidden;

- *sibhara* is a bark used to "loosen a tight chest";

- *Rosalina*, a sweet-smelling bark, is also taken in water for chest conditions;

- *Nukana* bark is boiled in water, cooled and taken internally for chest conditions; dose, two to three drops;

- *Vinbela*, python fat, a white, solid substance is rubbed on the head at night "to glow and keep off evil spirits";

- *hippopotamus hide* is rubbed on sores, to heal them;

- *monkey flesh* is sold as a medicine, not a food;

- *I Yesa le Gudisa*, a dark, mottled, beanlike seed which will blister the skin, is a laxative which is said to be capable of blasting the insides out, but the natives "have strong stomachs";

- *Mmcamamfenc*, a black powder obtained from baboon's urine, is used by pregnant women from the sixth month to term, a teaspoonful of the powder to a bottle of water, size unspecified; dose a teaspoonful three times a day.

An interesting sidelight on the psychology of this business is that the store is kept "primitive" but clean, since the natives would lose confidence if it became "a white man's store."

Before shrugging off these items, it might be well to reflect that reptile skins have been found to contain active chemical principles; bark of the cinchona tree gave us quinine and that of the willow produced the basis for aspirin; inhalants have been found useful in treating diseases of the nose and chest; many plants have laxative qualities; and animal urine has been the source of many of the sex hormones now in use.

It is to sources like these that the world-wide pharmaceutical industry is turning for new drugs and additional sources for drugs already known. These projects are the subjects of the fascinating book, *Green Medicine*, by Margaret Kreig, to which the reader is referred for first-hand information as well as entertaining reading.

The scouts whom pharmaceutical manufacturers and scientists are sending into the far corners of the earth, face rigorous challenges of climate, difficult terrain, drought and flood, accident, voracious insects, poisonous spiders, venomous snakes, carnivorous fish, loss of equipment, scarcity of food and becoming lost in the wilderness or marooned through failure of transportation by land, water or air. Mrs. Kreig, who looks more like a debutante than a rugged frontierswoman, has experienced these hazards in person, and relates them vividly in her book.*

Here are a few of the highlights of the renewed search for sources of important drugs required in huge quantities at prices which are not prohibitive:

When cortisone first crashed into the headlines as an almost magical treatment for rheumatoid arthritis, it took the bile from forty head of cattle to produce enough drug to treat one patient for one day. A three weeks' supply cost $18,000 for one patient. There had to be another way. Several American pharmaceutical manufacturers, with co-operation from the Government, scoured Africa in competition with Swiss expeditions to find specimens of an arrow poison derived from a flowering plant, *Strophanthus*, which had already yielded a drug useful in treating certain heart conditions. The search came to nothing. But success came from another quarter; what Mrs. Kreig calls taming the wild Mexican yams, which are now an important source of steroids. I wouldn't think of spoiling her story by telling it here; it is too good to miss. Steroids are playing an increasingly important role in medicine, even in the treatment of cancer of the female breast with a male hormone. The more plant sources that can be found for such important drugs, the cheaper they can be made for the patient.

* *Green Medicine* (*op. cit.*).

Most of the more useful synthetic drugs have been modifications of naturally occurring substances, plant or animal.

This is but one example of millions of dollars being spent annually in the search for new drug sources, under the sea as well as on the land.

Previous reference has been made to sarsaparilla as a root much esteemed in folk medicine, but not in the modern sense. At least, not as such, nor in the traditional sense. Sarsaparilla, known since the sixteenth century, was used as treatment for syphilis, rheumatism and other conditions, and perhaps became best known in this country as a spring tonic, and for restoring "lost manhood." The home remedies long current, like sarsaparilla, were forerunners of the hormones now recognized, which are derived from sarsaparilla, yams (not sweet potatoes), Trillium and hundreds of other plants. Many of these were known to natives; some became ingredients in "female weakness" patent medicines. The male and female hormones were isolated chemically from saponins, sudsing substances which yielded steroids. The use of these hormones is manifold; the best known, of course, is the contraceptive pill.

Garlic, widely exploited by quacks and faddists, is being investigated by serious scientists, who find that extracts of garlic and bloodroot have some activity against cancers *in animals*. There is, however, at this time, no contradiction in recognizing this highly preliminary indication and at the same time rejecting the false claims for the crude substance. It is often a long road from the popular belief in a remedy to the scientific proof; sometimes the strongest hopes fail to be realized.

Another plant that is now interesting scientists working with anticancer drugs, is the periwinkle, related to the common "running myrtle," a ground-cover plant. The former yields a large number of alkaloids, some of which show activity against cancer. The ordinary myrtle does not, at least so far. The periwinkle which has given hope of usefulness against cancer is a shrub, with white, pink or crimson blossoms; all have red centers.

These examples could be multiplied manifold. They are typical examples of the difficulties encountered in research. Among many related plants, some may show activity, others none. The presence of an inhibiting influence on tumors in animals, or other specific action in relation to other diseases, does not necessarily mean a cure. This is particularly true in cancer, which is not one disease, but many. It now appears unlikely that there will ever be one successful treatment for all forms of cancer.

Medical scientists have learned a great deal from the seas, much of it based on folklore. The Japanese used seaweed as a food or medicine long before the value of iodine was recognized as essential to thyroid function, and to the treatment and prevention of goiter. The story of fish-liver oils in the prevention of rickets has been told too often to need retelling here, beyond noting its place in this context. Electric eels pointed the way to the synthesis of a crystalline penicillin preparation (PAM) as an antidote for nerve gas, and the Portuguese man-of-war stings played a key role in explaining allergies, anaphylaxis and shock reactions. Plankton, the microscopic animals and plants that flourish in the oceans, are attracting scientific interest as possible sources of useful medicinal agents. So are algae of all kinds which grow in the waters. Research vessels and divers are scouring the seas, to beaches and the bottoms for specimens, which will be subjected to intensive chemical and botanical scrutiny. Isolated chemical entities will have biological tests for possible medical activity. The bacterial life associated with these plants will also be intensively investigated.

The inhabitants of oceanic islands and shores will not be overlooked. Their traditional use of marine plants, fish and crustaceans for food and for medicine will be investigated for clues to the possibilities of modern applications based on their folklore.

Seaweed, already mentioned in connection with goiter, has had many other uses: as a poultice to favor healing of wounds; for treating infections and skin diseases; for inflammations and for digestive disturbances. As a dietary item, seaweed supplies many other minerals besides iodine. Alaskan Indians use a tubelike stem of kelp to treat earache, inserting one end into the ear canal and placing the other end on a hot stone (Kreig). The steam generated is comforting if not always curative. A jellylike substance, agar, is a valuable culture medium for bacterial research, and is useful in producing slow-acting drugs, and as a laxative.

So, from all over the world, on land and sea and under the

sea, the search is on for nature's sources of medicinal principles which seem endless in number and variety, and miraculous in their recognized and their possibly hidden potentialities.

Not least in importance, from the viewpoint of this book, is the fact that medical folklore began earlier than recorded history. Founded in magic, myth, witchcraft and witch doctoring, it led man on a never-ending quest for a better image of himself. Along the way he learned of medicinal plants and herbs, and the medicinal properties in foods. He learned much from animals and paid his debt to them through the very knowledge they gave him, by easing them as well as himself of pain and disability. He recognized the psychic values in beauty. He learned that "Grandma is not always wrong," and that new therapies could rise from old remedies. Experience taught him that some beautiful plants are poisonous. Perhaps most important of all, he learned that the search for scientific truth never ends, and that each new discovery opens a fresh, unexplored vista, leading him on, and on and on.

Chapter Fourteen

POPULAR BELIEFS THAT ARE NOT SO

In summary, and for convenience, a listing is here presented of some two hundred and fifty commonly held, medical-folklore beliefs, gathered by the American Medical Association from its correspondence with lay inquirers seeking information, from surveys published in medical literature, and from physicians who have encountered these ideas in their practice.

Many of these beliefs have been discussed in more or less detail in the preceding chapters; here they are grouped to suggest their validity, if any, and to give an overview of the scope of medical folklore, and its persistence to the present time, despite advances in science. Better methods of communication, and long-continued efforts at health education in schools, colleges and through books, magazines, newspapers, radio, television and lectures, have not been sufficient to overcome many false beliefs. These are not limited to uneducated people; many college students have been quizzed, and have been found to hold a great many erroneous beliefs, often based on folklore.

In order to avoid tiresome, repetitious comment, the items which follow have been divided roughly into three lists:

I   Medical folklore which has become the basis for scientifically authenticated modern knowledge; often basic belief has been greatly modified in the process.

II Medical-folklore traditions which have had justification and a limited usefulness in the absence of anything better, but are now outmoded.

III Medical folklore which appears, at this writing, to be without validity.

One never knows, of course, how the future growth of knowledge may alter this classification. So here goes:

LIST I
Forerunners of Modern Medical Knowledge

Children of first cousins are likely to be feeble-minded.
True only where mental defects exist, or where intermarriages have taken place in many generations.

Eating lettuce will induce sleep.
Roman emperors thought so; modern science recognizes lettuce only as a useful foodstuff.

Growing pains are a natural part of growing up.
No, but they have served a useful purpose in calling attention to matters needing timely care.

Malaria is due to night air.
No, but its prevalence led to suspicions directed at mosquitoes, which tend to fly at night, and so led to ultimate means for conquering the disease.

Tuberculosis is inherited.
No, but its prevalence in family groups was at least one factor which led to discovery of its contagious nature.

Stop nosebleeds by placing a silver coin under the upper lip or dropping a cold key down the nape of the neck.
Ineffective, but placing a pack of gauze under the upper lip helps to compress an artery leading to the nose.

An expectant mother must eat for two.
Yes, but not in the original sense; we now know that she must eat for two qualitatively, but not in excessive amounts.

The mother loses a tooth for every child.
She used to, but she needn't any more.

Sleepiness is due to acid products accumulated during the day.
Not entirely, but fatigue is now recognized as due to lactic acid, among other factors.

To combat alkaline reactions in the blood due to running the human motor in high gear, take two teaspoonfuls of vinegar in a glass of water while dressing for breakfast.

Like the preceding item, curiosity about acid and alkaline reactions has been satisfied by the knowledge that the normal human body is slightly alkaline, with the exception of stomach juices, urine, perspiration and (sometimes) saliva.

An apple a day will keep the doctor away.
Of course not, but this does represent an instinctive recognition of the value of fruit in the diet (see also lettuce, above).

Fish, a brain food, will make you quick-witted.
It won't, but it is a useful source of protein, and deep-sea fish is valuable for its iron content.

Human or animal urine has many medicinal values.
In the primitive sense, no, but today human urine is of great value in diagnosis, and animal urine is a valuable source of sex hormones and others.

Bee venom can cure arthritis.
It is not a cure, but has been used in some instances; it is not without hazard, and is not a commonly accepted treatment.

Darkness is necessary for sound slumber.
Too sweeping a statement; darkness helps, but anyone can sleep in the presence of light if sufficiently fatigued, and many can do so at any time and in any place.

Sunlight is important in combating tuberculosis.
To a limited extent, yes, but only under medical supervision, since too much can do harm.

Summer sun and warmth help prevent subsequent winter ills.
Perhaps; certainly summer is a welcome relief from the rigors of winter.

Lines and markings in the hands foretell the future.
Not in the fortuneteller sense, but recent observations indicate that palm patterns may have diagnostic significance.

To sleep well, eat one or two lobsters before retiring; ocean-grown food acts as a sedative.
Not true, but seafood has definite food values, especially for goiter prevention; two lobsters would be quite a challenge!

A poultice made of a freshly killed chicken or dove, split, or one of cow manure, will cure pneumonia (or other illnesses).

The principle of heat, which underlies these repulsive measures, has found a genuine place in modern medicine, with pleasanter and more effective methods.

LIST II

Folk Remedies of Limited Usefulness in the Absence of More Effective Measures

To get a cinder out of an eye, rub the other.
This seldom helps, but it is better than rubbing the eye with the cinder in it.

Anyone exposed to scarlet fever will get measles.
These are different diseases, but any idea that will discourage exposures can't be all bad.

An hour of sleep before midnight is worth two afterward.
Literally untrue, but probably a good motivation for getting enough sleep.

Bowels should move every day without fail.
True for many people, untrue for many, but it approaches the correct basic idea, the importance of good elimination at regular intervals.

Brushing teeth three times a day will prevent cavities.
It will help, but the real secret of prevention for tooth decay remains somewhat in doubt.

A beautiful coat of tan is a sign of good health.
It isn't, and tanning can be overdone, but exercise in the open air is a good health practice.

Sleeping with windows open will cause frequent head colds.
True only if the sleeper becomes excessively chilled.

As a rule, slender persons become ill in the spring, stocky ones in the fall.
Not necessarily, but the germ of an idea is here, namely that body types have an influence on health.

Wounds should be cauterized with hot sand, or oil, or with eagle down, scrapings from tanned hides, or cobwebs, to combat infection and control bleeding.
Limited usefulness, but primitive, and more likely to introduce infection than control it.

LIST III
Superstitions Without Basis Other Than Coincidence and the Tendency of Many Diseases to Recover Spontaneously

Milk from the mother's breast squirted into an infant's sore eyes is beneficial.

Piercing the ears of the newborn with needles insures good eyesight.

If the newborn lies on his left side, he will be left-handed.

If a child looks in a mirror before its first birthday, it will die before the age of two.

The expectant mother will strangle her baby if she lifts her arms above her head.

High heels worn by a pregnant woman will bring a cross-eyed child.

Babies born at seven months have a better chance of living than those born at eight months.

The mother's blood circulates through the body of the unborn child.

Birthmarks are due to mothers witnessing unpleasant or frightening sights.

Cutting baby's hair before he can go to a barbershop is unlucky.

Babies who walk before they are a year old will be bowlegged.

Expectant mothers should sleep with a pair of open scissors under their mattresses, to have an easy birth and a healthy child.

An open Bible with the blood of the expectant mother on each page, will help a woman in labor if placed under her bed.

Good-looking babies grow up ugly, and vice versa.

Weak, sore eyes may be helped by wearing golden earrings.

After a nail puncture has been sustained in the foot, grease the nail and carry it in the pocket to prevent tetanus.

Madstones (calcified formations found in animal intestines) will cure rabies.

For dog bites, use a plaster of goose grease and hair of the dog that bit you.

A hair of the dog that bit the person will prevent rabies, if applied to the wound.

Yeast strengthens "internal muscles" and intestines, cures constipation and acne and aids digestion.

Cure syphilis by fasting, followed by a milk diet; or by eating only grapes.

Vaccination against smallpox causes syphilis.

Use whiskey as an antidote for snakebite.

Cats kill infants by sucking their breath.

Cutting the hair often, encourages thicker growth.

Color blindness is curable.

Children cannot have a communicable disease oftener than once.

Cancer is inherited.

Tomatoes induce cancer.

Boils purify the blood.

Oysters cause ptomaine poisoning in months without an "r."

Grape seeds cause appendicitis.

Feed a cold and starve a fever.

If a child's fingernails are cut before the ninth month, he will grow up to be a thief.

A deer's foot, warmed and rubbed over the skin, will relieve toothache, swellings and itching.

Stop nosebleed by wearing a red string around the little finger or a necklace of red-corn kernels.

Elm bark stripped from the tree downward will act as a laxative; upward as an emetic.

A sty is quickly cured by rubbing it with a gold ring.

Brown paper soaked in vinegar and bound about the head, will cure "sick" headache.

A black cotton thread tied around the neck will prevent croup.

An opal loses brilliance when the wearer is ill.

A necklace of peony roots will prevent convulsions in children.

Peony roots carried in the pocket will protect against "insanity."

Small branches of mistletoe, cut with a golden knife, will protect against epilepsy and against poisoning if worn around the neck.

A leather strap made from a horse's harness will strengthen muscles and cure sprains and local infections, if worn about the wrist.

For cramps: the kneecap of a sheep applied to the skin in the affected area and tucked under the pillow at night; a "cramp" ring, made from a coffin nail removed from the graveyard (China, England, U.S.A.).

Prevent rheumatism by carrying the right forepaw of a rabbit in a pocket.

Dog days are so named because that's when dogs go mad most often.

Grinding teeth during sleep indicates intestinal worms.

Measles patients' rooms must be darkened and sealed against drafts and fresh air.

Bed-wetting is hereditary.

You will become blind if you sleep with the moon shining on you (or "insane"—lunatic from *luna*, the moon).

A vein showing across the nose indicates a short life.

Getting out of bed backward or from the left side means misfortune.

Constipation is normal in pregnant women.

Drowning people come to the surface three times before they die.

Intelligent children are prone to be weak and physically retarded.

Pasteurization of milk removes proteins.

Cucumbers and cream, eaten together, will kill you.

"Every part (of an animal) strengthens a part" of the individual who eats the animal part or organ.

If you are always hungry, you are a "boarding house" for tapeworms.

Thunder causes milk to sour.

To avoid cancer, do not eat fruits of trees which develop tumors, especially apricot, peach and pear trees.

Goiter is caused by a germ found in water and meat; too much salt also causes goiter.

Pasteurization destroys good germs as well as bad.

Aluminum cooking utensils cause cancer.

Red hair signifies a violent temper.

Hairy arms signify strength.

Greenish-gray eyes are found less often in trustworthy people than those with blue or brown eyes.

Brunettes are more trustworthy than blondes.

You can assess a person's intelligence just by studying his face.

Long, slender hands indicate an artistic nature.

Herbal bitters and astringents will relieve physical depression.

To cure cirrhosis of the liver, kill a cat each night in the cemetery for three months and drink the blood.

The skin of a black cat, cut into two parts and bound on either wrist, is very good for high fever.

Poultices draw poisons out of wounds.

To get a cinder out of an eye, blow the nose on the opposite side.

Drink two quarts of whiskey to cure snakebite.

Chewed tobacco or pipe dottles placed over wounds will promote healing; tobacco smoke is a disinfectant.

Cut onions in pieces and place them in stockings or socks or wear them in gloves to "sidetrack" fevers of all kinds.

To reduce fever, split two salt-white herrings and apply them to the soles of the patient's feet.

If you are afraid of a disease, you will catch it.

For a sore throat, wind one of patient's own stockings around his neck when he goes to bed.

If a child sleeps with his textbook under his pillow, he will know his lessons in the morning.

A sound sleeper sleeps "like a log."

Northern people, like polar bears, are fair and blond to help them hide against the snow; tropical people are dark so that they may hide in the shadows of the jungle.

Beans soaked in blood, with a bit of the bark of a tree, will cure skin troubles and reduce swellings.

To make your hair grow better, cut it while the moon is new.

Handle a toad and you'll get warts (or cure them!).

Wearing a hat causes baldness.

Hair may turn gray or white overnight from fright.

Lemon juice cures freckles.

A *stolen* horse chestnut or a potato will protect against rheumatism.

A *stolen* Italian chestnut worn under the breasts prevents cancer.

A nutmeg in your pocket will ward off rheumatism.

Amber beads about baby's neck will prevent croup (and goiter).

If the afterbirth is promptly put into a pot with earth, together with some flower seeds, the child will live long and successfully if the seeds grow and the plant thrives.

If "shingles" encircles your body, you will die.

A high forehead indicates superior intelligence.

Cold hands indicate a warm heart.

Brains and beauty rarely go together.

A square jaw is a sign of great will-power.

Fat people are always good-natured.

Insanity is influenced by the moon.

A full moon makes a simple-minded person eccentric.

Mental disorders result from too intense study.

Pores in the skin open and close just like tiny trap doors.

A prominent Roman nose means a strong fighting instinct.

Seed pods of Job's-tears (spiderwort) hung around the neck of a child help to cut his teeth.

Give your heart the natural sugar from honey instead of from refined white sugar.

Vinegar and honey supply the mineral needs of the body—the vinegar brings minerals from the apple cider and the honey does likewise from the flowers.

Milk forms a curd in the stomach and should be replaced in the diet by cheese, which doesn't.

Discard muscle meats and instead use fish, seafood, liver, heart, kidneys and tripe.

Citrus fruits and juices should be replaced in the diet by grape, apple and cranberry juices.

Honey contains important ingredients for new blood; it acts as a sedative to assure sound sleep, and it prevents constipation, and in the unborn it helps to develop a sound nervous system if taken by the mother.

A teaspoonful of apple-cider vinegar taken by a pregnant woman, will provide necessary acids and help with morning sickness.

When a pregnancy is desired, both husband and wife should exchange wheat breads and cereals for products of rye, oats or corn, use honey instead of white sugar and cold-climate fruits (apples, grapes and cranberries) in place of citrus fruits.

If you have brown or hazel eyes, chestnut brown or black hair, and a round head (broad between the ears), you should use land-grown foods and meat from game, flocks and herds.

If you have a dark skin, dark eyes, black hair and a long head, you can eat all kinds of food, but especially corn cereals, grapes and grape juice.

People with big ears usually like vegetables and bulky foods; those with small ears prefer meat and more concentrated foods.

Apple-cider vinegar, alone or in combination with honey, has been highly esteemed and sometimes commercially exploited. In folk medicine, it was usually advised for internal use in a glass of water several times a day, to:
relieve arthritic pains
relieve pain of sinusitis (seven doses a day)
destroy bacteria in the intestines
correct the cause of morning vomiting
help overcome diarrhea
cure kidney inflammation
reduce a woman's dress size from fifty to forty-two
promote energy (by using as a "handbath")
relieve migraine headache (by inhaling the fumes from vinegar and water boiling on the stove)
relieve sore throat by gargling, then swallowing the solution with honey, better than shots for hay fever

Honey, too, with or without vinegar, has been popular, and commercially profitable for:
bed-wetting, a teaspoonful at bedtime;
stuffy nose, eat honeycomb;
sinusitis, chew a mouthful of honeycomb every hour for fifteen minutes; repeat four to six times daily.

A high-protein, low-vegetable and -fruit diet will make you more susceptible to colds, bronchitis and "flu."

Making the urine more acid will help to cure a cold.

Simmer short, bud-bearing twigs and needles from a pine tree in water for three days. The brown liquid is run through a sieve and thickened with honey; a teaspoonful of this mixture several times a day will end sickness in the breathing tract.

Fresh gum from a spruce tree will cure a sore throat.

Castor oil rubbed on warts will remove them; do this night and morning, rubbing twenty times, until the warts are gone.

Castor oil applied to the breasts of nursing mothers will increase the flow of milk.

Liver spots on the skin will disappear if they are rubbed with castor oil morning and evening.

One tablespoonful of corn oil at breakfast and again at the evening meal, within one month's time will generally cure scaliness and granulation of the eyelids.

One tablespoon of corn oil at one or all three meals helps to control allergic swellings.

To relieve lameness, beat up the yolk of one egg with a tablespoon each of apple-cider vinegar and turpentine, and rub it into the skin thoroughly.

For poison ivy, use equal parts of apple-cider vinegar and water; dab it on the skin and let it dry. Repeat often.

Apple-cider vinegar will cure shingles, night sweats, and impetigo and may be used for burns and varicose veins.

Sheep and other animals will not eat poisonous mushrooms.

Poisonous mushrooms grow in the woods; edible ones in the open fields.

If a mushroom is boiled with a silver spoon and the spoon is darkened, the mushroom is poisonous; otherwise not.

A wolf's liver boiled in thin wine, bacon of an herb-fed sow, and the flesh of a she-donkey; eat these with the broth; this is a sure cure for tuberculosis.

Various "cures" for tuberculosis:
Drink cows' milk direct from the udder.
Cram yourself with milk and eggs.
Drink goats' milk to counteract the tuberculosis.
Take okra pods and sweet pine kernels at each meal.
Take "sugar" of roses.

Mixtures of oak bark, pomegranate, mimosa and acacia in a decoction.

Eat a vulture's lung burned on logs, mixed in wine with a lily blossom.

Spit into the mouth of a tree frog and give him the disease.

Eat the "middle" of a snake, then run for an hour; if you don't get sick, you'll be cured.

Bathe in cold water, then breathe into a hole cut in the wet earth.

Pass the patient three times through a hole in a tree.

Take mummy powder made from a woman with red hair who had been well-nourished for twenty years, then drowned in honey and aromatics, and sealed up for 120 years.

Since TB is due to witchcraft, drink milk from cows fed in a churchyard.

Polynesians believed TB was caused by a demon, Mumu. A priest swung a spear over the patient's head and sang, "Oh, Mumu, I am about to spear you." If the spear did not slip and kill the patient, he was supposed to be cured as the demon fled his body.

Place a piece of amber on the nose to stop nosebleeds.

Indians packed wounds with hot sand, eagles' down and scrapings from tanned hides.

Wounds were cauterized with malacca cane dipped in hot grease (Canary Islands).

When the Dionne quintuplets were drawing crowds of tourists, a large box filled with stones dug from their farmland, was kept by their gate for people to take with them as fertility talismans. Dr. Dafoe, their physician, remarked deadpan that sometimes it worked—or maybe it was the vacation. Anyway, it kept one man busy keeping the box filled.

The unborn was supposedly influenced by mother's musical, cultural or artistic activities.

Eat alkaline foods for a boy baby, acid for girls!

Looking at the sky will give a baby crossed eyes, so will trying to look over his shoulder.

Spunk water for warts—rain water gathered in rotten stumps. Must be approached at midnight, backing up against the stump, and saying: Barleycorn, barleycorn, injun-meal shorts; spunk water, spunk water, swallow these warts (Mark Twain).

Or go to a graveyard with a dead cat when someone wicked has been buried, and as the devil comes to take him away, you heave your cat after him, saying, "Devil follow corpse, cat follow devil, warts follow cat. I'm done with ye!"

White eggs are better than brown eggs.

Appetite is the best guide to proper eating.

Dark breads are less "fattening" than white breads.

Never eat fish and milk at the same meal.

Water with your meals washes the vitamins away.

Toasted bread is less fattening than untoasted bread.

Spicy food is good for blood and complexion; acid foods like lemons are bad.

Tiger's blood and moss burning, drive away devils (Chinese).

Eyelids of frogs, and a kei stone worn around the neck, are Chinese charms against illness.

Scientists cannot ignore superstition. They must examine, analyze and determine the value, if any, of superstitions and popular beliefs. If they fail to do so, they themselves are guilty of superstition. Science is a method for separating the true from the false; if there is truth in any given belief, science should prove it; if not, science is obligated to disprove it. In the end, we must all rely on science, not mere belief.

PRINCIPAL SOURCES OF INFORMATION

A *Pictorial History of Magic and the Supernatural*: Maurice Bessy, Spring Books, London, 1964 (Original in French, 1961)

A *Syllabus of Medical History*: Fred B. Rodgers, M.D., Little, Brown & Company, Boston, 1962

A *Textbook of Pharmacognosy*: George Edward Trease, 8th Ed., 1961, Balliere, Tindall & Cox, London, W.C. 2

A *Treasury of Mexican Folkways*: Frances Toor, Crown Publishers, New York, 1952

Biblical Antiquities: Edwin Cone Bissell, The American Sunday-School Union, Philadelphia, Pa.

B.P.O.E. (*Elks*): personal communication from Otho de Vilbiss, Director of Public Relations, Chicago, Ill., 1967

Chinese Folk Medicine: Heinrich Wallnofer and Anna von Rottauscher, Crown Publishers, New York, 1965

Classics of Medicine and Surgery: C. N. B. Camac, Dover Publications, New York, 1909

Daffodils Are Dangerous: Hubert Creekmore, Walker & Company, New York, 1966

Digging Into the Past: Sir Leonard Woolley, Charles Scribner's Sons, New York, 1931

Edible Wild Plants of Eastern North America: Reed C. Rollins, Harper & Bros., New York, 1958

Encyclopedia Britannica, 1967: Chicago, Illinois

Encyclopedia of Bible Life: Madeleine S. Miller and J. Lane Miller, Harper & Bros., New York and London

Everything But Money: Sam Levenson, Simon & Schuster, New York, 1966

Folklore and Symbolism of Flowers, Plants and Trees: Ernest and Hohan Lehner, Tudor Publishing Company, New York

From the Tablets of Sumer: Samuel Noah Kramer, The Falcon's Wing Press, Indian Hills, Colorado, 1956

Givaudanian: Givaudan Corporation, New York

Greek Mythology: Paul Hamlyn (Translated by Delano Ames), First published by Auge, Gillon, Hollier, Moreau et Cie, printed in London by Westbrook House, Fulham Broadway, 1963

Green Medicine: Margaret B. Kreig, Rand McNally & Company, Chicago

Herbal: Joseph Wood Krutch, Putnam, 1965.

History of Medicine: Fielding H. Garrison, W. B. Saunders & Company, Philadelphia, Pa., 4th Edition

History of Salt: Morton Salt Company, courtesy of Salt Institute, Alexandria, Va.

How Did It Begin?: R. Brasch, David McKay Company, New York, 1966

Magical Transference of Disease (in Folklore Studies in Honor of Arthur Palmer Hudson): North Carolina Folklore Society, Chapel Hill, N.C., 1965

Midwest Pioneer: Madge E. Pickard and R. Carlyle Buley, Banta, Crawfordsville, Ind., 1945

New Standard Encyclopedia: Standard Education Society, Inc., Chicago, Ill., 1965

News and Pesticide Review, Vol. 23, No. 5, June, 1965

Nutritional Nonsense and Food Fanatics: Proceedings of the Third National Congress on Medical Quackery, American Medical Association, Chicago, Ill., 1966

Readings in Pharmacology: B. Holmstedt and G. Liljestrand, Pergamon Press, London, Macmillan, New York, 1963

Science and Secrets of Early Medicine: Jurgen Thorwald, Harcourt, Brace and World, Inc., New York, 1962

Source Book of Medical History: Logan Clendenning, Harper & Bros., New York, 1942

Superstitions About Salt: William B. Wilkinson, Cayuga Salt Co., Ithaca, N.Y.

The Amazing World of Medicine: Edited by Helen Wright and Samuel Rapport, Harper & Row, New York, 1963

The Conquest of Civilization: James Henry Breasted, Harper & Bros., New York and London, 1926, 1938

The Dawn of Conscience: James H. Breasted, Charles Scribner's Sons, 1933

The Golden Bough: Sir James George Frazer, Macmillan, New York, 1925

The Old Egyptian Medical Papyri: Chauncey D. Leake, University of Kansas Press, Lawrence, Kansas, 1965

The Oldest Code of Laws in the World: C. H. W. Johns, T. & T. Clark, 38 George St., Edinburgh, Scotland, 8 impressions, 1903–1926

The Romance of Human Progress: Arthur Stanley Riggs, The Bobbs-Merrill Company, Indianapolis, Ind., 1938

The Story of Medicine: Kenneth Walker, Oxford University Press, New York, 1955

Today's Health Magazine: American Medical Association, Chicago, 1964

Using Plants for Healing: Nelson Coon, Hearthside Press, New York, 1963

INDEX